The Nature and Origin of Compression in Passive Margins

Geological Society books refereeing procedures

The Society makes every effort to ensure that the scientific and production quality of its books matches that of its journals. Since 1997, all book proposals have been refereed by specialist reviewers as well as by the Society's Books Editorial Committee. If the referees identify weaknesses in the proposal, these must be addressed before the proposal is accepted.

Once the book is accepted, the Society Book Editors ensure that the volume editors follow strict guidelines on refereeing and quality control. We insist that individual papers can only be accepted after satisfactory review by two independent referees. The questions on the review forms are similar to those for *Journal of the Geological Society*. The referees' forms and comments must be available to the Society's Book Editors on request.

Although many of the books result from meetings, the editors are expected to commission papers that were not presented at the meeting to ensure that the book provides a balanced coverage of the subject. Being accepted for presentation at the meeting does not guarantee inclusion in the book.

More information about submitting a proposal and producing a book for the Society can be found on its web site: www.geolsoc.org.uk.

It is recommended that reference to all or part of this book should be made in one of the following ways:

JOHNSON, H., DORÉ, A. G., GATLIFF, R. W., HOLDSWORTH, R., LUNDIN, E. R. & RITCHIE, J. D. (eds) 2008. *The Nature and Origin of Compression in Passive Margins*. Geological Society, London, Special Publications, **306**.

RITCHIE, J. D., JOHNSON, H.,QUINN, M. F. & GATLIFF, R. W. 2008. The effects of Cenozoic compression within the Faroe–Shetland Basin and adjacent areas. *In*: JOHNSON, H., DORÉ, A. G., GATLIFF, R. W., HOLDSWORTH, R., LUNDIN, E. R. & RITCHIE, J. D. (eds) *The Nature and Origin of Compression in Passive Margins*. Geological Society, London, Special Publications, **306**, 121–136.

GEOLOGICAL SOCIETY SPECIAL PUBLICATION NO. 306

The Nature and Origin of Compression in Passive Margins

EDITED BY

HOWARD JOHNSON
British Geological Survey, Edinburgh, UK

TONY G. DORÉ
StatoilHydro, USA

ROBERT W. GATLIFF
British Geological Survey, Edinburgh, UK

ROBERT W. HOLDSWORTH
Durham University, UK

ERIK R. LUNDIN
StatoilHydro, Norway

and

J. DEREK RITCHIE
British Geological Survey, Edinburgh, UK

2008
Published by
The Geological Society
London

THE GEOLOGICAL SOCIETY

The Geological Society of London (GSL) was founded in 1807. It is the oldest national geological society in the world and the largest in Europe. It was incorporated under Royal Charter in 1825 and is Registered Charity 210161.

The Society is the UK national learned and professional society for geology with a worldwide Fellowship (FGS) of over 9000. The Society has the power to confer Chartered status on suitably qualified Fellows, and about 2000 of the Fellowship carry the title (CGeol). Chartered Geologists may also obtain the equivalent European title, European Geologist (EurGeol). One fifth of the Society's fellowship resides outside the UK. To find out more about the Society, log on to www.geolsoc.org.uk.

The Geological Society Publishing House (Bath, UK) produces the Society's international journals and books, and acts as European distributor for selected publications of the American Association of Petroleum Geologists (AAPG), the Indonesian Petroleum Association (IPA), the Geological Society of America (GSA), the Society for Sedimentary Geology (SEPM) and the Geologists' Association (GA). Joint marketing agreements ensure that GSL Fellows may purchase these societies' publications at a discount. The Society's online bookshop (accessible from www.geolsoc.org.uk) offers secure book purchasing with your credit or debit card.

To find out about joining the Society and benefiting from substantial discounts on publications of GSL and other societies worldwide, consult www.geolsoc.org.uk, or contact the Fellowship Department at: The Geological Society, Burlington House, Piccadilly, London W1J 0BG: Tel. +44 (0)20 7434 9944; Fax +44 (0)20 7439 8975; E-mail: enquiries@geolsoc.org.uk.

For information about the Society's meetings, consult *Events* on www.geolsoc.org.uk. To find out more about the Society's Corporate Affiliates Scheme, write to enquiries@geolsoc.org.uk.

Published by The Geological Society from:
The Geological Society Publishing House, Unit 7, Brassmill Enterprise Centre, Brassmill Lane, Bath BA1 3JN, UK

(*Orders*: Tel. +44 (0)1225 445046, Fax +44 (0)1225 442836)
Online bookshop: www.geolsoc.org.uk/bookshop

The publishers make no representation, express or implied, with regard to the accuracy of the information contained in this book and cannot accept any legal responsibility for any errors or omissions that may be made.

British Library Cataloguing in Publication Data

A catalogue record for this book is available from the British Library.

ISBN 978-1-86239-261-8

Typeset by Techset Composition Ltd, UK

Printed by MPG Books Ltd, Bodmin, UK

Distributors

North America
For trade and institutional orders:
The Geological Society, c/o AIDC, 82 Winter Sport Lane, Williston, VT 05495, USA
Orders: Tel +1 800-972-9892
             Fax +1 802-864-7626
             E-mail gsl.orders@aidcvt.com

For individual and corporate orders:
AAPG Bookstore, PO Box 979, Tulsa, OK 74101-0979, USA
Orders: Tel +1 918-584-2555
             Fax +1 918-560-2652
             E-mail bookstore@aapg.org
             Website http://bookstore.aapg.org

India
Affiliated East-West Press Private Ltd, Marketing Division, G-1/16 Ansari Road, Darya Ganj, New Delhi 110 002, India
Orders: Tel +91 11 2327-9113/2326-4180
             Fax +91 11 2326-0538
             E-mail affiliat@vsnl.com

Contents

Preface

The tectonic evolution of passive continental margins is a topic not only of fundamental scientific interest, but also has relevance to various commercial developments, not least of which is the exploration and development of oil and gas resources. Increasingly, researchers have reported that passive margins do not show a simple uninterrupted thermal sag pattern of post-rift subsidence following continental separation as predicted by the McKenzie model for sedimentary basin development. Rather, the structural and stratigraphic development of such margins may record evidence of complex phases of differential subsidence and/or exhumation and fold development. Consequently, some passive margins have been considered to be 'anything but passive'. There are many ways in which post-breakup tectonism on passive margins can significantly affect petroleum systems. Some effects may be positive with respect to petroleum prospectivity, such as the development of large trapping structures. For example, some structural domes form major oil and gas fields, such as the Ormen Lange gas field offshore Norway, and others form possible future exploration targets. However, other effects may be negative with respect to petroleum prospectivity, such as uplift, trap tilting, fault reactivation, seal breach, and late timing of the structuring with respect to source rock maturation. Some of the fold structures observed on passive continental margins appear to be related to regional stresses transmitted through basement rocks, whereas others are related to gravitational sliding and toe-thrusting. Especially on volcanic passive margins, morphologically similar, but generically quite separate types of fold structures occur that are related to igneous intrusion or the emplacement of remobilized crust or magmatically underplated material at depth. This special publication concentrates on the first of these categories, that is compressive structures that appear to have formed on passive margins in the absence of an obvious gravitational sliding regime. The volume is derived from a joint Petroleum Group/Tectonic Studies Group 2-day international conference 'Compressional deformation within passive margins: nature, causes and effects' which was held at the Geological Society, London in October 2005.

The first section of the volume consists of three regional overview papers that consider the fundamental driving mechanisms that have been proposed to account for the generation, location and orientation of post-breakup compressional structures. A common theme in these papers is their emphasis upon the importance of structural inheritance through the reactivation of pre-existing structural architecture, which commonly exerts a strong local influence on the location and orientation of subsequent fold development. The relative merit of the potential driving mechanisms on the volcanic margin of the NE Atlantic is discussed by **Doré et al**. They present the results of interdisciplinary studies to provide an introduction to the topic of post-breakup compression on passive margins in general before going on to review the complex nature, timing and distribution of post-breakup fold development on the NE Atlantic passive margin in particular. They recognize the importance of a number of primary and secondary driving mechanisms and also present some interesting new ideas on the potential importance of body force exerted by the Iceland Insular Margin, and on the factors governing location of the structures. **Cloetingh et al**. use examples from European passive margins and rifts to demonstrate that polyphase deformation of a compressional nature is a common feature in their post-rift evolution. The mode of compressional deformation appears to be strongly affected by the rheological structure of the underlying lithosphere and is characterized by a spectrum of spatial wavelengths spanning several tens of kilometres up to several hundreds of kilometres and by substantial differential vertical motions and late-stage anomalies in subsidence and uplift patterns. **Hillis et al**. summarize and compare present-day intraplate stresses, seismicity and neotectonic deformation in the Australian continent, focusing on its passive margins, in order to evaluate the extent to which this deformation can be accounted for in terms of the boundary forces acting on the plate. They argue that plate boundary forces are effectively transmitted thousands of kilometres into the Australian plate's interior where they are responsible for intraplate deformation.

The next section of this volume comprises four papers that examine post-breakup compression and uplift along the NE Atlantic margin and the Irish Sea. **Holford et al**. present a synthesis of extensive apatite fission-track analysis, vitrinite reflectance and a compaction database derived from sonic velocity and density log-derived porosities to demonstrate kilometre-scale Neogene exhumation driven by compressional deformation in the Irish Sea basin system. This interpretation contrasts with many previous studies which have attributed the exhumation of this region to processes

associated with the early Palaeogene initiation of
the Iceland Plume. **Ritchie** *et al.* describe the
effects of Cenozoic compression within the
Faroe–Shetland Basin and surrounding areas,
which are mainly manifested in the form of
growth folds. Evidence is presented for a number
of pulses of compression. Raised sea bed profiles
over some of the anticlinal features may suggest
that the effects of compressional stress continue
into Pliocene to Recent times. **Smallwood** presents
a Cenozoic topographic model for the Faroe–
Shetland Basin that takes account of permanent
uplift from igneous underplating, which is computed from gravity anomaly data, transient regional
uplift and a simple elevation-dependent erosion
term, under isostatic balance. The sediment
volume balance suggests that around thirty per
cent of the Paleocene sediments currently in the
basin were sourced from a westerly provenance
area, the pre-basalt Faroes platform terrane or
East Greenland. **Ziska** *et al.* interpret previously
unreleased commercial seismic profiles within the
region to the SW of the Faroe Islands and suggest
that these ridges were primarily initiated by a transient rifting event in the early Paleocene and were
subsequently modified by significant compressive
phases.

The final section of the volume comprises three
papers that examine various pure and applied
aspects of post-breakup tectonism in the West
Iberia and Australia regions. **Péron-Pinvidic** *et al.*
use seismic reflection data to examine localized
deformation on the West Iberia margin associated
with Eocene and Miocene compressive tectonic
events that probably resulted from collision

between Iberia, Europe and Africa. **Keep &
Harrowfield** present a synthesis of Neogene tectonism in the Browse and Bonaparte basins along
Australia's North West Shelf and attempt to reconcile the growth of major Neogene depocentres with
brittle normal faults in a convergent plate boundary
setting. **Rogers** *et al.* utilize a geomechanical model
of the *in situ* stress field, the mechanical properties
of the fault rock and the orientations of existing
faults to assess the propensity of fault reactivation
within a proposed demonstration site for the subsurface geological storage of carbon dioxide
located in southeastern Australia.

Any publication of this nature requires the help
of a large number of people. We would like to
thank the staff of the Conference Office at
Burlington House for their help in organizing the
meeting in October 2005, and the conference spon-
sors BP, Shell and Statoilhydro. We also thank staff
of the Geological Society Publishing House for
their assistance in producing the volume. Finally,
we thank the following colleagues in the British
Geological Survey, academia and industry who
gave their time to review the papers published
here: Andy Chadwick, Dave Ellis, Richard
England, Neil Grant, Richard Hillis, Geoff
Kimbell, David Moy, Emma Nelson, Kevin Smith
and Ian Walker.

HOWARD JOHNSON
TONY DORÉ
ROBERT GATLIFF
ROBERT HOLDSWORTH
ERIK LUNDIN
DEREK RITCHIE

Potential mechanisms for the genesis of Cenozoic domal structures on the NE Atlantic margin: pros, cons and some new ideas

A. G. DORÉ[1], E. R. LUNDIN[2], N. J. KUSZNIR[3] & C. PASCAL[4]

[1]*StatoilHydro Gulf of Mexico, 2103 Citywest Boulevard, Suite 800, Houston, Texas 77042, USA*
(e-mail: agdo@statoilhydro.com)

[2]*Statoil Research Centre, Postuttak, 7005 Trondheim, Norway*

[3]*Department of Earth and Ocean Sciences, University of Liverpool, Liverpool L69 3BX, UK*

[4]*Geological Survey of Norway (NGU), P.O. Box 3006, N-7002 Trondheim, Norway*

Abstract: The mild compressional structures of Cenozoic age on the passive margins bordering Norway, the UK, the Faroes and Ireland have been the subject of much discussion in the literature. Nevertheless, their origin remains enigmatic. Candidate mechanisms must be able to explain the generation of sufficient stress to cause deformation, the episodic nature of the structures and why they developed where they did. We examine these mechanisms and conclude that multiple causes are probable, while favouring body force as potentially the most important agent.

The geometry and setting of the structures are incompatible with gravitational sliding and toe-thrusting, probably the commonest 'compressive' structuring around the Atlantic margins. A passive mode of origin featuring drape or flank sedimentary loading probably emphasized some of the structures, but cannot be invoked as a primary mechanism. Likewise, reactivation of basement structure probably focused deformation but did not initiate it. Far-field orogenic stress from Alpine orogenic phases and from the West Spitsbergen–Eurekan folding and thrusting is also examined. This mechanism is attractive because of its potential to explain episodicity of the compressional structures. However, difficulties exist with stress transmission pathways from these fold belts, and the passive margin structures developed for much of their existence in the absence of any nearby contemporaneous orogeny. Breakup and plate spreading forces such as divergent asthenospheric flow have potential to explain early post-breakup compressional structuring, for example on the UK–Faroes margin, but are unlikely to account for later (Neogene) deformation.

Ridge push, generally thought to be the dominant body force acting on passive margins, can in some circumstances generate enough stress to cause mild deformation, but appears to have low potential to explain episodicity. It is proposed here that the primary agent generating the body force was development of the Iceland Insular Margin, the significant bathymetric-topographic high around Iceland. Circumstantially, in Miocene times, this development may also have coincided with the acme of the compressional structures. We show that, dependent on the degree of lithosphere–asthenosphere coupling, the Iceland Plateau may have generated enough horizontal stress to deform adjacent margins, and may explain the arcuate distribution of the compressional structures around Iceland.

Assuming transmission of stress through the basement we argue that, through time, the structures will have developed preferentially where the basement is hotter, weaker and therefore more prone to shearing at the relatively low stress levels. This situation is most likely at the stretched and most thermally-blanketed crust under the thickest parts of the young (Cretaceous–Cenozoic) basins. Although several elements of this model remain to be tested, it has the potential to provide a general explanation for passive margin compression at comparatively low stress levels and in the absence of nearby orogeny or gravitational sliding.

At the time of plate separation in the NE Atlantic in the early Eocene (53.7 Ma, Chron 24B) the oceanic margins were bounded by a thick sedimentary pile that had accumulated during a succession of extensional episodes lasting some 350 Ma (Doré *et al.* 1999). The sedimentary pile is up to 17 km thick (in the Møre Basin) and consists primarily of Cretaceous and Cenozoic sediments. On outer parts of the margin, the basin fill is further increased by thick breakup-related flood basalts of Paleocene–Eocene age.

During and subsequent to breakup, the basins marginal to the NE Atlantic were deformed into a series of domes, generally elongate anticlines with 4-way closure at Cretaceous–Cenozoic level, generally simply inverted without a marked directional asymmetry, but in some instances verging in the direction of a reverse fault system in the core of the fold. The domes are generally assumed to have a compressional element, but at low strain levels representing only a few percent shortening (e.g. Vågnes *et al.* 1998). They can, however, be

From: JOHNSON, H., DORÉ, A. G., GATLIFF, R. W., HOLDSWORTH, R., LUNDIN, E. R. & RITCHIE, J. D. (eds)
The Nature and Origin of Compression in Passive Margins. Geological Society, London, Special Publications,
306, 1–26. DOI: 10.1144/SP306.1   0305-8719/08/$15.00 © The Geological Society of London 2008.

areally large and this factor, combined with the presence of potential reservoir sandstones in the Cretaceous and Cenozoic successions, makes them interesting targets for petroleum exploration. Members of this structural suite have been identified between Hatton Bank and the Faroe–Shetland Basin (e.g. Johnson *et al.* 2005), on the Faroes shelf (e.g. Boldreel & Andersen 1993) and on the Mid-Norwegian margin (e.g. Blystad *et al.* 1995; Doré & Lundin 1996; Lundin & Doré 2002). Similar, albeit lesser studied, features have been identified onshore East Greenland (Price *et al.* 1997) and

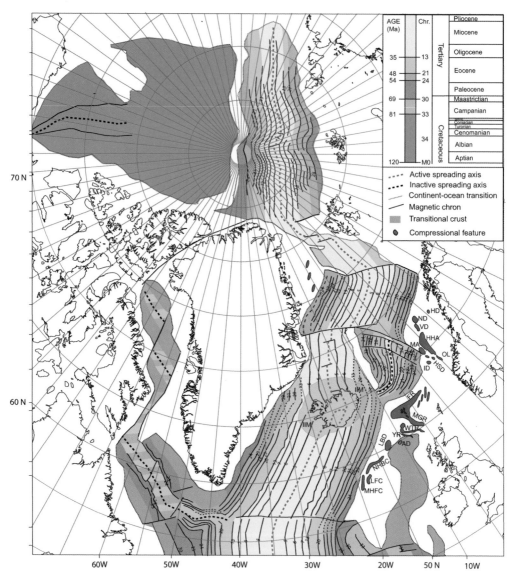

Fig. 1. Super-regional plate tectonic map of the NE Atlantic, Labrador Sea/Baffin Bay, and Arctic Ocean, with inversion features marked in red. Seafloor spreading anomalies marked with respective numbers and colour coded. Abbreviations: AD, Alpin Dome; FR, Fugløy Ridge; HD, Hedda Dome; HHA, Helland Hansen Arch; HSD, Havsule Dome; ID, Isak Dome; IIM, Iceland Insular Margin; LBD, Lousy Bank Dome; LFC, Lyonesse Fold Complex; MA, Modgunn Arch; MGR, Munkagunnar Ridge; MHFC, Mid-Hatton Bank Fold Complex; ND, Naglfar Dome; NHBA, North Hatton Basin Anticline; NHBC, North Hatton Bank Fold Complex; OL, Ormen Lange Dome; VD, Vema Dome; WTR, Wyville Thomson Ridge; YR, Ymir Ridge. Red dashed lines, active spreading axes; Black dashed lines, abandoned spreading axes. Polar stereographic north projection. Modified after Lundin (2002).

briefly described offshore NE Greenland (Hamann *et al.* 2005; Tsikalas *et al.* 2005) (Fig. 1).

We believe that on a very generic level it is important to distinguish between two classes of domes, both of which are evident and lie in close juxtaposition on the Mid-Norwegian shelf (Fig. 2). They are superficially similar in morphology but appear to differ in timing and origin. The first and earlier class is of Late Cretaceous to Paleocene age and is related to breakup magmatism. We term these features 'tectonomagmatic' because the broad domal uplifts appear to be associated with intrusion or the emplacement of remobilized crust or magmatically underplated material at depth. Examples include the Gjallar Ridge, which has been characterized as an incipient core complex (Lundin & Doré 1997; Doré *et al.* 1999; Ren *et al.* 1998; Gernigon *et al.* 2003), the palaeo-Vema

Dome, in which an early uplift collapsed in Paleo-cene times and was infilled by sediments prior to the later (Miocene) doming event (Lundin & Doré 2002), and the Isak Dome (informal name) which had an early phase of doming in latest Cretaceous time and subsequently one in Miocene time. The second and later class of features, which we term 'compressional-compactional' are post-breakup in age (i.e. early Eocene to Recent) and form the main subject of this paper. On the Mid-Norwegian shelf they include the Ormen Lange Dome, Havsule Dome, Modgunn Arch, and Isak Dome at the Vøring–Møre Basin transition. To the north lies the largest of these features, the Helland-Hansen Arch with a north–south fold axis in the order of 200 km in length and an amplitude in the order of 1000 m (Fig. 3) and, farther north still, the Vema, Naglfar, and Hedda (informal name)

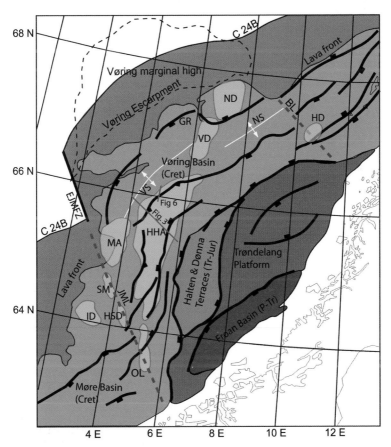

Fig. 2. Simplified structural map of mid-Norway illustrating the inversion features in relationship to main structural provinces and structures. Abbreviations: BL, Bivrost Lineament; EJMFZ, East Jan Mayen Fracture Zone; GR, Gjallar Ridge; HD, Hedda Dome; HHA, Helland Hansen Arch; HSD, Havsule Dome; ID, Isak Dome; JML, Jan Mayen Lineament; MA, Modgunn Arch; ND, Naglfar Dome; NS, Någrind Syncline; OL, Ormen Lange Dome; SM, Souther Modgunn Arch; VD, Vema Dome; VS, Vigrid Syncline. Red lines refer to seismic profiles shown in Figures 3 & 6. UTM Zone 33 projection.

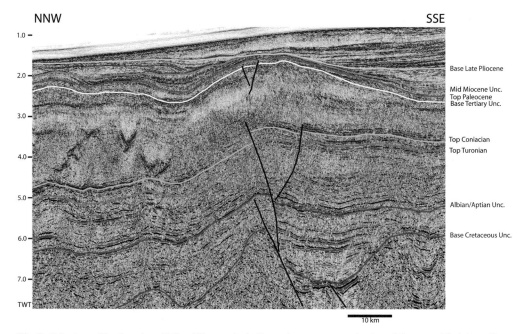

NNW   SSE

Base Late Pliocene

Mid Miocene Unc.
Top Paleocene
Base Tertiary Unc.

Top Coniacian
Top Turonian

Albian/Aptian Unc.

Base Cretaceous Unc.

10 km

Fig. 3. Seismic profile of southern Helland Hansen Arch, illustrating reverse reactivation of the normal fault bounding the western side of the Rås sub-basin. Line of section shown on Figure 2.

domes (Figs 1 & 2). Structures generally assigned to this suite in the UK and Faroes sector to the south include the Pilot Whale Anticline and Wyville Thompson, Munkegrunnur and Ymir ridges (e.g. Boldreel & Andersen 1998; Johnson *et al.* 2005) (Fig. 1).

Numerous potential mechanisms have been suggested for the formation of the post-breakup domal structures. These include deformation of the sedimentary pile by far-field orogenic (principally Alpine) forces (e.g. Brekke 2000; Vågnes *et al.* 1998), reactivation of basement lineaments under spreading forces and particularly during plate reorganization (Doré & Lundin 1996), topographic body forces such as ridge push (e.g. Doré & Lundin 1996; Boldreel & Andersen 1998), mantle drag (e.g. Mosar *et al.* 2002) emphasized by pulses in flux of a supposed Iceland plume (e.g. Lundin & Doré 2002), and sedimentary flank loading and differential compaction (e.g. Stuevold *et al.* 1992; Kjeldstad *et al.* 2003). The main purpose of this paper is to review these and other potential mechanisms and assess their relative merits.

Timing (Fig. 4) is probably the most critical factor in distinguishing between potential mechanisms, because it allows us to equate phases of structural development with external factors such as plate boundary forces. For this purpose, key events during the development of the NE Atlantic

are described with reference to a series of four plate reconstructions (Fig. 5 a–d).

Rotation poles used for moving Greenland with respect to a fixed Eurasia, after Gaina *et al.* (2002) are:

Time (Ma)	Latitude (° N)	Longitude (° W)	Rotation angle (°)
53	52.28	123.2	11.2
33	68.22	131.53	7.64
18	68.58	132.58	4.5

Early Eocene (c. 53 Ma) (Fig. 5a)

An immediate precursor of breakup in the NE Atlantic was uplift and subaerial erosion along the line of incipient separation, together with voluminous basaltic magmatism (e.g. White *et al.* 1987). Plate reconstructions suggest that plate separation in the Labrador Sea and Baffin Bay occurred approximately in Campanian time (*c.* 82 Ma), close to the time proposed by Srivastava & Roest (1999), although the initial phase of plate separation was probably characterized by mantle exhumation (Louden *et al.* 1996). In late Maastrichtian time (*c.* 68 Ma) classic seafloor spreading with formation of basaltic oceanic crust began. This

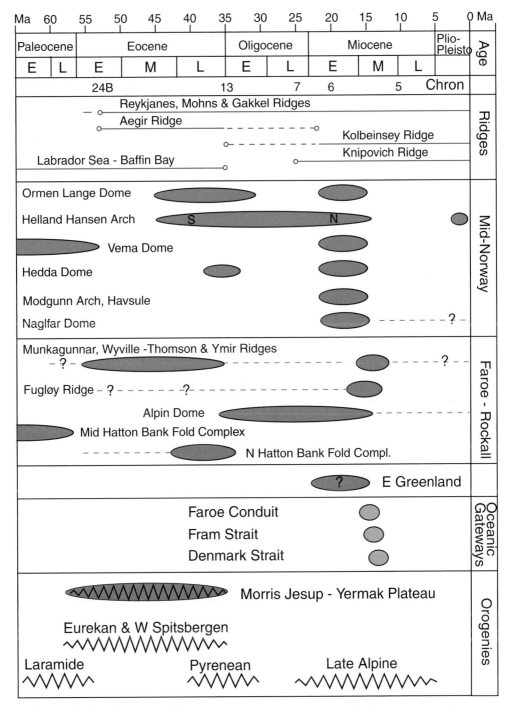

Fig. 4. Chronological diagram illustrating the approximate timing of inversion and its relationship to seafloor spreading, orogeny and oceanographic events. Modified after Lundin & Doré, 2002; Johnson *et al.* 2005; Smallwood 2004; Stoker *et al.*, 2005*a*, *b*.

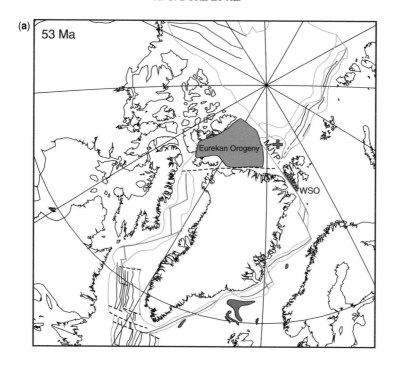

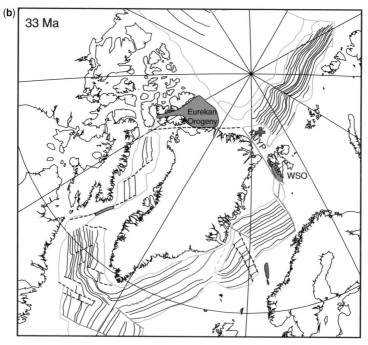

Fig. 5. A series of plate reconstructions for the NE Atlantic and Arctic to illustrate key events relating to development of the compressional structures (red blobs). Continent–ocean boundaries or transitions (orange lines), fracture zones (blue, active, black dashed, inactive), spreading axes (red, active, green, inactive) and isochrones (black). Passive margin compressional features undergoing development at the time of the reconstruction are shown in bright red. Orogens or areas of significant compression are marked with orange. Isochrons in the Eurasia Basin are mainly after Gaina *et al.* (2006), in the Labrador Sea after Oakey (2005), and in the NE modified after Lundin (2002) (further references therein) and Gaina *et al.* (2006). Continent–ocean boundaries in the Fram Strait are after Engen *et al.* (2008). Software used for

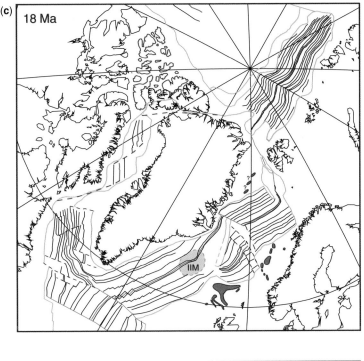

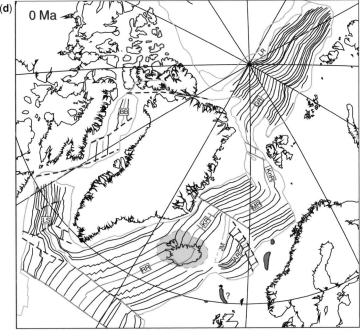

Fig. 5. (*Continued*) the reconstructions is SPlates (Torsvik *et al.* 2006). (**a**) Plate reconstruction to Chron 24 b, 53 Ma. WSO, West Spitsbergen orogenic belt. The plus sign and MJYP represents the Morris Jesup Rise and Yermak Plateau, areas of anomalously high ocean floor which, highly conjecturally, may represent extensions of the orogenic belt. (**b**) Plate reconstruction to Chron 13, 33 Ma. (**c**) Plate reconstruction to Chron 5, 18 Ma. IIM, Iceland Insular Margin. (**d**) Plates at present, 0 Ma. AR, Aegir Ridge; BB, Baffin Bay; GR, Gakkel Ridge; JM, Jan Mayen microcontinent; KR, Kolbeinsey Ridge; KnR, Knipovitch Ridge; LR, Lomonosov Ridge; LS, Labrador Sea; MR, Mohns Ridge; RR, Reykjanes Ridge.

estimate is somewhat earlier than that proposed by Chalmers & Pulvertaft (2001) (Chron 27, 61 Ma). Upon opening of the NE Atlantic in early Eocene (53.7 Ma), the simultaneous spreading in the two arms of the North Atlantic resulted in Greenland being driven northward relative to the Barents Sea and Canadian Arctic margins, with the development of a transpressional shear margins at the Barents–Greenland boundary, whereas near perpendicular convergence at the North America–Greenland boundary in Nares Strait formed the Eurekan orogenic belt. Immediately following breakup much of the anomalously elevated separation line collapsed and was inundated, but topographically positive areas were maintained along the shear margins and in the orogen to the north. The crustal nature (oceanic versus continental) of the Yermak Plateau and Morris–Yesup Rise at the termination of the Nansen–Gakkel Ridge against northern Greenland is still not resolved. However, these anomalously elevated areas may concievably be elements of the Eurekan and West Spitsbergen foldbelt.

Offshore Mid-Norway, initial growth of compressive structures such as the Ormen Lange Dome and Helland-Hansen Arch began in the middle Eocene (Lundin & Doré 2002) while farther southwest in the Faroes–Rockall area some authors claim compressional deformation may have begun at the time of breakup, i.e as early as late Paleocene–early Eocene (e.g. Boldreel & Andersen 1998).

Early Oligocene (c. 33 Ma) (Fig. 5b)

At the onset of Oligocene time, at Chron 13, drift between Greenland and Norway switched from a NW–SE to a more east–west vector, resulting in a radical reconfiguration of the North Atlantic spreading geometries (e.g. Faleide *et al.* 1993). The reason for the change of motion is unclear, but in terms of plate-wide kinematics, it may have been related to the contemporaneous Pyrenean phase of Tethyan closure (Fig. 4), which radically affected the southwestern margin of the Eurasian Plate.

A spreading link had begun to develop between Jan Mayen and East Greenland, via the Kolbeinsey Ridge to the Mohns Ridge. Linkage was achieved between the northward propagating Kolbeinsey Ridge and the Mohns Ridge at Chron 13. Activity on the shear margin between the Barents Sea–Spitsbergen and Greenland ceased and gave way to rifting and eventually to passive drift, with the gradual linkage of the Nansen–Gakkel Ridge in the Nansen Basin with the Mohns Ridge via the nascent Knipovich Ridge. At the same time, all the compressional belts around Greenland, in the Davis Strait, on Spitsbergen along the SW Barents

Sea margin, and the Eurekan Orogeny in the Canadian Arctic ceased, as did the development of the anomalously high ocean-floor between North Greenland and Spitsbergen comprising the Yermak Plateau and Morris–Jesup Rise. Spreading in the Labrador Sea and Baffin Bay is generally accepted to have ceased at Chron 13 times, with the result that Greenland became effectively part of the North American Plate (Kristoffersen & Talwani 1977).

Moderate landmass uplift took place at this time on the Norwegian mainland and in East Greenland, with continuing minor evolution of compressional structures in the Norwegian Sea (Lundin & Doré 2002) and Faroes–Rockall area (Johnson *et al.* 2005).

Middle Miocene (c. 18 Ma) (Fig. 5c)

The middle Miocene saw an important phase of development of the compressional features, both in the Norwegian Sea (Lundin & Doré 2002) and Faroes–Rockall area (Johnson *et al.* 2005). This interval was not marked locally by significant changes in spreading direction, but nevertheless included some important events in the development of the NE Atlantic.

To the south, in the Betic Chain (southern Spain), the main phase of orogenic compression occurred at this time (Berástegui *et al.* 1998), also roughly contemporaneous with the Late Alpine Tethyan closure phase, which lasted from Miocene to early Pliocene (e.g. Ziegler 1988).

The Wyville–Thomson Ridge complex (eastern part of the Greenland–Faroe Ridge) became breached at this time, possibly due to compressional buckling, resulting in development of the Faroe Conduit (Stoker *et al.* 2005a, b). Breaching this major bathymetric barrier permitted oceanic circulation between the Norwegian–Greenland Sea and the northern Atlantic, and led to deposition of major contourite drift deposits (Fig. 6).

Rifting that had started in earliest Oligocene times in the Fram Strait and along the SW Barents Sea margin gave way to seafloor spreading in middle Miocene time (c. 18 Ma according to our in-house work, and 16 Ma according to Engen *et al.* 2008). Thereby, a continuous Atlantic spreading ridge was established between the southern tip of the South Atlantic and the tip of the Gakkel Ridge in the Laptev Sea of the Arctic, spanning approximately half the Earth's circumference. It is intriguing to speculate whether this fundamental link-up resulted in any circulation changes in the underlying mantle, with potential implications for uplift and body force, as suggested in a later (late Pliocene) context by Stoker *et al.* (2005a). Certainly, uplift of landmasses can, locally, be timed

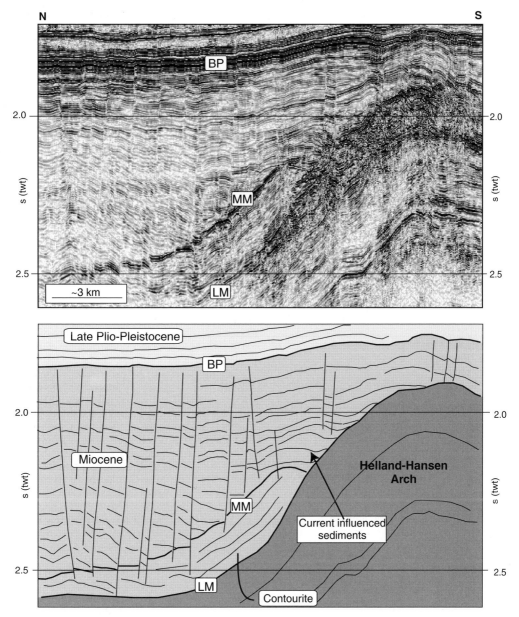

Fig. 6. Seismic profile of northern Helland Hansen Arch, illustrating the mid-Miocene growth phase. Two phases of Miocene contourite deposition along the western flank of the arch have been interpreted to reflect a significant mid-Miocene change in the bottom-current circulation system in response to the compressive episode (Hjelstuen *et al.* 2004; Stoker *et al.* 2005*a*). BP, Base Late Pliocene; MM, Middle Miocene unconformity; LM, Top Lower Miocene. After Hjelstuen *et al.* 2004. Line of section shown on Figure 2.

to the middle Miocene. Southern Norway was uplifted and sediments were shed southwards toward the Central Graben and Denmark (e.g. Jordt *et al.* 2000; Rasmussen 2004). The northern North Sea was subject to uplift, subaerial erosion, and associated valley incision into Oligocene strata during the Miocene (Jordt *et al.* 2000 and references therein) and seismic mapping has led to proposed incised valleys draining NW into the Møre Basin (Martinsen *et al.* 1999). Major eastward

shelf progradation off NE Greenland has been proposed to be of Miocene age based on seismic
interpretation (Hamann *et al.* 2005), and must
reflect a major uplift event of the NE Greenland
margin regardless of the precise age. Notably,
these seismically mapped sequences remain uncali-
brated by drilling and their significance cannot be
appreciated fully until better time constraints have
been obtained.

The Iceland Insular Margin is an enigmatic
feature in the NE Atlantic, whose origin remains
poorly understood. The *c.* 500 km wide plateau
may have originated from lower crustal flow
above the presumed Iceland plume (Jones &
Maclennan 2005). Another possibility is that the
plateau represents a major phase of subaerial flood
basalt flow, over pre-existing oceanic crust.
Lacking firm evidence from age dated cores, the
age of the Iceland Insular Margin is only loosely
confined to the Miocene (Ellen, 2002). However,
it is remarkable that the dominant phase of NE
Atlantic compression occurred in middle Miocene
time and that these compressional features form an
arc centred on Iceland (e.g. Figs 1 & 8). A causal
relationship is therefore possible, and is discussed
in detail later.

Late Pliocene to Recent (illustrated by reconstruction at 0 Ma) (Fig. 5d)

The Late Pliocene marked a significant environmental change in the northern hemisphere, reflecting the interaction between climate deterioration
and a pre-existing landscape. Major prograding
wedges forming mouth trough fans are especially
well developed off the Mid-Norwegian, the SW
and north Barents Sea margins, and to a smaller
extent off central East Greenland (Vorren &
Laberg 1997). Smaller prograding wedges exist as
far south as offshore northern Ireland (Stoker
et al. 2005a).

Stoker *et al.* (2005a) have argued convincingly
that early Pliocene tectonic uplift predated the late
Pliocene glaciation. Recent redating of the Molo
Formation offshore mid-Norway (Eidvin *et al.*
2007), places this prominent and widespread
fluvial delta in the earliest Pliocene. The delta
marks a significant basinward shift of the Norwegian palaeocoastline along the formation's
mapped extent from Lofoten to mid-Norway (e.g.
Henriksen & Weimer 1996). These fluvial deposits
are geometrically and compositionally different
from the volumetrically much larger overlying
late Pliocene and younger glaciomarine prograding
wedges of the Naust Formation. The timing and
environmental change between the Molo and
Naust formations agree with Stoker *et al.*'s

(2005a) suggestion of an early Pliocene tectonic
uplift predating the climatic change and associated
erosional and isostatic uplift.

It has been proposed that an early Pliocene plate
reorganization caused the development of the
Panama Isthmus (Cloetingh *et al.* 1990), ending
communication between the Atlantic and Pacific
Oceans, and instead forcing the equatorial Atlantic
waters to circulate northward (Lear *et al.* 2003).
Such a development would support the proposal
that already existing topographic highs acted as
nucleation points upon which the ice caps started
to grow (Eyles 1996).

Potential mechanisms for development of the compressional structures

Gravity loading, spreading and sliding

The outer parts of many passive margins are characterized by deep-water foldbelts, commonly kinematically coupled to extension near the shelf break.
Most of these foldbelts are gravity induced. They
did not form by tectonic shortening but were essentially a result of rapid sediment input into the
passive margin basins. They are by far the most
common of the compressional features around the
Atlantic, occurring for example offshore West
Africa, off Brazil and in the USA Gulf of Mexico.
The foldbelts generally formed as a result of gravitational gliding on a dipping low-friction substrate
or by gravitational spreading by differential
loading of sedimentary systems. Coupling between
the extensional and compressional regimes is particularly efficient where a laterally continuous
weak layer can be utilized as a decollement.
When exceptionally weak layers are present, such
as salt, gravity gliding of the overburden initiates
on very low-angle dip slopes (e.g. Vendeville &
Jackson 1992). Passive margins obtain dip
through basinward increasing thermal subsidence.
Hence, gravity gliding and associated deep-water
foldbelts are common along some passive margin
regions, particularly where a widespread weak post-
rift layer is present. The West African and Brazilian
Aptian salt basins are such examples.

The deep-water foldbelts readily form where the
low-friction substrate terminates basinward, such
as against the outer high of the West African and
Brazilian margins, where the salt terminates laterally (e.g. Cramez & Jackson 2000; Mohriak *et al.*
1998, 2002). Lacking a basinward regional dip, a
sedimentary succession above a mechanically
weak layer can still be induced to extend by
asymmetric loading, such as from a prograding
shelf. Such deformation is termed gravity spreading
(Vendeville & Jackson 1992) and can also be

coupled with foldbelts. Large deltas generate such asymmetric loading and commonly are associated with deep-water foldbelts (e.g. McClay *et al.* 1998); the Niger delta is an example. In these settings, coupling between extension near the shelf break and the deep-water foldbelt may occur via overpressured shales, or possibly via source rocks going through the window of maturation.

However, evidence of this kind of linkage is missing in the NE Atlantic setting. Although detachments along locally developed Triassic halites have been proposed for the Halten Terrace (Withjack *et al.* 1989) these developments appear to be local, without the potential to form a universal detachment surface throughout the margin. There is no known seismic evidence to suggest that the Cenozoic domes detach at depth. The compressional structures tend to be basin-centred, not at the seaward edge of the margin as is the case for many of the southern Atlantic gravity-induced foldbelts. Finally, the hinterland loading – detachment – foldbelt assemblage is not observed in the area, although as we shall see below, sedimentary loading enhanced the flanks of some structures. As also shown earlier, there is evidence of hinterland uplift and associated sedimentary input to the passive margin basins in the mid-Miocene (Stoker *et al.* 2005*b*; Davies *et al.* 2004). However, in the main areas where compressional structures are observed (Norwegian Sea and Faroes–Rockall) they do not seem to be associated with contemporaneous mid-Miocene progradation. The one potential candidate for such a progradation, the Molo Formation off mid-Norway (Løseth & Henriksen 2005) has recently been redated as early Pliocene (Eidvin *et al.* 2007).

Flank enhancement by sedimentary loading

The major Helland Hansen Arch off mid-Norway has been proposed to relate to asymmetric loading from a major prograding Plio-Pleistocene glaciomarine sequence, in combination with asymmetric thermal subsidence (e.g. Stuevold *et al.* 1992; Kjeldstad *et al.* 2003). This therefore appears to be a mechanism requiring no tectonic shortening at all. Although we recognize the importance of late asymmetric sedimentary loading to forming the east flank of the Helland Hansen Arch (Lundin & Doré 2002) it is less clear that asymmetric thermal subsidence has generated the western flank of the compressional feature. 3D backstripping and thermal subsidence modelling revealed that the Helland Hansen Arch cannot be completely removed when the asymmetric eastern load is stripped off and when a western asymmetric

thermal effect is applied (Roberts *et al.* 2002). The presence of a mid-Miocene unconformity over the top of the arch (Brekke 2000) is strong evidence that the feature did not initiate only from lateral loading by the Plio-Pleistocene wedge of sediments. Certainly, Plio-Pleistocene loading cannot be a universal dome-forming mechanism in the NE Atlantic since many domes exist beyond the influence of such loads (Stoker *et al.* 2005*a*). It is probably more correct to view the Plio-Pleistocene progradation as a mechanism sustaining or enhancing pre-existing compressional features rather than one forming them.

More probably, all or most of the domes may have been enhanced by sedimentation and differential compaction on the flanks. Recent work by Gómez & Vergés (2005) using sequential backstripping has led them to propose a tectonic contribution to the Helland Hansen Arch of as little as 27% of the total amplitude, with an equivalent value of 37% for the Vema Dome. The rest of the amplitude in both cases is interpreted to result from loading and differential compaction of the structures' flanks. Should this prove to be the case, the tectonic strain levels required to create the passive margin domes (i.e. crustal shortening) may be even lower than previously supposed – a fraction of a percent according to Gómez & Vergés (2005).

Transfer of orogenic stress

From latest Paleocene to the end of the Eocene, a shear margin existed along the Barents Sea western margin, relaying spreading between the Norwegian Sea and Eurasian Basin, while orogeny took place in Spitsbergen and the Canadian Arctic islands due to the northerly movement and impact of Greenland on North American–Arctic lithosphere (see earlier sections and Lundin & Doré 2005) (Figs 5a, b). Restraining and releasing bends along the shear margin created transpressive (Hornsund Fault Zone) and transtensional (Sørvestsnaget Basin) segments (e.g. Faleide *et al.* 1993; Steel *et al.* 1985). The West Spitsbergen Orogeny has been attributed to convergent dextral slip along the shear margin, although the direction of structural transport appears to have been from west to east, orthogonal to the margin (Faleide *et al.* 1988). In the Canadian Arctic (Eurekan) orogen thrusting was to the SE, almost perfectly coincident with the convergence vector between Greenland and North America (Oakey 1994, 2005).

The Eurekan and West Spitsbergen foldbelts formed from northward translation of Greenland in Eocene time (between Chrons 24 and 13). Collision with the North American and Eurasian plates ended in earliest Oligocene (Chron 13) when Eurasia moved obliquely away. Plate reconstructions back to Chron 13 reveal that the Yermak Plateau (NW of Svalbard) and the Morris Jesup Plateau north of Greenland formed a single feature prior to Chron 13 (Fig. 5b). This common plateau, here called the Morris Jesup–Yermak Plateau (MJYP) was located between the Eurekan and West Spitsbergen orogens. Based simply on the location of the MJYP, it is tempting to include it as part of a more widespread region of compression north of Greenland (e.g. Brozena *et al.* 2003). However, the MJYP remains somewhat enigmatic because it is not proven whether the plateau consists of continental crust, oceanic crust or a combination of the two. For alternative interpretations see Feden *et al.* (1979) and Ritzmann & Jokat (2003).

This occurrence of orogeny, transpression and transtension on a section of continuous shelf is a factor frequently overlooked in the search for candidate mechanisms for the NE Atlantic inversion structures. In terms of timing, the middle Eocene and early Oligocene initiation of structures such as Ormen Lange and Helland Hansen on the Mid-Norwegian shelf began during this activity (Lundin & Doré 2002), while some structuring farther south in the Faroes–Rockall area essentially began at breakup time (Johnson *et al.* 2005). It is therefore tempting to envisage a regime of distributed compression along the NE Atlantic margin in Eocene times associated with plate interaction between Greenland and North America. It is similarly attractive to postulate a link between the NE Greenland shelf structures (Hamann *et al.* 2005) and the adjacent Barents shear margin. Problems with this concept are: (1) stresses would need to have been propagated between the orogen and Mid-Norwegian shelf via a developing ocean basin, or south of the southern termination of the Senja Fracture Zone where little shear should have been taking place (Fig. 5a, b); (2) logically, such propagation along the NE Atlantic shelf should have involved strike-slip zones parallel to the basin axes; no evidence has been brought forward for such activity; and (3) propagation of such stress as far south as Rockall is unlikely.

Transmission of stress from the Alpine orogen—essentially representing Tethyan closure and the collision of Africa and Eurasia—has commonly been cited as a likely cause of the compressive deformation on the NE Atlantic shelves, e.g. for the Rockall Trough (Roberts 1989), and for mid-Norway (Vågnes *et al.* 1998 and most notably Brekke 2000). Transmission of stress away from collisional fronts for distances up to 1300 km has been documented for a wide range of orogenic forelands (Ziegler 1988). Orientations of present-day maximum compressive stress from such sources as earthquake focal plane mechanisms and borehole break-outs are NW–SE for much of central and northern Europe, and for the adjacent Atlantic margin (see Fig. 7, an extract from the World Stress Map: Reinecker *et al.* 2005). This direction is consistent with the direction of closure between Eurasia and Africa. However the maximum compressive stress orientation is almost normal to the NE Atlantic spreading ridges and parallel to the direction of spreading. Hence, it is not possible to attribute the present day stress regime on the NE Atlantic margin conclusively to either Eurasia–Africa convergence or to NE Atlantic ridge push.

The Alpine orogeny began in the Early Cretaceous (Austrian Phase). Cenozoic movements were extremely complex, but three phases of more intense tectonic activity are generally recognized. They comprise the Early Alpine ('Laramide') of late Paleocene age, the Main Alpine ('Pyrenean') approximately straddling the Eocene–Oligocene boundary and the Late Alpine (Miocene–Pliocene starting about 20 Ma) (Fig. 4). See Ziegler (1988) for the most complete description of this activity as related to associated foreland deformation.

It is possible to equate these phases, in a broad sense, with growth of the domes. Brekke (2000) attributes particular importance to the Main Alpine (Eocene–Oligocene) events, although precise dating appears to place this episode between mid-Eocene inception and main Miocene growth of the mid-Norwegian domes. The Late Alpine orogeny appears to correspond roughly in time with the latter growth phase, and is a plausible causative factor (Fig. 4). Our main issue with this initially attractive hypothesis relates to the distribution of foreland deformation in central Europe. The Alpine phases, although varying in time, space and intensity, caused inversion in the basins of central Europe and propagated northwestwards into the southern North Sea to invert depocentres such as the Broad Fourteens, Sole Pit and West Netherlands basins (Ziegler 1988). This deformation is observed in the south Central Graben and, west of Britain, the Celtic Sea basins, but no further north. The northern North Sea and Møre Basin are essentially devoid of compressive deformation (Pascal & Gabrielsen 2001). It is thus difficult to understand why such activity should pick up again in, say, the Faroe–Shetland Basin, and even more difficult to envisage in the Vøring Basin, where the Baltic Shield separates the area from the Alpine orogen. Finally, compressive domes identified in East Greenland (Price *et al.* 1997) and on the NE Greenland shelf (Hamann *et al.* 2005) cannot be attributed to direct propagation of Alpine stress since these areas were decoupled

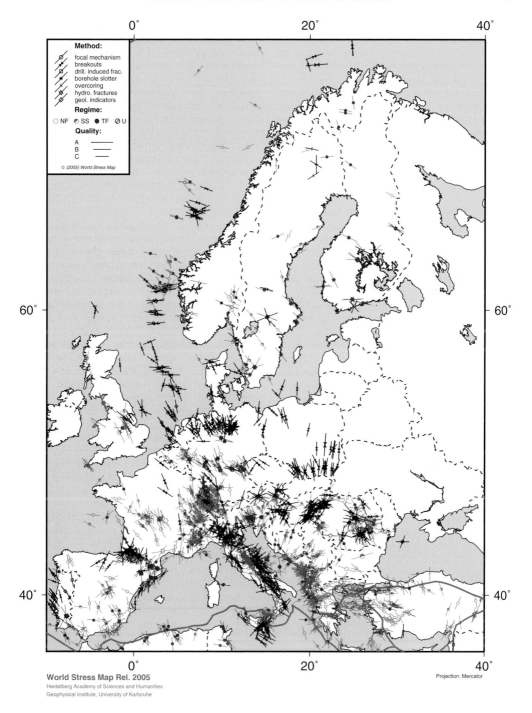

Fig. 7. Present day stress map for Europe. Extract from the World Stress Map (Reineker *et al.* 2005). Long axes of stress plots show orientation of present day maximum compressive stress from earthquake focal plane mechanisms, borehole breakouts and other sources.

from the Alpine orogen by an intervening spreading ridge.

Further investigation of links between the Alpine deformation and the NE Atlantic structures would require a more in-depth examination of 'time and place' in the orogenic belt. Correlation with generalized Alpine phases is probably over-simplistic. During the orogeny different parts of the foldbelt were active at different times in terms of thrusting and nappe formation. This in turn caused varying penetration of deformation into the Central European foreland along the strike of orogenic belt at any given time. Furthermore, the conditions for long-distance transmission of stress are not fully understood. Ideally, this process would require coupling between the collisional plates at the subduction zone. The lithospheric level at which such coupling takes place, and whether this would correspond with a well defined phase of thrusting/nappe formation, are issues that remain to be resolved.

Reactivation of basement lineaments

The long-axes of the compressional domes on the NE Atlantic seaboard show a rough correspondence with those of the the Mesozoic basins, with a pre-ponderance of NE–SW and north–south trends (Figs 1 & 2). It is thus a workable *a priori* assumption that the structures resulted from inversion of the Mesozoic basins by classic mechanisms such as basin-centre bulge, reverse reactivation and half-graben extrusion. The Helland Hansen Arch (Figs 3 & 6) appears to correspond well to this type of mechanism. On its NW flank, NW- or west-vergent folding is linked to reversely reactivated segments of the Fles Fault Complex, an easterly-verging Jurassic–Cretaceous normal fault system (Doré & Lundin 1996). However, in most cases, evidence of classic inversion is essentially circumstantial (trend-based) and is not supported by a direct fault linkage. This principle is well illustrated in the UK portion of the Faroe–Shetland Basin (Davies *et al.* 2004; see also earlier work by Roberts 1989). Here, up to 17 elongate NE–SW and NNE–SSW highs, interpreted to have formed due to middle–late Miocene compression, appear to overlie the thickest parts of the Mesozoic basin system. The seismic evidence does not provide a conclusive link between these features and under-lying basin faults. Evidence of reactivation is cir-cumstantial (albeit strong) and is provided by thickness considerations (see above), trends and fold wavelengths.

In other cases there appears to be no link at all to a basin-parallel fault or half-graben. Examples include the Ormen Lange, Havsule Dome, and Modgunn Arch at the transition between the

Vøring and Møre Basins. The junction between these basins occurs at a diffuse NW–SE trending basin cross-cutting dislocation, the Jan Mayen Lineament (Blystad *et al.* 1995). This lineament also coincides with a marked offset between the two basin axes, and links northwestward with a major oceanic fracture zone, the East Jan Mayen Fracture Zone (Fig. 2). The domes appear to be arrayed along the length of the Jan Mayen Linea-ment, suggesting an association.

The NW lineaments are part of a structural suite that extends over the whole NE Atlantic margin (e.g. Lundin & Rundhovde 1993; Rumph *et al.* 1993) and in the UK–Faroes sector includes the Judd, Erlend and Clair Transfers. They are gener-ally presumed to have formed as transfer zones (cf. Morley *et al.* 1990), accommodating displace-ment between different rift segments during exten-sion of the Mesozoic basins. They may in some cases have an older origin, having been predisposed to develop at major basement (Caledonian and older) dislocations; see for example Dicken (1992) on offshore British Isles, and Fichler *et al.* (1999) on offshore mid-Norway. Although workers on the UK and Faroes margin attribute the compressional structures primarily to buttres-sing against basin-parallel structures, these sources also provide evidence for implication of the NW–SE transfer suite. This influence may be mainly a function of the fact that the transfer zones affected the original basin configuration, and hence the location of any compressive reactiva-tion (e.g. Johnson *et al.* 2005; Kimbell *et al.* 2005). In some instances, however, late Cenozoic strike-slip reactivation of NW–SE zones such as the Magnus Lineament is suggested by changes in strike and mud diapirism (Johnson *et al.* 2005; Kimbell *et al.* 2005).

Doré & Lundin (1996) suggested that the driving force for reactivation of the NW–SE lineaments was ridge push from the Atlantic spreading centre. Following previous workers (e.g. Brekke & Riis 1987) it was proposed that the main period of reac-tivation could be attributed to the change in spread-ing direction from NW–SE to a more east–west vector that took place at the beginning of the Oligocene (Chron 13, 33 Ma: see geological history section). According to this hypothesis, the change in plate motion created a sinistral transpres-sive regime via shear adjustments along the NW–SE lineaments. It was supported by the presence of an apparent sinistral wrench structural assemblage along the NW–SE lineaments, particu-larly the Jan Mayen Lineament (e.g. north–south trending folds with local east–west tensional faults). Doré & Lundin (1996) suggested a similar strike-slip association of compressive structures with other NW–SE lineaments offshore mid-Norway (e.g. Vema Dome with the Surt Lineament, Hedda Dome with the Bivrost Lineament).

Subsequent work has led us to re-evaluate this hypothesis. Although the evidence for a sinistral wrench suite is still strong (on the mid-Norwegian shelf at least) the tie to the Chron 13 plate reorganization is less persuasive, for the following reasons: (1) new evidence from drilling and interpretation of 3D datasets emphasizes the importance of the early to middle Miocene phase of growth of the north–south anticlines along the Jan Mayen Lineament (Ormen Lange Dome, Havsule Dome and Modgunn Arch), i.e. some 15–20 Ma after onset of plate reorganization; and (2) change in plate motion would not have affected the direction of ridge push, since this effect is a body force from the elevated spreading ridge. These arguments do not preclude reactivation of members of the NW–SE transfer suite by either body forces such as ridge push or by directional forces associated with spreading such as basal drag—they simply de-emphasize the link between these potential mechanisms and plate reorganization.

The array of north–south anticlines along the diffuse onshore projection of the East Jan Mayen Fracture Zone (Fig. 2) remains a strong indicator of probable wrench movement along the lineament, from whatever cause. This observation encapsulates the basement reactivation argument. Although there is strong circumstantial evidence that basement structure was implicated in the formation of the compressional structures, basement lineaments were essentially conduits for expression of strain and not an *a priori* cause of the deformation.

Plate driving forces

Candidate driving forces for lithospheric plates are: (1) the plate boundary forces, i.e. ridge-push and slab-pull; and (2) shear traction (mantle-drag) forces excerted at the base of the lithosphere by the convecting asthenosphere. Ziegler (1993) suggested that interaction of mantle drag forces with deviatoric tensional stresses in the lithosphere above upwelling asthenosphere cells are important to the breakup of large continental masses such as Pangaea, whereas the plate boundary forces may play a more important role during continent dispersal.

The North Atlantic–Arctic evolved from overall northward propagation of the Central Atlantic spreading axis, possibly interacting with a separate Arctic spreading system. The current spreading axes separate North America from Eurasia; however, a three-plate system including Greenland existed for approximately 20 Ma in the Eocene–earliest Oligocene. Disregarding pre-breakup rifting, the oldest plate separation in the NE Atlantic region dates back approximately to late Maastrichtian time (Chron 31, *c.* 68 Ma) when the Labrador Sea opened. Some 15 Ma later, in early Eocene time (Chron 24b, *c.* 53 Ma), the NE Atlantic and Norwegian–Greenland Sea opened. The two arms of seafloor spreading, Labrador Sea and NE Atlantic, were kinematically linked with the Gakkel Ridge in the Eurasia Basin; both arms were active until earliest Oligocene time (Chron 13, *c.* 33 Ma).

The effect of opening the NE Atlantic was to translate Greenland north-northwestward. Greenland's triangular shape permitted it being squeezed by two opposed spreading forces, analogous to squeezing a lemon seed. As a result, Greenland impinged upon the Canadian Arctic islands and the SW Barents Sea margin, resulting in the Eurekan and West Spitsbergen orogenies (see earlier sections). The significance of this observation is that a plate-driving force capable of causing these orogenies would easily be able to create the low-strain passive margin domes. It appears possible to exclude traditional 'passive' mechanisms such as slab-pull as the driving force: we know of no evidence for a relict subduction zone within the Eurekan orogen. Ridge-push, which most published work suggests is only capable of generating stresses of approximately 2–$3 \times 10^{12}\,\mathrm{N\,m^{-1}}$ (Haxby & Turcotte 1978; Dahlen 1981; Fleitout & Froidevaux 1982; Kusznir 1991), is insufficient to have caused the observed compressional shortening in the Eurekan orogen. So what force caused the orogenies? Potential candidates include:

1) Ziegler's (1993) idea of constructive interference between plate boundary forces and overall lithospheric motion relative to the deep mantle. Palaeomagnetically-constrained plate tectonic reconstructions reveal that North America, Greenland, and Eurasia all travelled northwestward relative to the deep mantle, although simultaneously moving away from each other as a result of plate separation (Torsvik *et al.* 2001). During Eocene time (Chron 24b–13) when Greenland acted as a separate plate, the NE Atlantic arm of spreading could conceivably have interfered constructively with the overall lithospheric drift applied to Greenland, pushing Greenland into North America and causing the Eurekan Orogeny. However, the mechanism for this common overall motion of dispersing plates is poorly understood.

2) Bott's (1993) proposal of enhanced ridge-push from anomalously warm asthenosphere (basically a plume). The current anomalous elevation of the NE Atlantic spreading axis, above sea-level on Iceland, and the widespread positive North Atlantic geoid anomaly may reflect an upper mantle thermal anomaly. As for normal ridge-push forces, Bott's enhanced mantle-drag force ought to act

symmetrically, i.e. affect both the Greenland and Eurasian plates. If one opts for the possibility that this force was responsible for the Eurekan Orogeny, it is still unclear why the more proximal areas along the NE Atlantic margins were only mildly deformed.

The model proposed by Kusznir *et al.* (2005) and Kusznir & Karner (2007) for continental lithosphere thinning leading to continental breakup and seafloor spreading initiation predicts that for volcanic margins the young continental margin lithosphere is placed into horizontal compression. In this model, developed to explain apparent depth-dependent stretching at continental margins, deformation and thinning of continental lithosphere leading to breakup occurs in response to an upwelling divergent flow field emanating from the asthenosphere. Such flow could occur ahead of the propagating tip of a spreading ridge or, locally, from a mantle plume. Differing breakup lithosphere geometries are explained through the interplay between the upwelling divergent flow field (with a velocity V_z) and the rate of plate separation (V_x). During the formation of volcanic margins, V_z is significantly larger than V_x due to thermal buoyancy (Neilsen & Hopper 2003) and the young continental margin lithosphere suffers horizontal compression during early seafloor spreading.

This model therefore holds the possibility of compression, which could be validated by searching for examples of contractional structures close to the margins and associated with breakup. In the NE Atlantic margin, this mechanism would be mainly expected to apply at time of breakup and shortly thereafter, when the upwelling flow field was close to, and acting upon, the margin. It may be a candidate for the earliest Cenozoic compressive deformation phases recorded off mid-Norway (Lundin & Doré 2002) and in the Faroes–Rockall area (Boldreel & Andersen 1998; Johnson *et al.* 2005) but is unable to explain later compressional structuring including the regional peak in the mid-Miocene (Fig. 4).

Body forces

Differences in topography and/or lithospheric density between adjacent areas, and the resulting lithostatic head, can create a horizontal pressure gradient and thus the potential for crustal deformation. Unless bordered by exceptionally high continental topography, the primary body force influencing passive margins is likely to be ridge push, i.e. the gravitational force exerted by a thermally elevated spreading ridge (eg Turcotte & Schubert 1982). As indicated earlier, ridge-push is capable of generating stresses of approximately $2–3 \times 10^{12} \, \mathrm{N \, m^{-1}}$ (Haxby & Turcotte 1978;

Dahlen 1981; Fleitout & Froidevaux 1982; Kusznir 1991), which could be enhanced in the region of an asthenosphere anomaly such as a mantle plume. These forces are capable of creating mild compressive deformation on the adjacent margin, depending on its structure and elevation. However, timing remains a critical problem. The Eocene–Oligocene inception of the compression does not appear to leave time for the generation of sufficient relief between the ocean ridge and the young rifted continental margin. In addition, young oceanic lithosphere might be too weak to serve as efficient stress guide and transmit stresses to the margin. More importantly, the episodic nature of the compression with a significant phase in the mid-Miocene seems difficult to attribute to ridge push, which should be a constant or gradually developing effect. To seek a solution, it is necessary to examine the interaction between the NE Atlantic ridges and Iceland during the Cenozoic.

Although the opening of the NE Atlantic and Norwegian–Greenland Sea can be described by a common pole of rotation (e.g. Talwani & Eldholm 1977), it is well recognized that the central segment of the NE Atlantic spreading system, consisting of the Aegir and Kolbeinsey ridge pair, is more complicated. Prior to the abandonment of the Aegir Ridge, the asymmetric fan-shaped spreading of Aegir Ridge was compensated by opposed asymmetric spreading along the Kolbeinsey Ridge. Of key interest too is the time of abandonment of the Aegir Ridge and/or the time when spreading along the Kolbeinsey Ridge changed from a northward propagating pattern to 'orthogonal' opening described by the overall NE Atlantic pole of rotation. Unfortunately, the time of abandonment of the Aegir Ridge remains unclear since the anomaly of the central axis appears to be a fused mix of magnetic signatures post-dating Chron 13 (33 Ma) (Jung & Vogt 1997). The final phase of spreading along the Aegir Ridge was ultra-slow, and the exact time of abandonment depends on how slow one allows the rate to become (e.g. Breivik *et al.* 2006). Another option is indirectly to determine the time of abandonment by the onset of 'orthogonal' opening along the Kolbeinsey Ridge. This appears to have occurred near Chron 6a (*c.* 21 Ma). Stacked aeromagnetic flight tracks (Vogt *et al.* 1980) centred on Chron 4 reveal parallel anomalies out to Chron 6a, while Chron 6b deviates in orientation and is here interpreted to be the last anomaly related to northward fan-shaped spreading (cf. Nunns 1983; Lundin & Doré 2005). Thus we argue that the Kolbeinsey Ridge had taken over most of the spreading from the Aegir Ridge by Chron 6a (*c.* 21 Ma, late early Miocene). The significance of this observation will become clear when we discuss (below) the distribution of domes on the adjacent Mid-Norwegian shelf.

We propose that there is a connection between the body force from the development of the Iceland Insular Margin and the widespread middle Miocene pulse of compression. Such an interpretation is attractive because: (1) the feature would seem to have potential for generation of a greater body force than a less elevated spreading ridge; and (2) it may provide a means to explain the onset of increased stress in mid-Cenozoic times. The interpretation is hampered, however, by the absence of conclusive dating of the Iceland Insular Margin. The offshore part of the plateau has not been sampled and age dated. An IODP drilling site in this area seems overdue.

The oldest basalts onshore Iceland are located along the west and east sides of the island and are of middle Miocene age (Jóhannesson & Sæmundsson 1998). Northward projection of the well-defined magnetic isochrons related to the Reykjanes Ridges onto the Greenland–Faroes Ridge and the Iceland Plateau yields different ages against the west and east side of the plateau (approx. Chron 13 and Chron 20 respectively) (Fig. 8). Making the simple assumption that the west and east sides formed simultaneously it can be argued that at least the east side of the plateau is considerably younger than the substrate of the Greenland–Faroes Ridge. This would be the case if a surge of magmatism had caused flood basalts to spread out radially over pre-existing oceanic crust. Extending this argument further, we propose as a testable working hypothesis that the Iceland Insular Margin as expressed by current bathymetry was initiated in middle Miocene time during a major magmatic event. The build-up of the Iceland Insular Margin would have induced a body force directed radially towards the margins of the NE Atlantic.

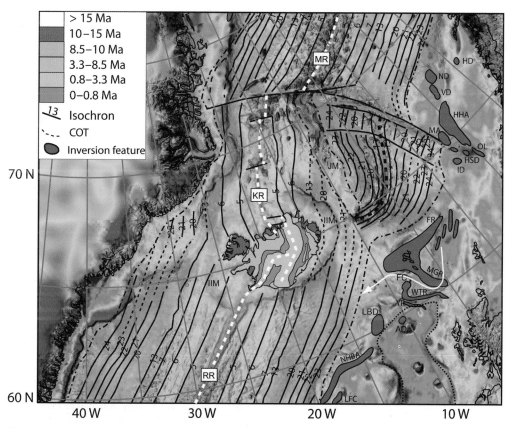

Fig. 8. Free air gravity draped on bathymetry and topography, with seafloor spreading isochrons, approximate continent–ocean transition, spreading axes and bedrock ages in Iceland from Jóhannesson & Sæmundsson (1998). For abbreviations see Figure 1. Polar stereographic north projection.

Body force generated by the Iceland Insular Margin

As indicated earlier, more accurately determining the time at which the present plateau developed could help to establish this link, since the structures developed spasmodically with an acme in the mid-Miocene. Of equal importance is whether the elevated Iceland Insular Margin could have created enough body force to cause deformation of the margins.

Figure 9a shows geoid elevation relative for the Iceland–NE Atlantic area, using the EGM96 geoid model relative to the reference shape of the Earth

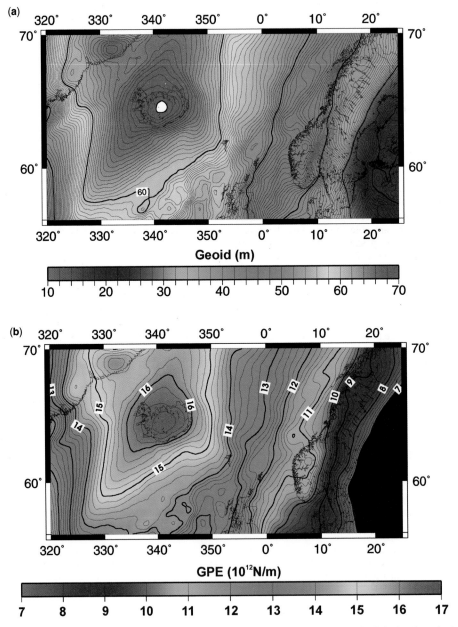

Fig. 9. (**a**) Geoid height anomaly map for the NE Atlantic, using the EGM96 geoid model. (**b**) Calculated gravitational potential energy based on (a). Regular Mercator Projection, central meridian 352.5°.

(Lemoine *et al.* 1996). Using the assumption of local isostasy, gravitational potential energy values (GPE) can be directly derived from geoid undulations (Turcotte & Schubert 1982). Bott (1991) demonstrated that the results obtained from this simplified approach do not differ significantly from those obtained applying more complex numerical models. The NE Atlantic GPE values are shown in Figure 9b. The difference in GPE between the Iceland Insular Margin and the adjacent Norwegian continental margin, and thus the force applied to the margin, is about 5×10^{12} N m^{-1}. Assuming that all the force is transmitted to a $c.$ 100 km-thick lithosphere and no dissipation takes place, a rough estimation for the horizontal stress gives 50 MPa applied to the whole lithospheric column, or $c.$100 to 150 MPa if we consider that the force concentrates on the mechanical boundary layer of the lithosphere (Parsons & McKenzie 1978; Kusznir 1991). This value appears to be higher than needed to cause yielding and shortening of the basement (e.g. Kusznir 1991; Ranalli 1995).

Note that this calculation is for the fully-expanded geoid, which in turn represents signals from sources located both at lithosphere levels and greater depths. If the geoid is truncated at higher degrees and orders, or conversely for long wavelengths, we are able to eliminate the signals associated with deep sources, e.g. located at the core–mantle interface (Bowin 1991) that are unlikely to transmit stresses to the lithosphere directly. As a consequence lower stress magnitudes than proposed above would be calculated. On the other hand, geoid trucation can also result in eliminating long-wavelength signals associated with relatively shallow sources (e.g. at asthenospheric levels) but having significant lateral extension. Thus, although our simple computation appears to show that the Iceland Insular Margin and associated mantle structure can create enough body force to cause deformation, the computed stress magnitudes rely on the true depth of the sources producing the geoid anomaly centred at the location of the plateau and appear to be dependent on the degree of coupling between the lithosphere and asthenoshere.

What governs the location of the compressional structures?

Assuming transmission of this stress through the lithosphere, it is reasonable to assume that it is propagated through the basement rather than through the young and ductile Cretaceous–Cenozoic basin fills on the margin. What factor, therefore, governs the position at which the basement will fail, either through new simple shear or through re-activation of existing shears, and thereby

generating compressional structures in the cover rocks? In general, the hotter the basement, the lower the stress levels required for fracturing to take place (Ranalli 1995). On a passive margin, hottest (and therefore weakest) basement would logically be found where the crystalline crust is thinnest and blanketed by the thickest overlying sedimentary pile.

To test this supposition, we have examined sedimentary thicknesses on the Norwegian Atlantic margin. These are plotted in Figure 10, the values broadly derived from the work of Ebbing *et al.* (2006). From the depth to basement map we generated a total sediment thickness map. From this map in turn we subtracted the thickness of the Plio-Pleistocene Naust formation (Riise *et al.* 2005) in order to reveal the pre-glacial sediment thicknesses. Also shown on Figure 10 are the approximate locations and shapes of the Cenozoic domal structures and the weakly inverted Vigrid and Någrind synclines, and it can be seen that there is a reasonably good correspondence between the structures and the sedimentary 'thicks' representing the deepest Cretaceous–Cenozoic basins. An exception is the more inboard basin of the Halten Terrace, where compressional structures are minor or absent. The thick sedimentary succession of the Halten Terrace is mainly of Triassic–Jurassic age, and it is therefore possible that the thinnest, hottest and weakest basement is to be found under the younger, more recently stretched Vøring Basin. This idea is also supported by geothermal gradients from unpublished industry well data. Although these data are generally recorded on structural 'highs' and should be regarded with some caution, the data available for the Norwegian margin show gradients in the order of 30–40 °C km^{-1} for the shelf, increasing to 40–50 °C km^{-1} in the deep basins.

Therefore, there are reasonable grounds to support the speculation that the hottest basement under the young, deep sedimentary basins of the margin was predisposed to shear under the influence of body forces from the adjacent ocean, with the largest contribution to these forces in the NE Atlantic coming from the Iceland Insular Margin. This force may not, on the other hand, have been sufficient to deform cooler basement areas. Our next research step will be to carry out numerical simulations to test whether this hypothesis, at present only supported by empirical observation, can be be sustained at the likely ranges of horizontal stress and basement temperature on the NE Atlantic margin. It also remains to be seen whether this idea forms a general explanation for compressive deformation of passive margins in the absence of nearby orogenic influences.

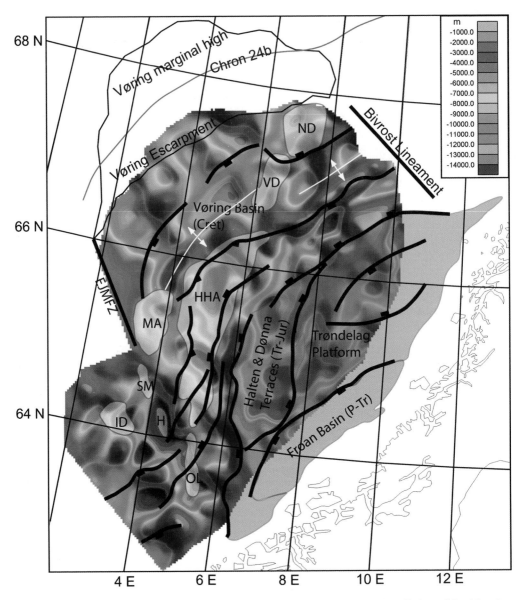

Fig. 10. Total sediment thickness map (excluding the thickness of the Plio-Pleistocene Naust Fm), overlain with main structural provinces, main fault systems and inversion features. A reasonably good correspondence between the inversion structures and the deepest Cretaceous–Cenozoic Basins is evident. For abbreviations see Figures 1 & 2. UTM Zone 33 projection.

Why are there few or no compressional features along the Møre margin?

The distribution of Cenozoic compressional features along the NE Atlantic margins is notable for the lack of such features along the Møre margin of Norway, in spite of a thick and presumably easily deformable sedimentary fill in the Møre Basin, up to 17 km in axial parts. If there is indeed a connection with body force generated from the Iceland Plateau, the Møre Basin should be in prime position for compression, and yet little is observed.

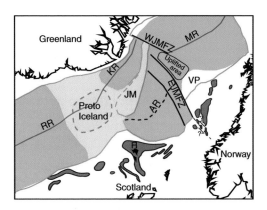

Fig. 11. Simplified crustal thickness map at Middle Miocene time (18 Ma), with inversion features marked in red. Abbreviations: AR, Aegir Ridge; EJMFZ, East Jan Mayen Fracture Zone; FI, Faroe Islands; JM, Jan Mayen microcontinent; MR, Mohns Ridge; KR, Kolbeinsey Ridge; RR, Reykjanes Ridge; VP, Vøring Plateau; WJMFZ, West Jan Mayen Fracture Zone. Blue, thin crust; orange, thick crust; yellow, significantly thicker crust. Area marked 'uplifted' represents Miocene uplift (Breivik *et al.* 2006). Simplified after Greenhalgh & Kusznir 2007.

Notably, this portion of the margin lies inboard of the extinct Aegir Ridge, suggesting a causative relationship. We suggest that the development of the Iceland Insular Margin not only provided the gravitational force responsible for the compressional deformation, but also was the decisive factor making the Kolbeinsey Ridge succeed over the Aegir Ridge and thereby generate the single spreading ridge in the central segment of the NE Atlantic. If so, the Aegir Ridge conceivably absorbed the compression by slowing down to ultraslow spreading, thereby shielding the Møre margin from this force (Figs 5c & 11).

A potential flaw in this argument is that the Aegir Ridge would also interpose between the Iceland Insular Margin and the Vøring Basin, where compressional domes are developed. This objection could be overcome if there was strain partitioning by lateral movement along the East Jan Mayen Fracture Zone and its margin prolongation, the Jan Mayen Lineament (Figs 2 & 11). This could conceivably allow transmission of stress to the Vøring Basin while allowing accomodating by shortening around the Aegir Ridge. The oceanic bathymetric high identified by Breivik *et al.* (2006) just NE of the East Jan Mayen Fracture Zone ('uplifted area' in Fig. 11) has been identified as overthickened oceanic crust associated with Late Miocene underplating, but speculatively may also be a result of strain accommodation along fracture zone.

Conclusions

(1) A suite of compressional structures is now well-documented on the Faroes–Rockall and Mid-Norwegian passive continental margins. Minor representatives of the suite have also been identified onshore SE Greenland and offshore NE Greenland. Although developed at very low strain levels, the structures include domes of substantial areal extent and structural relief. They are therefore interesting as petroleum exploration targets.

(2) By context, the structures are different from the gravity-induced foldbelts commonly found in the deep-water delta front settings elsewhere around the Atlantic (West Africa, Brazil and Gulf of Mexico).

(3) The structures developed from early Eocene breakup to Recent times, but underwent episodes of greater activity. A marked compressive episode in the middle Miocene is recorded by authorities working on Rockall, the Faroe–Shetland Basin and the Norwegian Sea. This episode also coincided with the development of a continuous Atlantic spreading system from the Laptev Sea in the Arctic to the southernmost South Atlantic. We further suggest a link with the inception of the Iceland Insular Margin, generally believed to have taken place in the Miocene but poorly constrained by dating. Conceivably, the development of this melting anomaly could reflect linkage of Arctic and Atlantic mantle convection systems.

(4) Sedimentary loading, either from progradation of thick Plio-Pleistocene deposits or consisting of simple differential compaction, enhanced the flanks of some or all of the compressional structures. This mechanism, however, cannot be used to model all of the relief of the features and is unlikely as a primary cause of the structures; an initial tectonic impetus is necessary.

(5) A mechanism involving far-field transmission of orogenic stress from the Alpine orogen to the south and/or the West Spitsbergen–Eurekan orogen to the north remains attractive, not least because of the episodic nature of the deformation. A problem with the Alpine hypothesis is the apparent absence of notable compression in intervening areas such as the northern North Sea. The West Spitsbergen–Eurekan system is separated from the area of interest by the Senja Fracture Zone, and evidence of stress transmission lengthways along the shelf by (for example) strike-slip is not observed. We have examined the driving force generating these northern orogenies, because it appears that they occurred in the absence of traditional 'passive' plate-driving mechanisms such as slab pull, suggesting in turn generation of compression by an 'active' drive from the spreading

ridges. We have not yet, however, settled on a convincing explanation for this apparent anomaly.

(6) There is a strong association throughout the margin between the compressional structures and the grain of the underlying Mesozoic basins and basement. Cross-cutting NW–SE transfer zones and lineaments also appear to have influenced some structures, with the association of the Jan Mayen Lineament with domes such as Ormen Lange being particularly impressive. Basement reactivation appears to influence strain localization, but does not provide an explanation for the primary cause of the compressive stress.

(7) Recent models of continental breakup involving divergent asthenospheric flow are capable of inducing compressive deformation on the margins, specifically where the rate of divergent flow exceeds the rate of plate separation, as postulated to be the case on volcanic margins. Compression in such cases would primarily be expected at or close to time of breakup, and has the potential to explain early Cenozoic deformation recorded offshore mid-Norway and in the Faroes–Rockall area. It would not explain the acme of the NE Atlantic margin compressive structures in mid-Cenozoic time.

(8) Ridge push, generally thought to be the dominant body force affecting passive margins, can in certain circumstances generate enough force to cause mild deformation. However, this mechanism alone does not seem to be able to explain either the episodic timing or the location of the structures.

(9) We suggest that development of the topographically high Iceland Insular Margin, currently rather loosely constrained to a magmatic event in the Miocene, may be strongly associated with development of the structures. This idea has the potential to explain the episodic development, specifically the pulse in the early middle Miocene, and the location of the structures in an apparent arc around Iceland.

(10) Modelling of the Gravitational Potential Energy (GPE) of the geoid undulation associated with the Iceland Insular Margin shows that enough horizontal stress can be generated to deform adjacent margins. This result depends on the depth filter applied, with greater forces deriving from greater lithosphere depths. Such values rely on the deep asthenospheric root of the plateau as well as the surface topography, and appear to be dependent on the degree of coupling between the lithosphere and asthenosphere.

(11) Accomodation of compression along the ultraslow-spreading Aegir Ridge, or in the anomalously thin oceanic crust of the adjacent Norway Basin, may explain the puzzling near-absence of compressional structures from the Møre Basin.

This model would require strain partitioning along the Jan Mayen Lineament, and idea that is strongly supported by the series of probably wrench-related anticlines along the lineament.

(12) We propose that the locus of the structures is predisposed by the position of hottest, weakest and most easily sheared basement, usually in the axial Cretaceous–Cenozoic depocentres. A superimposition of sedimentary thickness and the Cenozoic domes on the mid-Norway margin provides good empirical support for this hypothesis. Whether this idea could be a paradigm for passive margin compression depends on testing of additional areas.

(13) Critical future research is proposed to include: (a) further, more sophisticated modelling of the potential body force from the Iceland Insular Margin; (b) numerical simulations to determine whether there is indeed a connection between the locus of the compressive structures, the likely ranges of horizontal stress and basement temperature on the NE Atlantic margin; and (c) more precise dating of the Iceland Insular Margin, a surprisingly neglected line of research that could be accomplished via an IODP site or other offshore drilling.

The authors thank Howard Johnson and Martyn Stoker for thorough and constructive reviews. We gratefully acknowledge the use of the SPlates plate reconstruction software, developed in collaboration with the Geological Survey of Norway, and thank Carmen Gaina for her efforts in this project. The plate reconstructions were carried out in-house and we thank Phil Ball for his input to this. Grateful thanks to Berit Hjelstuen for allowing us to reproduce the section in Figure 6.

References

BERÁSTEGUI, X., BANKS, C. J., PUIG, C., TABERNER, C., WALTHAM, D. & FERNÁNDEZ, M. 1998. Lateral diapiric emplacement of Triassic evaporites at the southern margin of the Guadalquivir Basin, Spain. *In*: MASCLE, A., PUIGDEFÁBREGAS, C., LUTERBACHER, H. P. & FERNÁNDEZ, M. (eds) *Cenozoic Foreland Basins of Western Europe*. Geological Society, London, Special Publications, **134**, 49–68.

BLYSTAD, P., BREKKE, H., FÆRSETH, R. B., LARSEN, B. T., SKOGSEID, J. & TØRUDBAKKEN, B. 1995. Structural elements of the Norwegian continental shelf. Part II: The Norwegian Sea region. *Norwegian Petroleum Directorate Bulletin*, 8.

BOLDREEL, L. O. & ANDERSEN, M. S. 1993. Late Paleocene to Miocene compression in the Faroe–Rockall area. *In*: PARKER, J. R. (ed.) *Petroleum Geology of Northwest Europe. Proceedings of the 4th Conference*. Geological Society, London, 1025–1034.

BOLDREEL, L. O. & ANDERSEN, M. S. 1998. Tertiary compressional structures on the Faeroe–Rockall Plateau in relation to northeast Atlantic ridge-push and Alpine foreland stresses. *Tectonophysics*, **300**, 13–28.

BOTT, M. H. P. 1991. Ridge push and associate plate interior stress in normal and hot spot regions. *Tectonophysics*, **200**, 17–32.

BOTT, M. H. P. 1993. Modelling the plate-driving mechanism. *Journal of the Geological Society of London*, **150**, 941–951.

BOWIN, C. 1991. The Earth's gravity field and plate tectonics, *Tectonophysics*, **187**, 69–89.

BREIVIK, A. J., MJELDE, R., FALEIDE, J. I. & MURAI, Y. 2006. Rates of continental breakup magmatism and seafloor spreading in the Norway Basin – Iceland plume interaction. *Journal of Geophysical Research*, **111**, B07102, doi:10.1029/2005JB004004.

BREKKE, H. 2000. The tectonic evolution of the Norwegian Sea Continental Margin with emphasis on the Vøring and Møre Basins. *In*: NØTTVEDT, A. (ed.) *Dynamics of the Norwegian Margin*. Geological Society, London, Special Publications, **167**, 327–378.

BREKKE, H. & RIIS, F. 1987. Tectonics and basin evolution of the Norwegian shelf between 62° and 72°N. *Norsk Geologisk Tidskrift*, **67**, 295–321.

BROZENA, J. M., CHILDERS, V. A., LAWVER, L. A., GAHAGAN, L. M., FORSBERG, R., FALEIDE, J. I. & ELDHOLM, O. 2003. New aerogeophysical study of the Eurasia Basin and Lomonosov Ridge: implications for basin development. *Geology*, **31**, 825–828.

CHALMERS, J. A. & PULVERTAFT, T. C. R. 2001. Development of the continental margins of the Labrador Sea: a review. *In*: WILSON, R. C. L., WHITMARSH, R. B., TAYLOR, B. & FROITZHEIM, N. (eds) *Non-Volcanic Rifting of Continental Margins: A Comparison of Evidence from Land and Sea*. Geological Society, London, Special Publications, **187**, 77–105.

CLOETINGH, S., GRADSTEIN, F. M., KOOI, H., GRANT, A. C. & KAMINSKI, M. 1990. Plate reorganization: a cause of rapid late Neogene subsidence and sedimentation around the North Atlantic. *Journal of Geological Society, London*, **147**, 495–506.

CRAMEZ, C. & JACKSON, M. P. A. 2000. Superposed deformation straddling the continental–oceanic transition in deep-water Angola. *Marine and Petroleum Geology*, **17**, 1095–1109.

DAHLEN, F. A. 1981. Isostasy and the ambient state of stress in the oceanic lithosphere. *Journal of Geophysical Research*, **86**, 7801–7807.

DAVIES, R. J., CLOKE, I., CARTWRIGHT, J., ROBINSON, A. & FERRERO, C. 2004. Post-breakup compression of a passive margin and its impact on hydrocarbon prospectivity: and example from the Tertiary of the Faroe–Shetland Basin, United Kingdom. *American Association of Petroleum Geologists Bulletin*, **88**, 1–20.

DICKEN, A. P. 1992. Evidence for an Early Proterozoic crustal province in the North Atlantic region. *Journal of Geological Society, London*, **149**, 483–486.

DORÉ, A. G. & LUNDIN, E. R. 1996. Cenozoic compressional structures on the NE Atlantic margin: nature, origin, and potential significance for hydrocarbon exploration. *Petroleum Geoscience*, **2**, 299–311.

DORÉ, A. G., LUNDIN, E. R., JENSEN, L. N., BIRKELAND, Ø., ELIASSEN, P. E. & FICHLER, C. 1999. Principal tectonic events in the evolution of the northwest Eurpoean Atlantic margin. *In*: FLEET, A. J. & BOLDY, S. A. R. (eds) *Petroleum Geology of Northwest Europe. Proceedings of the 5th Conference*. Geological Society, London, 41–61.

EBBING, J., LUNDIN, E., OLESEN, O. & HANSEN, K. 2006. The mid-Norwegian margin: a discussion of crustal lineaments, mafic intrusions, and remnants of the Caledonian root by 3D density modelling and structural interpretation. *Journal of the Geological Society, London*, **163**, 47–59.

EIDVIN, T., BUGGE, T. & SMELROR, M. 2007. The Molo Formation, deposited by coastal progradation on the inner Mid-Norwegian continental shelf, coeval with the Kai Formation to the west and the Utsira Formation in the North Sea. *Norwegian Journal of Geology*, **87**, 75–142.

ELLEN, S. M. O. 2002. *Geological Map, Land and Sea Areas of Northern Europe*. Scale 1:4 million. Geological Survey of Norway.

ENGEN, Ø., FALEIDE, J. I. & DYRENG, T. K. 2008. Opening of the Fram Strait gateway; a review of plate tectonic constraints. *Tectonophysics*, **450**, 51–69, doi:10.1016/j.tecto.2008.01.002.

EYLES, N. 1996. Passive margin uplift around the North Atlantic region and its role in Northern Hemisphere late Cenozoic glaciation. *Geology*, **24**, 103–106.

FALEIDE, J. I., MYHRE, A. M. & ELDHOLM, O. 1988. Eraly Tertiary volcanism at the Western Barents Sea margin. *In*: MORTON, A. C. & PARSON, L. M. (eds) *Early Tertiary Volcanism and the Opening of the NE Atlantic*. Geological Society, London, Special Publications, **39**, 135–146.

FALEIDE, J. I., VÅGNES, E. & GUDLAUGSSON, S. T. 1993. Late Mesozoic–Cenozoic evolution of the south-western Barents Sea in a regional rift-shear tectonic setting. *Marine and Petroleum Geology*, **10**, 186–214.

FEDEN, R. H., VOGT, P. R. & FLEMING, H. S. 1979. Magnetic and bathymetric evidence for the 'Yermak hot spot' northwest of Svalbard in the Arctic Basin. *Earth and Planetary Science Letters*, **44**, 18–38.

FICHLER, C., RUNDHOVDE, E., OLESEN, O., SÆTHER, B. M., RUESLÅTTEN, H., LUNDIN, E. & DORÉ, A. G. 1999. Regional tectonic interpretation of image enhanced gravity and magnetic data covering the mid-Norwegian shelf and adjacent mainland. *Tectonophysics*, **306**, 183–197.

FLEITOUT, L. & FROIDEVAUX, C. 1982. Tectonics and topography for a lithosphere containing density heterogeneities. *Tectonics*, **1**, 21–56.

GAINA, C., ROEST, W.R. & MULLER, R.D. 2002. Late Cretaceous–Cenozoic deformation of Northeast Asia. *Earth and Planetary Science Letters*, **197**, 273–286.

GAINA, C., TORSVIK, T. H., REDFIELD, T. F. *ET AL.* 2006. *Frontier Science and Exploration: the Atlantic-Arctic*. Norwegian Geological Survey, report 2006.077.

GERNIGON, L., RINGENBACH, J. C., PLANKE, S., LE GALL, B. & JONQUET-KOLSTØ, H. 2003. Extension, crustal structure and magmatism at the outer Vøring Basin, Norwegian margin. *Journal of the Geological Society*, **160**, 197–208.

GÓMEZ, M. & VERGÉS, J. 2005. Quantifying the contribution of tectonics vs. differential compaction in the development of domes along the Mid-Norwegian Atlantic margin. *Basin Research*, **17**, 289–310.

GREENHALGH, E. E. & KUSZNIR, N. J. 2007. Evidence for thin oceanic crust on the extinct Aegir Ridge, Norwegian Basin, NE Atlantic derived from satellite gravity inversion. *Geophysical Research Letters*, **34**, L06305, doi:10.1029/2007GL029440.

HAMANN, N. E., WITTAKER, R. C. & STEMMERIK, L. 2005. Geological development of the Northeast Greenland Shelf. *In*: DORÉ, A. G. & VINING, B. A. (eds) *Petroleum Geology: North-West Europe and Global Perspectives. Proceedings of the 6th Petroleum Geology Conference*. Geological Society, London, 887–902.

HAXBY, W. F. & TURCOTTE, D. L. 1978. On isostatic geoid anomalies. *Journal of Geophysical Research*, **83**, 5473–5478.

HENRIKSEN, S. & WEIMER, P. 1996. High-frequency depositional sequences and stratal stacking patterns in Lower Pliocene coastal deltas, mid-Norwegian continental shelf. *American Association of Petroleum Geologists Bulletin*, **80**, 1867–1895.

HJELSTUEN, B. O., SEJRUP, H. P., HAFLIDASON, H., BERG, K. & BRYN, P. 2004. Neogene and Quaternary depositional environments on the Norwegian continental margin, 62°N–68°N. *Marine Geology*, **213**, 257–276.

JONES, S. M. & MACLENNAN, J. 2005. Crustal flow beneath Iceland. *Journal of Geophysical Research*, **110**, B9, doi:10.1029/2004JB003592.

JOHNSON, H., RITCHIE, J. D., HITCHEN, K., MCINROY, D. B. & KIMBELL, G. S. 2005. Aspects of the Cenozoic deformational history of the Northeast Faroe–Shetland Basin, Wyville-Thomson Ridge and Hatton Bank areas. *In*: DORÉ, A. G. & VINING, B. A. (eds) *Petroleum Geology: North-West Europe and Global Perspectives. Proceedings of the 6th Petroleum Geology Conference*. Geological Society, London, 993–1008.

JÓHANNESSON, H. & SÆMUNDSSON, K. 1998. Geological map of Iceland. Iceland Institute of Natural History, Reykjavik. Scale 1:500 000.

JORDT, H., THYBERG, B.I. & NØTTVEDT, A. 2000. Cenozoic evolution of the central and northern North Sea with focus on differential vertical movements of the basin floor and surrounding clastic source areas. *In*: NØTTVEDT, A. (ed.) *Dynamics of the Norwegian Margin*. Geological Society, London, Special Publications, **167**, 219–243.

JUNG, W.-Y. & VOGT, P. R. 1997. A gravity and magnetic study of the extinct Aegir Ridge, Norwegian Sea. *Journal of Geophysyical Research*, **102**, 5065–5089.

KIMBELL, G. S., RITCHIE, J. D., JOHNSON, H. & GATLIFF, R. W. 2005. Controls on the structure and evolution of the NE Atlantic margin revealed by regional potential field imaging and 3D modelling. *In*: DORÉ, A. G. & VINING, B. A. (eds) *Petroleum Geology: North-West Europe and Global Perspectives. Proceedings of the 6th Petroleum Geology Conference*. Geological Society, London, 933–945.

KJELDSTAD, A., SKOGSEID, J., LANGTANGEN, H. P., BJØRLYKKE, K. & HØEG, K. 2003. Differential loading by prograding sedimentary wedges on continental margins: An arch-forming mechanism. *Journal of Geophysical Research*, **108**, B1, 2036. doi:10.1029/2001JB001145.

KRISTOFFERSEN, Y. & TALWANI, M. 1977. Extinct triple junction south of Greenland and the Tertiary motion of Greenland relative to North America. *Geological Society of America Bulletin*, **88**, 1037–1049.

KUSZNIR, N. J. 1991. The distribution of stress with depth in the lithosphere: thermo-rheological and geodynamic constraints. *Philosophical Transactions of the Royal Society*, **337**, 95–110.

KUSZNIR, N. J., HUNSDALE, R. & ROBERTS, A. M. iSIMM Team 2005. Timing and magnitude of depth dependent lithosphere stretching on the S. Lofoten and N. Vøring continental margins offshore Mid-Norway: implications for subsidence and hydrocarbon maturation at volcanic rifted margins. *In*: DORÉ, A. G. & VINING, B. A. (eds) *Petroleum Geology: North-West Europe and Global Perspectives. Proceedings of the 6th Petroleum Geology Conference*. Geological Society, London, 767–783.

KUSZNIR, N. J. & KARNER, G. D. 2007. Continental lithosphere thinning leading to breakup and rifted margin formation in response to upwelling divergent flow: application to the Woodlark Basin, Newfoundland and Iberia Margins. *In*: KARNER, G. D., MANATSCHAL, G. & PINHEIRO, L. M. (eds) *Imaging, Mapping and Modelling Continental Lithosphere Extension and Breakup*. Geological Society, London, Special Publications, **282**, 389–419.

LEAR, C. H., ROSENTHAL, Y. & WRIGHT, J. D. 2003. The closing of a seaway: ocean water masses and global climate change. *Earth and Planetary Sciences*, **210**, 425–436.

LEMOINE, F. G., SMITH, D., SMITH, R. *ET AL.* 1996. EGM96, The NASA GSFC and NIMA Joint Geopotential Model. Proceedings of the International Symposium on Gravity, Geoid, and Marine Geodesy, Tokyo, Japan, September 30–October 4, 1996.

LOUDEN, K. E., OSLER, J. C., SRISASTAVA, S. P. & KEEN, C. E. 1996. Formation of oceanic crust at loe spreading rates: new constraints from an extinct spreading centre in the Labrador Sea. *Geology*, **24**, 771–774.

LØSETH, H. & HENRIKSEN, S. 2005. A Middle to Late Miocene compression phase along the Norwegian passive margin. *In*: DORÉ, A. G. & VINING, B. A. (eds) *Petroleum Geology: North-West Europe and Global Perspectives. Proccedings of the 6th Petroleum Geology Conference*. Geological Society, London, 845–859.

LUNDIN, E. R. 2002. Atlantic–Arctic seafloor spreading history. *In*: EIDE, E. A. (coord.) *BATLAS – Mid Norway plate reconstructions atlas with global and Atlantic perspectives*. Geological Survey of Norway, 40–47.

LUNDIN, E. R. & DORÉ, A. G. 1997. A tectonic model for the Norwegian passive margin with implications for the NE Atlantic: Early Cretaceous to break-up. *Journal of the Geological Society, London*, **154**, 545–550.

LUNDIN, E. & DORÉ, A. G. 2002. Mid-Cenozoic post-breakup deformation in the 'passive' margins bordering the Norwegian-Greenland Sea. *Marine and Petroleum Geology*, **19**, 79–93.

LUNDIN, E. R. & DORÉ, A. G. 2005. NE-Atlantic break-up: a re-examination of the Iceland mantle plume model and the Atlantic–Arctic linkage. *In*: DORÉ, A. G. & VINING, B. A. (eds) *North-West European Petroleum Geology and Global Perspectives. Proceedings of the 6th Conference*. Geological Society, London, 739–754.

LUNDIN, E. R. & RUNDHOVDE, E. 1993. Structural domains in the Møre Basin, Norway - from digital images of aeromagnetic data. EAPG 5th Annual Convention, Stavanger, Annual Convention Official Program, EO37.

MARTINSEN, O. J., BØEN, F., CHARNOCK, M. A., MANGERUD, G. & NØTTVEDT, A. 1999. Cenozoic development of the Norwegian margin 60–64 °N: sequences and sedimentary response to variable basin physiography and tectonic setting. *In*: FLEET, A. J. & BOLDY, S. A. R. (eds) *Petroleum Geology of Northwest Europe. Proceedings of the 5th Conference*. Geological Society, London, 293–304.

MCCLAY, K. R., DOOLEY, T. & LEWIS, G. 1998. Analog models of progradational delta systems. *Geology*, **26**, 771–774.

MOHRIAK, W. U., BASSETTO, M. & VIEIRA, I. S. 1998. Crustal architecture and tectonic evolution of the Sergipe-Alagoas-Jacúipe Basins, offshore northern Brazil. *Tectonophysics*, **288**, 199–220.

MOHRIAK, W. U., ROSENDAHL, B. R., TURNER, J. P. & VALENTE, S. C. 2002. Crustal architecture of South Atlantic margins. *In*: MENZIES, M. A., KLEMPERER, S. L., EBINGER, C. J. & BAKER, J. (eds) *Volcanic Rifted Margins*. Boulder, Colorado. Geological Society of America Special Paper **362**, 159–202.

MORLEY, C. K., NELSON, R. A., PATTON, T. & MUNN, S. G. 1990. Transfer zones in the East Africa rift system and their relevance to hydrocarbon exploration in rifts. *American Association of Petroleum Geologists Bulletin*, **74**, 1234–1253.

MOSAR, J., LEWIS, G. & TORSVIK, T. H. 2002. North Atlantic sea-floor spreading rates: implications for the Tertiary development of inversion structures of the Norwegian–Greenland Sea. *Journal of the Geological Society*, London, **159**, 503–515.

NIELSEN, T. K. & HOPPER, J. R. 2002. Formation of volcanic rifted margins: Are temperature anomalies required? *Geophysical Research Letters*, **29**, 2022–2025.

NUNNS, A. G. 1983. Plate tectonic evolution of the Greenland–Scotland Ridge and surrounding regions. *In*: BOTT, M. H. P., SAXOV, S., TALWANI, M. & THIEDE, J. (eds) *Structure and Development of the Greenland–Scotland Ridge: New Methods and Concepts*. Plenum Press, New York, 11–30.

OAKEY, G. 1994. A structural fabric defined by topographic lineaments: correlation with tertiary deformation of Ellesmere and Axel Heiberg Islands, Canadian Arctic. *Journal of Geophysical Research*, **99**(B10), 20,311–20,321.

OAKEY, G. N. 2005. *Cenozoic evolution and lithosphere dynamics of the Baffin Bay – Nares Strait region of Arctic Canada and Greenland*. Ph.D. thesis, Vrije Universiteit, The Netherlands.

PARSONS, B. & MCKENZIE, D. 1978. Mantle convection and the thermal structure of the plates, *Journal of Geophysical Research* **83**, 4485–4496.

PASCAL, C. & GABRIELSEN, R. H. 2001. Numerical modelling of Cenozoic stress patterns in the Mid Norwegian Margin and the northern North Sea. *Tectonics*, **20**/4, 585–599.

PRICE, S., BRODIE, J., WHITHAM, A. & KENT, R. 1997. Mid-Tertiary rifting and magmatism in the Traill Ø region, East Greenland. *Journal of the Geological Society*, London, **54**, 419–434.

RANALLI, G. 1995. *Rheology of the Earth*. Chapman and Hall, New York.

RASMUSSEN, E. S. 2004. The interplay between true eustatic sea-level changes, tectonics, and climate changes: what is the dominating factor in sequence formation of the Upper Oligocene-Miocene succession in the eastern North Sea Basin, Denmark? *Global and Planetary Change*, **41**, 15–30.

REINECKER, J., HEIDBACH, O., TINGAY, M., SPERNER, B. & MÜLLER, B. 2005. The release 2005 of the World Stress Map (available online at www.world-stress-map.org).

REN, S., SKOGSEID, J. & ELDHOLM, O. 1998. Late Cretaceous–Paleocene extension on the Vøring Volcanic Margin. *Marine Geophysical Researches*, **20**, 343–369.

RIISE, L., OTTESEN, D., BERG, K. & LUNDIN, E. 2005. Large-scale development of the mid-Norwegian margin during the last 3 million years. *Marine and Petroleum Geology*, **22**, 33–44.

RITZMANN, O. & JOKAT, W. 2003. Crustal structure of northwestern Svalbard and the adjacent Yermak Plateau: evidence for Oligocene detachment tectonics and non-volcanic breakup. *Geophysical Journal International*, **152**, 139–159.

ROBERTS, A. M., CORFIELD, R., MATTHEWS, S., KUSZNIR, N. J. & HOOPER, R. 2002. Mapping Palaeostructure and palaeobathymetry along the Norwegian continental margin. *Frontier Exploration of Volcanic Continental Margins*, Geological Society, London, 17–18 September 2002.

ROBERTS, D. G. 1989. Basin inversion around the British Isles. *In*: COOPER, M. A. & WILLIAMS, D. G. (eds) *Inversion Tectonics*. Geological Society, London, Special Publications, **44**, 131–150.

RUMPH, B., REAVES, C. M., ORANGE, V. G. & ROBINSON, D. 1993. Structuring and transfer zones in the Faroe Basin in a regional tectonic context. *In*: PARKER, J. R. (ed.) *Petroleum Geology of Northwest Europe. Proceedings of the 4th Conference*. Geological Society, London, 999–1010.

SMALLWOOD, J. R. 2004. Tertiary inversion in the Faroe–Shetland Channel and the development of major erosional scarps. *In*: DAVIES, R. J., STEWART, S. A., CARTWRIGHT, J. A., LAPPIN, M. & UNDERHILL, J. R. (eds) *3D Seismic Technology: Application to the Exploration of Sedimentary Basins*. Geological Society London, Memoir **29**, 187–198.

SRIVASTAVA, S. P. & ROEST, W. R. 1999. Extent of oceanic crust in the Labrador Sea. *Marine and Petroleum Geology*, **16**, 65–84.

STEEL, R., GJELDBERG, J., NØTTVEDT, A., HELLAND-HANSEN, W., KLEINSPEHN, K. & RYE-LARSEN, M. 1985. *The Tertiary Strike-Slip Basins and Orogenic Belt of Spitsbergen*. Society of Economic Palaeontologists and Mineralogists, Special Publication **37**, 339–360.

STUEVOLD, L. M., SKOGSEID, J. & ELDHOLM, O. 1992. Post-Cretaceous uplift events on the Voring continental margin. *Geology*, **10**, 919–922.

STOKER, M. S., PRAEG, D., SHANNON, P. M., HJELSTUEN, B. O., LABERG, J. S., NIELSEN, T., VAN WEERING, T. C. E., SEJRUP, H. P. & EVANS, D. 2005*a*. Neogene evolution of the Atlantic continental margin of NW Europe (Lofoten Islands to SW Ireland): Anything but passive. *In*: DORÉ, A. G. & VINING, B. A. (eds) *Petroleum Geology: North-West Europe and Global Perspectives. Proceedings of the 6th Petroleum Geology Conference.* Geological Society, London, 1057–1074.

STOKER, M. S., HOULT, R. J., NIELSEN, T., HJELSTUEN, B. O., LABERG, J. S., SHANNON, P. M., PRAEG, D., MATHIESEN, A., VAN WEERING, T. C. E. & MCDONNELL, A. 2005*b*. Sedimentary and oceanic response to early Neogene compression on the NW European margin. *Marine and Petroleum Geology*, **22**, 1031–1044.

TALWANI, M. & ELDHOLM, O. 1977. Evolution of the Norwegian-Greenland Sea. *Geological Society of America Bulletin*, **88**, 969–999.

TORSVIK, T. H., MOSAR, J. & EIDE, E. A. 2001. Cretaceous–Tertiary geodynamics: A North Atlantic exercise. *Geophysical Journal International*, **146**, 850–866.

TORSVIK, T. M., SMETHURST, M. A., REDFIELD, T. F., GAINA, C., STEINBERGER, B., ROUSSE, S., BUITER, S., MÜLLER, R. D. & GURNIS, M. 2006. "Splates: Paleogeographic reconstruction software", *Norwegian Geological Survey*, report 2006.060.

TSIKALAS, F., FALEIDE, J. I., ELDHOLM, O. & WILSON, J. 2005. Late Mesozoic–Cenozoic structural and stratigraphic correlations between the conjugate mid-Norway and NE Greenland continental margins. *In*: DORÉ, A. G. & VINING, B. A. (eds) *Petroleum Geology: North-West Europe and Global Perspectives. Proceedings of the 6th Petroleum Geology Conference.* Geological Society, London, 785–802.

TURCOTTE, D. L. & SCHUBERT, G. 1982. *Geodynamics*. John Wiley & Sons, New York.

VÅGNES, E., GABRIELSEN, R. H. & HAREMO, P. 1998. Late Cretaceous-Cenozoic intraplate contractional deformation at the Norwegian continental shelf: timing, magnitude and regional implications. *Tectonophysics*, **300**, 29–46.

VENDEVILLE, B. C. & JACKSON, M. P. A. 1992. The rise of diapirs during thin skinned extension. *Marine and Petroleum Geology*, **9**, 331–353.

VOGT, P. R., JOHNSON, G. L. & KRISJANSSON, L. 1980. Morphology and magnetic anomalies north of Iceland. *Journal of Geophysics*, **47**, 67–80.

VORREN, T. O. & LABERG, J. S. 1997. Trough mouth fans – palaeoclimate and ice-sheet monitors. *Quaternary Science Reviews*, **16**, 865–881.

WHITE, R. S., SPENCE, G. D., FOWLER, S. R., MCKENZIE, D. P., WESTBROOK, G. K. & BOWEN, A. N. 1987. Magmatism at rifted continental margins. *Nature*, **330**, 439–444.

WITHJACK, M. O., MEISLING, K. E. & RUSSELL, L. R. 1989. Forced folding and basement-detached normal faulting in the Haltenbanken area, offshore Norway. *In*: TANKARD, A. J. & BALKWILL, H. R. (eds) *Extensional Tectonics and Stratigraphy of the North Atlantic Margins.* American Association of Petroleum Geologists Memoir, **46**, 567–575.

ZIEGLER, P. A. 1988. *Evolution of the Arctic–North Atlantic and the Western Tethys.* American Association of Petroleum Geologists Memoir, **43**.

ZIEGLER, P. A. 1993. Plate-moving mechanisms: their relative importance. *Journal of the Geological Society, London*, **150**, 927–940.

Post-rift compressional reactivation potential of passive margins and extensional basins

SIERD CLOETINGH[1], FRED BEEKMAN[1], PETER A. ZIEGLER[2],
JAN-DIEDERIK VAN WEES[1,3] & DIMITRIOS SOKOUTIS[1]

[1]*Netherlands Research Centre for Integrated Solid Earth Sciences (ISES), Vrije Universiteit,
De Boelelaan 1085, 1081 HV Amsterdam, The Netherlands (e-mail: fred.beekman@falw.vu.nl)*

[2]*Geological–Palaeontological Institute, University of Basel, Bernoullistr, 32, 4065,
Basel, Switzerland*

[3]*Netherlands Institute of Applied Geosciences TNO, Princetonlaan 6, 3584 CB Utrecht,
The Netherlands*

Abstract: Poly-phase deformation of a compressional nature is a common feature in the post-rift evolution of passive margins and rifts. The compressional mode of deformation in these sedimentary basins, originally formed by extension in an intraplate setting, is characterized by a spectrum of spatial wavelengths spanning several tens of kilometres up to several hundreds of kilometres. The actual mode of compressional deformation appears to be strongly affected by the rheological structure of the underlying lithosphere, the level of the regional intraplate stress field, and the geometry of the rifted basin configuration prior to late-stage compressional reactivation. The interplay of plumes and intraplate compressional deformation can lead to temporal transitions from basin inversion to lithospheric folding. These modes of deformation lead to substantial differential vertical motions, late-stage anomalies in subsidence and uplift patterns. The development of innovative combinations of numerical and analogue modelling techniques is the key to differentiating different modes of compressional deformation of passive margins and extensional basins.

Post-rift deformation, involving tectonic reactivation, has strongly affected the structure and fill of extensional basins and passive margins. The long-lasting memory of the lithosphere appears to play a far more important role in basin reactivation than hitherto assumed (Van Wees & Beekman 2000; Ziegler *et al.* 2002). A better understanding of the 3D linkage between basin formation and basin deformation is, therefore, an essential step in research that aims at linking lithospheric forcing and upper mantle dynamics to crustal uplift and erosion and their effect on the dynamics of sedimentary systems (Garcia-Castellanos *et al.* 2000). Structural analysis of the basin architecture, including palaeostress assessment, provides important constraints on the transient nature of intraplate stress fields (Andeweg *et al.* 1999; Bada *et al.* 2001; Dèzes *et al.* 2004).

Field studies of kinematic indicators and numerical modelling of present-day- and palaeo-stress fields in selected areas (e.g. Gölke & Coblentz 1996; Bada *et al.* 1998, 2001) have yielded new constraints on the causes and the expression of intraplate stress fields in the lithosphere. Ziegler *et al.* (1998) demonstrated the key role of mechanical controls on collision related compressional intraplate deformation. These

authors discussed the build-up of intraplate stresses in relation to mechanical coupling between an orogenic wedge and its fore- and hinterlands, as well as the implications to the understanding of a number of first order features in crustal and lithospheric deformation.

Temporal and spatial variations in the level and magnitude of these stresses have a strong impact on the record of vertical motions in sedimentary basins (Cloetingh *et al.* 1985, 1990; Cloetingh & Kooi 1992; Zoback *et al.* 1993; Van Balen *et al.* 1998). Stresses at a level close to lithospheric strength propagating from the margins of the Black Sea Basin into its interior had a strong effect on the stratigraphic record and the observed late-stage subsidence acceleration, presumably induced by lithospheric folding (Cloetingh *et al.* 1999), similar to that recognized in the Pannonian and North Sea basins (Horváth & Cloetingh 1996; Van Wees & Cloetingh 1996). Over the last few years increasing attention has been directed to this topic, advancing our understanding of the relationship between changes in plate motions, plate-interaction and the evolution of rifted basins (Sclater & Christie 1980; Ziegler 1988; Janssen *et al.* 1995; Doré *et al.* 1997; Lundin & Doré 2002) and foreland areas Ziegler *et al.* (1995, 1998, 2001).

From: JOHNSON, H., DORÉ, A. G., GATLIFF, R. W., HOLDSWORTH, R., LUNDIN, E. R. & RITCHIE, J. D. (eds)
The Nature and Origin of Compression in Passive Margins. Geological Society, London, Special Publications,
306, 27–70. DOI: 10.1144/SP306.2   0305-8719/08/$15.00 © The Geological Society of London 2008.

A continuous spectrum of stress-induced vertical motions can be expected in the sedimentary record, varying from subtle faulting effects (Ter Voorde & Cloetingh 1996; Ter Voorde et al. 1997) and basin inversion (Brun & Nalpas 1996; Ziegler et al. 1998) to enhancement of flexural effects to lithosphere folds induced by high levels of stress approaching lithospheric strengths (Stephenson & Cloetingh 1991; Burov et al. 1993; Nikishin et al. 1993; Cloetingh & Burov 1996; Bonnet et al. 1998; Cloetingh et al. 1999).

Crustal and lithospheric folding can be an important mode of basin formation on plates involved in continental collision (Cobbold et al. 1993; Ziegler et al. 1995, 1998; Cloetingh et al. 1999). Numerical models have been developed for the simulation of the interplay of faulting and folding in intraplate compressional deformation (Beekman et al. 1996; Cloetingh et al. 1999; Gerbault et al. 1999). Models have also been developed to investigate the effects of faulting on stress-induced intraplate deformation in rifted margin settings (Van Balen et al. 1998).

In this paper we focus on the connection between lithospheric strength and the post-rift compressional reactivation potential of passive margins and extensional basins. We first review the temporal and spatial evolution of lithospheric strength, and its consequences for deformation modes of the crust and lithosphere, in particular for rifted continental margins. We demonstrate that the compressional yield strength of passive margins can vary considerably, depending on the lithospheric configuration, sedimentary cover and age. These factors set the stage for a wide spectrum of the intensity of post-rift compressional deformation. Analogue tectonic experiments allow examination of the mechanisms of post-rift shortening of passive margins and study of the modes of compressional deformation. It appears that the influence of pre-existing structural heterogeneity at the lithospheric scale is key for an assessment of the relative role of lithospheric folding and basin inversion in post-rift compressional reactivation of passive margins and extensional basins.

Subsequently, the role of lithospheric rheology in compressional reactivation is discussed for several extensional basins formed within continental Europe and its margins. Thermo-mechanical models demonstrate that a transition in the mode and distribution in intraplate deformation in northwestern Europe can be explained by a strength reversal, in which the long-term increase in lithospheric strength by conductive cooling is followed by a more abrupt decrease in lithospheric strength resulting from the combined effect of changes in Moho depth due to the transition from rifting into inversion and heating by mantle plumes.

The post-rift evolution of the lithospheric strength may also play an important role in localizing compressional deformation in either the interior parts of extensional basins and/or at their margins. This is illustrated for the Black Sea Basin where post-rift compressional deformation appears to be restricted to the edges of the basin.

Another example of compressional reactivation of extensional basins is provided by the Pannonian Basin system, which is characterized by a high level of vertical motions, associated with the indenting motion of Adria into Europe and ongoing inversion. This area is situated on the hottest and weakest lithosphere of continental Europe, where recent changes in the intraplate stress field make this weak back-arc system prone to a high level of compressional deformation.

These examples illustrate the need to understand and constrain the role of the pre-rift thermo-mechanical configuration of passive margins and extensional basin systems for an assessment of their compressional reactivation potential.

Evolution of lithosphere strength and deformation modes

Rheology of the lithosphere

The strength of continental lithosphere is controlled by its depth-dependent rheological structure in which the thickness and composition of the crust, the thickness of the mantle lithosphere, the temperature of the asthenosphere, and the presence or absence of fluids, as well as strain rates play an important role. By contrast, the strength of oceanic lithosphere depends on its thermal regime, which controls its essentially age-dependent thickness (Kusznir & Park 1987; Cloetingh & Burov 1996; Watts 2001).

Figure 1 gives synthetic strength envelopes for three different types of continental lithosphere and for oceanic lithosphere at a range of geothermal gradients (Ziegler & Cloetingh 2004). These theoretical rheological models indicate that thermally stabilized continental lithosphere consists of the mechanically strong upper crust, which is separated by a weak lower crustal layer from the strong upper part of the mantle lithosphere, which in turn overlies the weak lower mantle lithosphere. By contrast, oceanic lithosphere has a more homogeneous composition and is characterized by a much simpler rheological structure. Rheologically speaking, thermally stabilized oceanic lithosphere is considerably stronger than all types of continental lithosphere. However, the strength of oceanic lithosphere can be seriously weakened by transform faults and by the thermal blanketing effect of thick sedimentary prisms prograding onto it (e.g. Gulf of Mexico, Niger Delta, Bengal Fan; Ziegler *et al.* 1998).

The strength of continental crust depends largely on its composition, thermal regime and the presence of fluids, and also on the availability of pre-existing crustal discontinuities. Deep-reaching crustal discontinuities, such as thrust- and wrench-faults, cause significant weakening of the otherwise mechanically strong upper parts of the crust. These discontinuities are apparently characterized by a reduced frictional angle, particularly in the presence of fluids (Van Wees & Stephenson 2000). They are prone to reactivation at stress levels that are well below those required for the development of new faults. Deep reflection–seismic profiles show that the crust of Late Proterozoic and Palaeozoic orogenic belts is generally characterized by a monoclinal fabric that extends from upper crustal levels down to the Moho at which it either soles out or by which it is truncated (Ziegler & Cloetingh 2004). This fabric reflects the presence of deep-reaching lithological inhomogeneities and shear zones.

The strength of the continental lithospheric upper mantle depends to a large extent on the thickness of the crust but also on its age and thermal regime. Thermally stabilized, stretched, continental lithosphere with a 20 km thick crust and a lithospheric mantle thickness of 50 km is mechanically stronger than unstretched lithosphere with a 30 km thick crust and a 70 km thick lithospheric mantle (compare Fig. 1b & d). Extension of stabilized continental crustal segments precludes ductile flow of the lower crust and faults will be steep to listric and propagate towards the hanging wall, i.e. towards the basin centre (Bertotti *et al.* 2000). Under these conditions, the lower crust will deform by distributing ductile shear in the brittle–ductile transition domain. This is compatible with the occurrence of earthquakes within the lower crust and even close to the Moho (e.g. southern Rhine Graben: Bonjer 1997; East African rifts: Shudofsky *et al.* 1987).

On the other hand, in young orogenic belts, which are characterized by crustal thicknesses of up to 60 km and an elevated heat flow, the mechanically strong part of the crust is thin and the lithospheric mantle is also weak (Fig. 1c). Extension of this type of lithosphere, involving ductile flow of the lower and middle crust along pressure gradients away from areas lacking upper crustal extension into zones of major upper crustal extensional unroofing, can cause crustal thinning and thickening, respectively. This deformation mode gives rise to the development of core complexes with faults propagating towards the hanging wall (e.g. Basin and Range Province: Wernicke 1990; Buck 1991; Bertotti *et al.* 2000). However, crustal flow will cease after major crustal thinning has been achieved, mainly due to extensional decompression of the lower crust (Bertotti *et al.* 2000).

Generally, the upper mantle of thermally stabilized, old cratonic lithosphere is considerably stronger than the strong part of its upper crust (Fig. 1a, Moisio *et al.* 2000). However, the occurrence of upper mantle reflectors, which generally dip in the same direction as the crustal fabric and are probably related to subducted oceanic and/or continental crustal material, suggests that the continental lithospheric mantle is not necessarily homogenous but can contain lithological discontinuities that enhance its mechanical anisotropy (Vauchez *et al.* 1998; Ziegler *et al.* 1998). Such discontinuities, consisting of eclogitized crustal material, can potentially weaken the strong upper part of the lithospheric mantle. Moreover, even in the face of similar crustal thicknesses, the heat flow of deeply degraded Late Proterozoic and Phanerozoic orogenic belts is still elevated as compared to adjacent old cratons (e.g. Pan African belts of Africa and Arabia; Janssen 1996). This is probably due to the younger age of their lithospheric mantle and possibly also to a higher radiogenic heat generation potential of their crust. These factors contribute to weakening of former mobile zones to the end that they present rheologically weak zones within a craton, as evidenced by their preferential reactivation during the breakup of Pangaea (Ziegler 1989a, b; Janssen *et al.* 1995; Ziegler *et al.* 2001).

From a rheological point of view, the thermally destabilized lithosphere of tectonically active rifts, as well as of rifts and passive margins that have undergone only a relatively short post-rift evolution (e.g. 25 Ma), is considerably weaker than that of thermally stabilized rifts and of unstretched lithosphere (Fig. 1f & g; Ziegler *et al.* 1998). In this respect, progressive mechanical and thermal thinning of the lithospheric mantle and its substitution by the upwelling asthenosphere is accompanied during rifting, by a rise in geotherms causing progressive weakening of the extended lithosphere. In addition, permeation by fluids causes further weakening (Fig. 1g). Upon decay of the rift-induced thermal anomaly, rift zones are rheologically speaking, considerably stronger than unstretched lithosphere (Fig. 1). However, accumulation of thick syn- and post-rift sedimentary sequences results in thermal blanketing that causes a weakening of the strong parts of the upper crust and lithospheric mantle

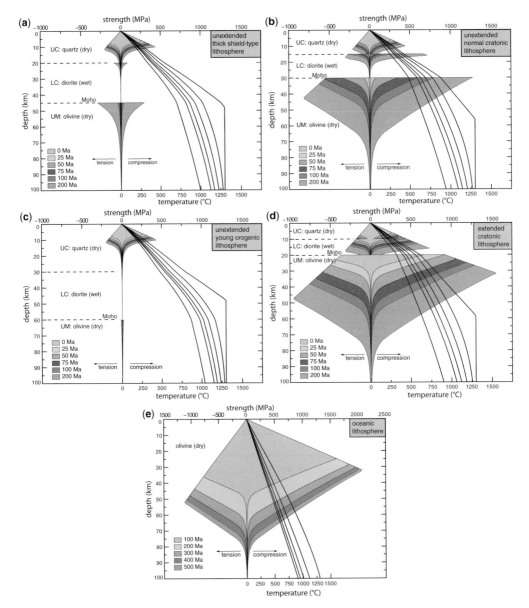

Fig. 1. Depth-dependent rheological models for various lithosphere types and a range of geothermal gradients. Assumed continental lithosphere is dry quartz/diorite/olivine mineralogy in panels (**a–e**) and dry and wet quartz/diorite/olivine in panels (**f–g**). (**a**) Unextended, thick-shield-type lithosphere with a crustal thickness of 45 km and a mantle lithosphere thickness of 155 km. (**b**) Unextended, 'normal' cratonic lithosphere with a crustal thickness of 30 km and a mantle lithosphere thickness of 70 km. (**c**) Unextended, young orogenic lithosphere with a crustal thickness of 60 km and a mantle lithosphere thickness of 140 km. (**d**) Extended, cratonic lithosphere with a crustal thickness of 20 km and a mantle lithosphere thickness of 50 km. (**e**) Oceanic lithosphere.

of rifted basins (Stephenson 1989). Moreover, as faults permanently weaken the crust of rifted basins, they are prone to tensional as well as compressional reactivation (Van Wees & Beekman 2000; Ziegler *et al.* 1995, 1998, 2001, 2002). As the structure of passive continental margin lithosphere is areally heterogeneous, its weakest parts start to yield first, once tensional or compressional intraplate stress levels equal their strength.

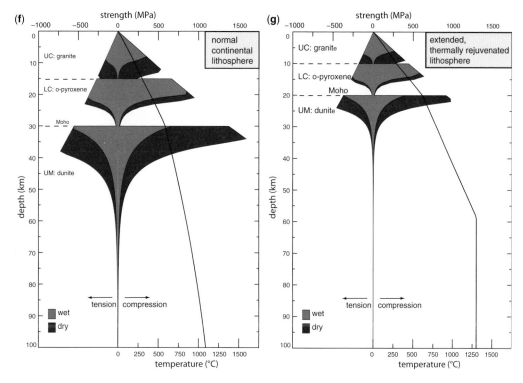

Fig. 1. (*Continued*) (**f**) Unextended, 'normal' cratonic lithosphere with a crustal thickness of 30 km and a mantle lithosphere thickness of 70 km. (**g**) Extended, thermally attenuated cratonic lithosphere with a crustal thickness of 20 km and a mantle lithosphere thickness of 38 km (after Ziegler & Cloetingh 2004).

Strength evolution of rifted continental margins

During rifting, culminating in the opening of new Atlantic-type oceanic basins, the continental lithosphere is stretched and the subcrustal mantle thermally attenuated (Fig. 2), particularly in the presence of a mantle plume. Upon termination of rifting activity, or after crustal separation has been achieved and the respective passive margins have moved away from the seafloor spreading axis, the thermally destabilized continental lithosphere re-equilibrates with the asthenosphere (McKenzie 1978; Steckler & Watts 1982; Wilson 1993; Ziegler 1996). During this process new mantle lithosphere, consisting of cooled asthenospheric material, is accreted to the attenuated old continental mantle lithosphere. This aspect is emphasized in Figure 2 as rheological properties of old and new mantle lithosphere may differ.

Rifts superimposed on ancient suture zones often display the geometry of simple-shear lithospheric extension (e.g. central Atlantic, Gulf of Suez; Favre & Stampfli 1992). Pre-existing crustal and mantle lithospheric discontinuities, as well as

the mechanical anisotropy of the lithospheric mantle, probably determine their location and polarity (Pique & Laville 1995; Vauchez *et al.* 1998). On the other hand, rifts cross-cutting the orogenic fabric of the crust (e.g. Labrador Sea, North Sea rift) are more prone to display a pure-shear geometry (Ziegler 1996). Under conditions of pure-shear lithospheric extension, conjugate passive margins are likely to display at the crustal separation stage a more or less symmetrical lithospheric configuration. Therefore, their post-rift evolution is similar with variations in their rheological structure depending largely on the thickness of the passive margin sedimentary wedge (starved versus overfilled, e.g. SE Greenland and Labrador margins; Chalmers & Laursen 1995). However, under conditions of simple-shear extension, the lithospheric configuration of conjugate margins can differ considerably at the end of the rifting stage (Fig. 3). At lower plate margins, the crust can be highly extended whereas the continental mantle lithosphere may be little attenuated; in their distal parts, the old mantle lithosphere can be denuded and in sheared contact with rotated upper crustal fault blocks and syn-rift sediments. In contrast, at

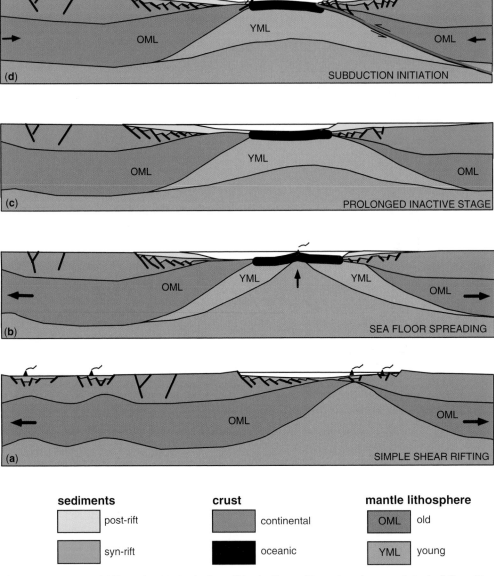

Fig. 2. Conceptual model illustrating (**a**) simple shear rifting leading to (**b**) opening of an oceanic basin, followed by (**c**) post-seafloor spreading evolution of mantle lithosphere, and (**d**) inception of a new subduction zone at the upper plate continental margin, employing the boundary between old and new mantle lithosphere, and contemporaneous minor intraplate deformations along the conjugate lower plate margin (not to scale) (after Ziegler *et al.* 1998).

upper plate margins, the crust may be less extended whereas the continental mantle lithosphere can be strongly attenuated with asthenospheric material ascending close to the base of the crust (Wernicke 1985; Wernicke & Tilke 1989; Boillot *et al.* 1989; Lister *et al.* 1991; Favre & Stampfli 1992; Pique & Laville 1995; Brun & Beslier 1996; Froitzheim & Manatschal 1996).

These differences in lithospheric configuration of simple-shear conjugate margins at the end of the rifting stage evidently have repercussions for their post-rift subsidence history and on their rheological structure, even after full thermal relaxation of the lithosphere.

Palaeostress analyses provide evidence for changes in the magnitude and orientation of intraplate stress fields on time scales of a few Ma (Bergerat 1987; Dèzes *et al.* 2004; Letouzey 1986; Philip 1987). Thus, in an attempt to understand the evolution of a post-rift basin, the effects of tectonic

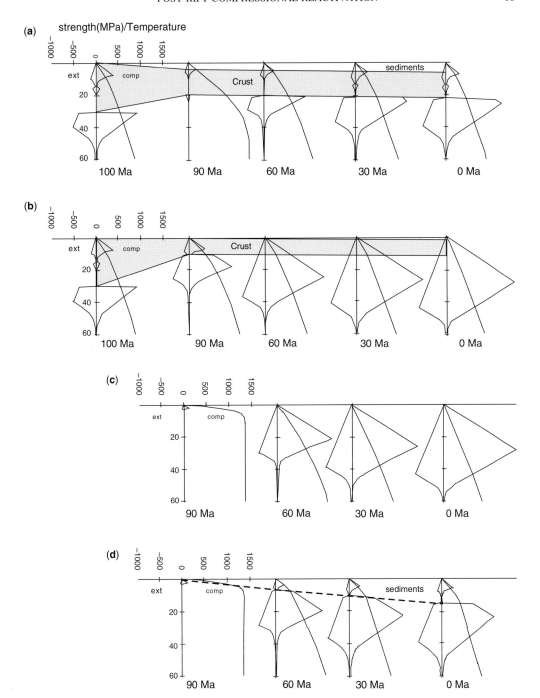

Fig. 3. Depth-dependent rheological models for the evolution of lower plate and upper plate passive margins and oceanic lithosphere. (**a**) Upper plate passive margin ($\delta = 2$, $\beta = 10$), characterized by complete sediment fill of accommodation space at end of post-rift phase ($\rho_s = 2100$ kg m^{-3}, 7.084 km sediments). (**b**) Lower plate passive margin ($\delta = 3$, $\beta = 1.1$), marked by sediment starvation at end of post-rift phase (1 km sediments). (**c**) Oceanic lithosphere with a thin sedimentary cover of 1 km. (**d**) Oceanic lithosphere with a gradually increasing sedimentary cover reaching a maximum of 15 km (after Ziegler *et al.* 1998).

stresses on subsidence must be separated from those related to thermal relaxation of the lithosphere (Cloetingh & Kooi 1992).

In response to the build-up of far-field compressional stresses, rifted basins, characterized by a strongly faulted and thus permanently weakened crust, are prone to reactivation at all stages of their post-rift evolution, resulting in their inversion (Ziegler 1990; Ziegler *et al.* 1995, 1998, 2001). Only under special conditions can gravitational forces associated with topography around a basin cause its inversion (Bada *et al.* 2001).

Rheological considerations indicate that the lithosphere of thermally stabilized rifts, lacking a thick post-rift sedimentary prism, is considerably stronger than the lithosphere of adjacent unstretched areas (Ziegler & Cloetingh 2004). This contradicts the observation that rift zones and passive margins are preferentially deformed during periods of intraplate compression (Ziegler *et al.* 2001). However, burial of rifted basins under a thick post-rift sequence contributes by thermal blanketing to weakening of their lithosphere (Stephenson 1989; Van Wees 1994), thus rendering it prone to tectonic reactivation.

In order to quantify this effect and to assess the reactivation potential of conjugate simple-shear margins during subduction initiation, their strength evolution was modelled and compared to that of oceanic crust (Ziegler *et al.* 1998). By applying a 1D two-layered lithospheric stretching model, incorporating the effects of heat production by the crust and its sedimentary thermal blanketing, the thermo-mechanical evolution of the lithosphere was analysed in an effort to predict its palaeorheology (Van Wees *et al.* 1996; Bertotti *et al.* 1997).

For modelling purposes, a time frame of 100 Ma was chosen. Of this, the first 10 Ma (between 100 Ma and 90 Ma in Fig. 3) correspond to the rifting stage, culminating in separation of the conjugate upper and lower plate margins, and the following 90 Ma to the seafloor spreading stage during which oceanic lithosphere is accreted to the diverging plates. For modelling purposes, it was assumed that the pre-rift crustal and mantle lithosphere thickness are 30 km and 70 km, respectively, and that at the end of the rifting stage the upper plate margin has a crustal thickness of 15 km ($\delta = 2$) and a remaining mantle lithosphere thickness of 7 km ($\beta = 10$), whereas the lower plate margin has a crustal thickness of 10 km ($\delta = 3$) and a mantle lithosphere thickness of 63.6 km ($\beta = 1.1$) (δ and β are respectively the crustal and subcrustal stretching factor (Royden & Keen 1980)). Results show that through time the evolution of strength envelopes for lower and upper plate passive margins differs strongly. In principle, during rifting increased heating of the lithosphere causes its weakening; this effect is most pronounced at the moment of crustal separation. However, upper and lower plate margins show a very different evolution, both during the rifting and post-rift stage.

At the moment of crustal separation, upper plate margins are very weak due to strong attenuation of the mantle lithosphere and the ascent of the asthenospheric material close to the base of the crust. During the post-rift evolution of such a margin, having a crustal thickness of 15 km, the strength of the lithosphere increases gradually as new mantle is accreted to its base and cools during the re-equilibration of the lithosphere with the asthenosphere (Figs 3a, 4a). In contrast, the evolution of a sediment starved lower plate margin with a crustal thickness of 10 km is characterized by a synrift strength increase due to extensional unroofing of the little attenuated mantle lithosphere; the strength of such a margin increases dramatically during the post-rift stage due to its progressive cooling (Figs 3b, 4b). At the time frame of 0 Ma, a sediment starved lower plate margin is considerably stronger than the conjugate upper plate margin for which a sedimentary cover of about 7 km was assumed. The strength evolution of an upper plate margin is initially controlled by the youthfulness of its mantle lithosphere and its thicker crust, and later by the thermal blanketing effect of sediments infilling the available accommodation space. On the other hand, the strength of oceanic lithosphere, that is covered by thin sediments only, increases dramatically during its 90 Ma evolution and ultimately exceeds the strength of both margins, even if these are sediment starved (Figs 3c, 4). However, the strength of 90 My old oceanic lithosphere that has been progressively covered by very thick sediments is significantly reduced (Fig. 3d) to the point that it approaches the strength of a sediment filled lower plate margin (Fig. 4).

To test the effects of sediment infill and thermal blanketing on the strength evolution of upper and lower plate passive margins, a wide range of models was examined, assuming that sediments completely fill the tectonically-created accommodation space (sediment overfilled), adopting different sediment densities and corresponding sediment thickness variations (Fig. 4). Results show that a thick syn- and post-rift sedimentary prism markedly reduces the integrated strength of a margin. However, despite the strong sediment fill effect on the integrated strength, earlier identified first order differences between upper and lower plate margins remain. Compared to oceanic lithosphere, both with a 1 km sedimentary cover (Figs 3c and Fig. 4) and a 15 km thick cover (Fig. 3d), a sediment overfilled upper plate margin (applying $\rho_s = 2100$ kg m^{-3}) is characterized by lower integrated strength values throughout its evolution. However, for a lower plate margin conditions are dramatically different. Up to 20–70 Ma after

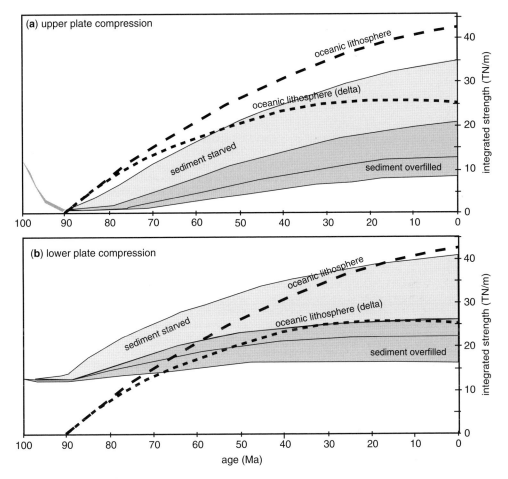

Fig. 4. Integrated compressional strength evolution of sediment-starved and sediment-filled (**a**) upper plate, and (**b**) lower plate passive margins, compared to the integrated strength evolution of oceanic lithosphere with thin and thick sediment cover as in Fig. 3. Shaded areas demonstrate strong sensitivity of integrated strength to sediment infilling, ranging from sediment starvation (highest strength values) to complete fill of accommodation space (dark shading, lowest strength values). Curves in dark shaded area correspond to different sediment densities and related range in sediment thickness (after Ziegler *et al.* 1998).

rifting, the lower plate integrated strength values are significantly higher than those for oceanic lithosphere, both with a thin and a thick sedimentary cover.

From these strength calculations it is evident, that at any stage the upper plate margin is weaker than oceanic lithosphere and the conjugate lower plate margin. This suggests that the upper plate margin is the most likely candidate for compressional reactivation and the initiation of a subduction zone. For realistic sediment density and infill values ($\rho_s \leq 2500$ kg m^{-3}), the upper plate margin tends to grow stronger in time, indicating that after a prolonged post-rift stage (>70 Ma) localization of deformation and subduction along such a margin, instead of on the adjacent continent, should be

facilitated by weakening mechanisms that are not incorporated in our standard rheological assumptions for the lithosphere, such as pre-existing crustal and mantle discontinuities and the boundaries between old and newly accreted lithospheric mantle.

The modelling shows that the compressional yield strength of passive margins can vary considerably, depending on their lithospheric configuration, sedimentary cover and thermal age. Lower plate margins, at which much of the old continental mantle lithosphere is preserved, are considerably stronger than upper plate margins at which asthenospheric material is accreted to the strongly attenuated old mantle lithosphere. Although mature oceanic lithosphere is characterized by a high compressional yield strength, it can be significantly weakened in areas where thick passive margin sedimentary prisms or deep-sea fans prograde onto it (e.g. Gulf of Mexico: Worrall & Snelson 1989; Niger Delta: Doust & Omatsola 1989; Bengal fan: Curray & Moore 1971).

Lithospheric folding and inversion

Folding of the lithosphere appears to play a more important role in the large-scale neotectonic deformation of extensional basin systems in intraplate areas than hitherto realized (Cloetingh *et al.* 1999). Lithospheric folding is a very effective mechanism for the propagation of tectonic deformation from active plate boundaries far into intraplate domains (e.g. Stephenson & Cloetingh 1991; Burov *et al.* 1993; Ziegler *et al.* 1995, 1998, 2002; Burov & Molnar 1998). The large wavelength of vertical motions associated with lithospheric folding (Cloetingh & Burov 1996) necessitates integration of available data from relatively large areas (Elfrink 2001), often going beyond the scope of regional structural and geophysical studies that target specific structural provinces. Recent studies of the German Basin (Bayer *et al.* 1999) have revealed the importance of its structural reactivation by lithospheric folding (Marotta *et al.* 2000). Similarly, folding of the Variscan lithosphere has been documented for Brittany (Bonnet *et al.* 2000), the adjacent Paris Basin (Lefort & Agarwal 1996; Guillocheau *et al.* 2000) and the Vosges–Black Forest arch (Dèzes *et al.* 2004).

The wavelength of the folds in Brittany is 250 km, pointing to a lithospheric mantle control of the deformation (Bonnet *et al.* 1998, 2000). As pointed out by Bonnet *et al.* (2000) the spatial pattern and the timing of the uplift inferred from river incision studies of Brittany is incompatible with a glacioeustatic origin. These authors link the observed patterns of vertical motions in NW France to the NW–SE directed principal compressional axis of the present-day intraplate stress field of NW Europe. The stress-induced uplift pattern appears to control the amount of fluvial incision in the area as well as the location of the main drainage divides. The area located at the western margin of the Paris Basin and the Atlantic rifted margin of France has been subject to thermal rejuvenation during Mesozoic extension related to North Atlantic rifting (Guillocheau *et al.* 2000; Robin *et al.* 2003; Ziegler *et al.* 2004) and subsequent compressional intraplate deformation (Ziegler *et al.* 1995), also affecting the Paris Basin (Lefort & Agarwal 1996). Levelling studies in this area (LeNotre

et al. 1999) also point towards its ongoing deformation.

An interesting analogue on the scale of a microcontinent affected by a succession of collisional events is provided by Iberia (Cloetingh *et al.* 2002), a well-documented natural laboratory for quantifying the interplay of neotectonics and surface processes (Garcia-Castellanos 2002; Garcia Castellanos *et al.* 2003; for a general discussion see Cloetingh *et al.* 1999 and Burov & Cloetingh 1997). An important factor in favour of a lithosphere-folding scenario for Iberia is the compatibility of the wavelength of observed deformations, the thermo-tectonic age of the lithosphere and the total amount of shortening with well documented examples of continental lithospheric folding coming from other cratonic areas (Cloetingh & Burov 1996).

A prominent example of lithospheric folding occurs in the Western Goby area of Central Asia, involving a lithosphere with a thermo-tectonic age of 400 Ma. In this area, mantle and crustal wavelengths are respectively 360 km and 50 km, with a shortening rate of *c.* 10 mm/a and a total amount of shortening of 200–250 km during 10–15 Ma (Burov *et al.* 1993; Burov & Molnar 1998).

The inferred wavelengths of these neotectonic lithosphere folds are consistent with the general relationship that was established between the wavelength of lithospheric folds and the thermo-tectonic age of the lithosphere on the base of an inventory of global examples of lithospheric folding (Cloetingh & Burov 1996). In a number of other areas of continental lithosphere folding, also smaller wavelength crustal folds have been detected, for example in Central Asia (Burov *et al.* 1993; Nikishin *et al.* 1993; Cobbold *et al.* 1993).

Compressional deformation of the lithosphere: insights from analogue tectonic experiments

Analytical, numerical and analogue modelling has focused mostly on buckling instabilities developing in a rheologically layered media representing the Earth's lithosphere in convergent tectonic environments (Zuber 1987; Martinod & Davy 1992, 1994; Burg *et al.* 1994; Martinod & Molnar 1995; Cloetingh *et al.* 1999; Gerbault *et al.* 1999; Montesi & Zuber 2003). Sokoutis *et al.* (2000, 2005) showed the strong influence of lateral variations in crustal thickness on the collisional deformation pattern. These findings suggest that adjacent parts of a compressionally reactivated system may exhibit different deformation styles depending on the local conditions. They demonstrate that the rheological properties of the lithosphere–asthenosphere system are essential to understand compressional deformation (Davy & Cobbold 1991 and references therein).

Below we discuss the mechanisms of shortening of continental lithosphere and the relationships of flexural buckling in the mantle layer and faulting in the uppermost brittle layer. The above aspects are approached through analogue experiments of Sokoutis *et al.* (2005) addressing the role of: (1) a suture zone separating blocks with different thickness; (2) weak crustal layers; and (3) mantle strengths.

Experimental setup

Two types of models are discussed: Type-1 experiments investigate shortening of a uniformly thick lithosphere, and Type-2 experiments simulate shortening of two welded lithospheres with different thickness (Fig. 5). The brittle–ductile layering of the continental lithosphere refers to geophysical data and extrapolation of laboratory experiments (e.g. Kirby 1983, 1985; Carter & Tsenn 1987; Ranalli 1995, 1997). Analogue materials were employed to construct 3-layer (brittle/weak ductile/strong ductile) systems (representing the lithosphere) floating on top of a heavy ductile fluid (representing the asthenosphere) (e.g. Davy & Cobbold 1991; Brun 1999, 2002).

The geometries and rheologies of analogue models necessarily simplify the natural complexity. The rheology of rocks is known to be strongly temperature dependent and therefore varies with depth (e.g. Ranalli 1995, 1997), but in analogue experiments the materials have a homogeneous rheology, which is a major simplification. However, representing the lower crust and upper mantle by a uniform layer, with depth-invariant properties is a justifiable first-order approximation that has been employed in other experiments (e.g. Davy & Cobbold 1988, 1991). On the other hand, since the detailed rheology of rocks in nature is imprecisely constrained, our choice of viscous rheology for the lower crust and upper mantle may be valid, though a non-linear rheology for these layers is perhaps more appropriate.

The Type-1 model represented a cold lithosphere with a relatively strong mantle. When subjected to horizontal shortening the primary mode of deformation of this model is characterized by buckling with a first-order wavelength (λ_1) of c. 7.7 cm (Fig. 6a,b). The surface structural pattern (Fig. 6a) is dominated by linear regions corresponding in sections (Fig. 6b) to prismatic pop-ups and pop-downs in the experimental upper brittle crust, still identifying a second-order wavelength (λ_2). In section, the deformed part of the model underwent thickening by box folding and thrusting. Again, shortening is taken up through

closure of prismatic basins lying above a down-warped mantle layer.

Influence of mantle strength

The role of the mantle rheology is made evident by comparing the results of Type-1 models, which have a normal mantle, and Type-2 models, which have a strong mantle. The Type-2 strong mantle allowed amplified folding of the experimental lithosphere configuring a megafold pair (Fig. 6d). The pre-existing suture focused the synclinal depression (Fig. 6c) in which the brittle crust thickened by complex wedging whereas a lithospheric anticline formed on the thinner block (Fig. 6d) (Burg *et al.* 2002). This geometry compares well with numerical models involving a strong upper mantle decoupled through a weak lower crust from the uppermost brittle crust (Cloetingh *et al.* 1999).

From buckling to thrusting and basin inversion

Model shortening followed three main phases in temporal sequence (see also Martinod & Davy 1994; Burg *et al.* 1994): (1) lithospheric buckling; (2) faulting at the inflection points of buckles that evolved in the orogenic areas to the development of: (3) large strain zones (Σ-belts) closing prismatic basins along upward-converging conjugate thrusts (Fig. 6b).

Buckling of continental and oceanic lithospheres has been recognized in theoretical, numerical and geophysical studies (e.g. Stephenson & Cloetingh 1991; Nikishin *et al.* 1993; Burg & Podlachikov 1999; Cloetingh *et al.* 1999, 2002; and references therein) as well as in experimental works (e.g. Martinod & Davy 1994). In the work presented here, the geometry of buckling depended on the rheology of the experimental lithosphere. Two-layer models may represent the oceanic lithosphere and any continental lithosphere without strong mantle (Martinod & Davy 1994). The scaled first-order wavelength in these models is c. 150–160 km, which is c. 4–5 times the lithospheric thickness. Three-layer models represent a thicker lithosphere with a strong mantle. The first-order buckling wavelength scales up to c. 385 km, about 3.8 times the lithospheric thickness. The spacing of structures in the upper crust corresponds to a second-order wavelength scaling to c. 165 km, which is c. 5.5 times the upper crustal thickness.

In the Type-2 model, up-scaled first-order wavelengths vary between c. 150–550 km, whereas the second-order wavelength of deformation is in the range of c. 80–150 km for the upper crust. In this model, normalization of

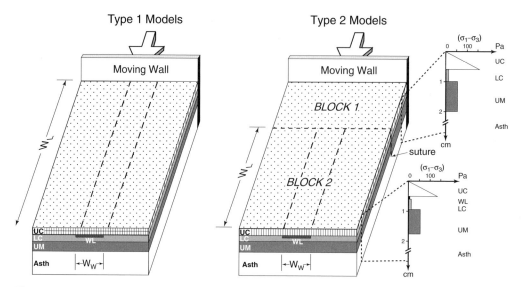

Fig. 5. Sketch of the experimental set-up. See text for materials used and rheological layering. The strength profiles represent the very initial deformation stage calculated using a pure shear strain rate approach for the ductile layers (Ramberg 1980) and the Mohr–Coulomb criterion for brittle layers. LC, lower crust; UC, upper crust; UM, upper mantle; Asth, asthenosphere; W_L and W_W represent the length and width, respectively, of the mid crustal soft layer (after Sokoutis *et al.* 2005).

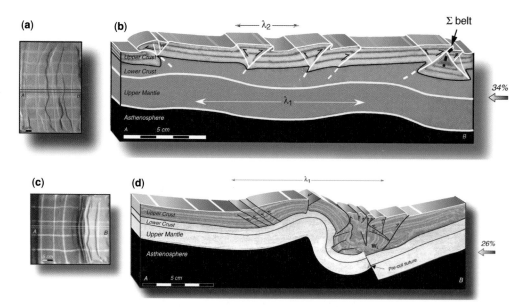

Fig. 6. Final deformation of analogue models investigating compressional reactivation of a cold lithosphere with a relatively strong mantle. (**a–b**) a 3-layer model of a uniformly thick lithosphere. (**c–d**) a 3-layer model with two welded lithospheres with different thicknesses. Left panels (a and c) show final top views. Right panels (b and d) show cross-sections with line drawings highlighting major structural features. λ_1 and λ_2 indicate first-order and second-order wavelengths, respectively. Arrows to the right indicate the direction of the moving wall (after Sokoutis *et al.* 2005).

the first-order wavelength to lithospheric thickness yields values of 4.1–5.5, and second-order wavelength normalized to the thickness of the upper crust is 4.6–6.

Plotting the depth–integrated strength (e.g. Davy & Cobbold 1991) scaled to nature versus scaled model wavelengths shows two distinct clusters depending upon the mantle strength (Fig. 7). Specifically, models built with a weak mantle exhibit a constant wavelength that is apparently not affected by the predefined suture (Sokoutis *et al.* 2005). Conversely, models with a strong mantle (i.e strong lithosphere) display: (1) longer wavelengths than those with relatively weak mantle; (2) the presence of a suture zone tends to increase the wavelength; and (3) a weak crustal layer decreases the wavelength (Fig. 7).

In essence, modelling results show the development of periodic instabilities at two distinct wavelengths, with first-order lithospheric folding (λ_1) on which a shorter wavelength (λ_2) of the brittle crust is superimposed. Both first-order and second-order wavelengths normalized to the lithospheric and brittle crust thickness, respectively, are in the range *c.* 4–6. These results are in good agreement with previous numerical and analytical estimates (e.g. Zuber 1987; Martinod & Davy 1992; Martinod & Molnar 1995; Cloetingh *et al.* 1999; Gerbault *et al.* 1999; Montesi & Zuber 2003) as well as analogue models (Burg *et al.* 1994; Martinod & Davy 1994). In nature, the wavelength of lithospheric and crustal folding mostly depends on the lithospheric strength and varies from 30 to 600 km (Cloetingh *et al.* 1999). The predicted first-order (130–550 km) and second-order (60–165 km) wavelengths are in the range of natural values.

Influence of a pre-existing suture zone

The suture zone introduced in the experiments to model a pre-existing lithospheric discontinuity controlled model evolution by localizing deformation. The lower crust and the Moho were both folded in correspondence with this discontinuity (see Fig. 6b). However, the suture installed between continental segments did not nucleate a singularity point, as prescribed in kinematic modelling (Escher & Beaumont 1997; Pfiffner *et al.* 2000). Instead, as in Burg *et al.* (2002), the prefigured suture has focused a synclinal depression on which the thickest crust is established through complex wedging while a crustal anticline formed on the weaker crust. The predefined sutures were not significantly reactivated during shortening; instead, they attracted the site of the closing basins because they bound an effective indenter. This behaviour is strongly controlled by the adopted model setup in which the pre-cut sutures were vertical, striking normal to direction of convergence. However, the analysis of experimental buckling suggests that the presence of a suture zone favours an increase of the wavelength of models with strong mantle.

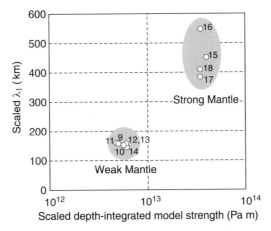

Fig. 7. Plot of depth-integrated model strength scaled to nature (logarithmic scale) versus scaled model wavelengths showing two distinct trends depending upon the mantle (i.e. lithospheric) strength. The lithospheric strength has been calculated by integrating the brittle/ductile differential stresses with depth and length (Corti *et al.* 2004). Models built with stronger mantle exhibit longer wavelengths than those with weaker mantle. The two main clusters of experimental data points are schematically highlighted by grey background. Numbers next to data points (white circles) indicate experiment numbers published by Sokoutis *et al.* (2005).

Europe's continental lithosphere: role of lithospheric rheology in basin (de)formation

Studies on the mechanical properties of the European lithosphere revealed a direct link between its thermo-tectonic age and bulk strength (Cloetingh & Burov 1996; Cloetingh *et al.* 2005; Pérez-Gussinyé & Watts 2005). On the other hand, inferences from P and S wave tomography (Goes *et al.* 2000*a*, *b*; Ritter *et al.* 2000, 2001) and thermo-mechanical modelling (Garcia-Castellanos *et al.* 2000) point to a pronounced weakening of the litho-sphere in the Lower Rhine area owing to high upper mantle temperatures. However, the Late Neogene and Quaternary tectonics of the Ardennes–Lower Rhine area appears to form part of a much wider neotectonic deformation system that overprints the Late Palaeozoic and Mesozoic basins of NW Europe. This is supported by geomorphological evidence and the results of seismicity studies in Brittany (Bonnet *et al.* 1998, 2000) and Normandy (Lagarde *et al.* 2000; Van Vliet-Lanoë *et al.* 2000), by data from the Ardennes–Eifel region (Meyer & Stets 1998; Van Balen *et al.* 2000), the southern parts of the Upper Rhine Graben (Nivière & Winter 2000), the Bohemian Massif (Ziegler & Dèzes 2005) and the North German Basin (Bayer *et al.* 1999).

Lithosphere-scale folding and buckling, in response to the build-up of compressional intraplate stresses, can cause uplift or subsidence of relatively large areas at time scales of a few Ma and thus can be an important driving mechanism of neotectonic processes. For instance, the Plio-Pleistocene accelerated subsidence of the North Sea Basin is attributed to down-buckling of the lithosphere in response to the build-up of the present-day stress field (Van Wees & Cloetingh 1996). Similarly, uplift of the Vosges–Black Forest arch, which at the level of the crust–mantle boundary extends from the Massif Central into the Bohemian Massif, commenced during the Burdigalian (±18 Ma) and persisted until at least early Pliocene times. Uplift of this arch is attributed to lithospheric folding controlled by compressional stresses originating at the Alpine collision zone (Ziegler *et al.* 2002; Dèzes *et al.* 2004; Ziegler & Dèzes 2005).

An understanding of the temporal and spatial strength distribution in the NW European litho-sphere may offer quantitative insights into the patterns of its intraplate deformation (basin inversion, upthrusting of basement blocks), and particularly into the pattern of lithosphere-scale folding and buckling.

Owing to the large amount of high quality geophysical data acquired during the last 20 years in Europe, its lithospheric configuration is well known, though significant uncertainties remain in many areas about the seismic and thermal thickness of the lithosphere (Babuska & Plomerova 1992; Artemieva & Mooney 2001). Nevertheless, the available data helps to constrain the rheology of the European lithosphere, thus enhancing our understanding of its strength.

So far, strength envelopes and the effective elastic thickness of the lithosphere have been calculated for a number of locations in Europe (e.g. Cloetingh & Burov 1996). As such calculations were made for scattered points only, or along transects, they provide limited information on lateral strength variations of the lithosphere. Although lithospheric thickness and strength maps have already been constructed for the Pannonian Basin (Lankreijer *et al.* 1999) and the Baltic Shield (Kaikkonen *et al.* 2000), such maps are not yet available for all of Europe.

As evaluation and modelling of the response of the lithosphere to vertical and horizontal loads requires an understanding of its strength distribution, efforts were dedicated to map the strength of the European foreland lithosphere by integrating 3D strength calculations (Cloetingh *et al.* 2005).

Strength calculations of the lithosphere depend primarily on its thermal and compositional structure and are particularly sensitive to thermal uncertainties (Ranalli & Murphy 1987; Ranalli 1995; Burov & Diament 1995). For this reason, the workflow aimed at the development of a 3D strength model for Europe was two-fold: (1) construction of a 3D compositional model; and (2) calculating a 3D thermal cube. The final 3D strength cube was obtained by calculating 1D strength envelopes for each lattice point (x, y) of a regularized raster covering NW Europe. For each lattice-point the appropriate input values were obtained from a 3D compositional and thermal cube (Fig. 8). A geological and geophysical geographic database was used as reference for the construction of the input models.

For continental realms, a 3D multi-layer compositional model was constructed, consisting of one mantle lithosphere layer, 2–3 crustal layers and an overlying sedimentary cover layer, whereas for oceanic areas a one-layer model was adopted. For the depth to the different interfaces several regional or European-scale compilations were available, which are based on deep seismic reflection and refraction or surface wave dispersion studies (e.g. Panza 1983; Calcagnile & Panza 1987; Suhadolc & Panza 1989; Blundell *et al.* 1992; Du *et al.* 1998; Artemieva *et al.* 2006). For the base of the lower crust, we relied strongly on the European Moho map of Dèzes & Ziegler (2004) (Fig. 9a). Regional compilation maps of the seismogenic lithosphere thickness were used as reference to the base of the thermal lithosphere in subsequent thermal modelling (Babuska & Plomerova 1993, 2001; Plomerova *et al.* 2002).

Figure 10a shows the integrated strength under compression of the entire lithosphere of Western and Central Europe, whereas Figure 10b displays the integrated strength of the crustal part of the lithosphere. As evident from Figure 10, Europe's lithosphere is characterized by major spatial mechanical strength variations, with a pronounced contrast between the strong Proterozoic lithosphere of the East European Platform to the east of the Teisseyre–Tornquist line and the relatively weak Phanerozoic lithosphere of Western Europe.

A similar strength contrast occurs at the transition from strong Atlantic oceanic lithosphere to the relatively weak continental lithosphere of Western Europe. Within the Alpine foreland,

pronounced NW–SE trending weak zones are recognized that coincide with such major geological structures as the Rhine Graben System and the North Danish–Polish Trough, that are separated by the high-strength North German Basin and the Bohemian Massif. Moreover, a broad zone of weak lithosphere characterizes the Massif Central and surrounding areas.

The presence of thickened crust in the area of the Teisseyre–Tornquist suture zone (Fig. 9b) gives rise to a pronounced mechanical weakening of the lithosphere, particularly of its mantle part. Whereas the lithosphere of Fennoscandia is characterized by a relatively high strength, the North Sea rift system corresponds to a zone of weakened lithosphere. Other areas of high lithospheric strength are the Bohemian Massif and the London–Brabant Massif both of which exhibit low seismicity. A pronounced contrast

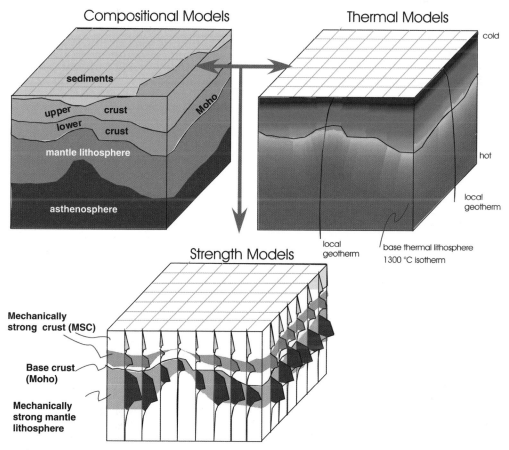

Fig. 8. From crustal thickness (top left) and thermal structure (top right) to lithospheric strength (bottom): conceptual configuration of the thermal structure and composition of the lithosphere, adopted for the calculation of 3D strength models.

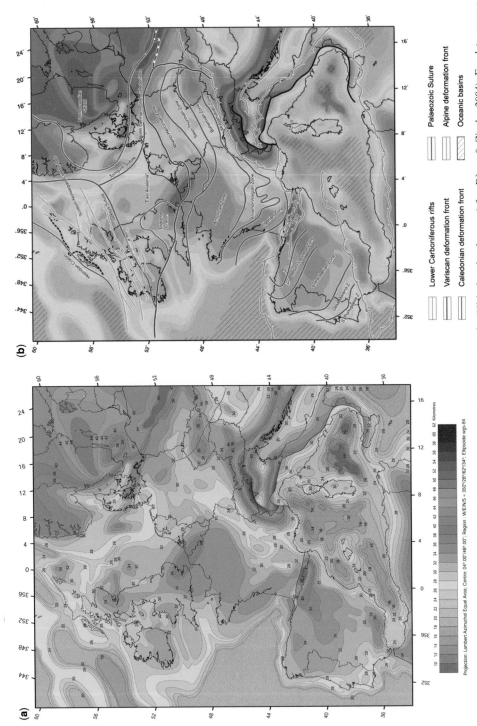

Fig. 9. (**a**) Crustal thickness map of western and central Europe, constructed by integration of published regional maps (after Dèzes & Ziegler 2004). For data sources see http://comp1.geol.umibas.ch/. Red lines (solid and stippled) show offsets of the Moho discontinuities. (**b**) Caledonian and Variscan structures superimposed on the crustal thickness map.

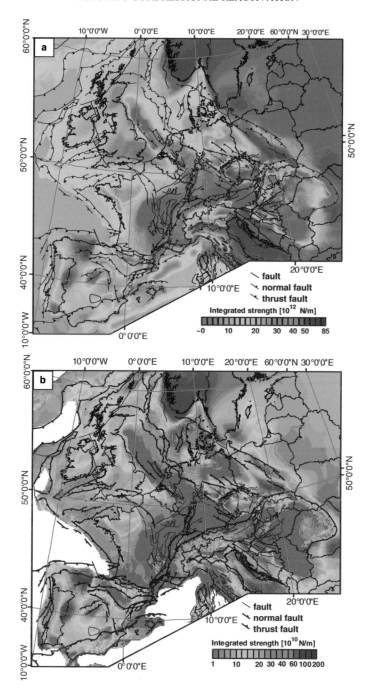

Fig. 10. Integrated strength maps for intraplate Europe. Adopted composition for upper crust, lower crust and mantle is based on a wet quartzite, diorite and dry olivine composition, respectively. Rheological rock parameters are based on Carter & Tsenn (1987). The adopted bulk strain-rate for creep deformation of continental lithosphere (Carter & Tsenn, 1987) is 10^{-16} s^{-1}, compatible with constraints from GPS measurements (see text). Contours represent integrated strength in compression for (**a**) total lithosphere, and (**b**) crust. The main structural features of Europe are superimposed on the strength maps (after Ziegler 1988; Dèzes *et al.* 2004).

in strength can also be noticed between the strong Adriatic indenter and the weak Pannonian Basin area (see also Fig. 10).

Comparing Figures 10a and b reveals that the lateral strength variations of Europe's intraplate lithosphere are primarily caused by variations in the mechanical strength of the mantle lithosphere, whereas variations in crustal strength appear to be more modest. The variations in lithospheric mantle strength are primarily related to variations in the thermal structure of the lithosphere, that can be related to thermal perturbations of the sub-lithospheric upper mantle imaged by seismic tomography (Goes *et al.* 2000*a*), with lateral variations in crustal thickness playing a secondary role, apart from Alpine domains which are characterized by deep crustal roots. High strength in the East European Platform, the Bohemian Massif, the London–Brabant Massif and the Fenno-Scandian Shield reflects the presence of old, cold and thick lithosphere, whereas the European Cenozoic Rift System coincides with a major axis of thermally weakened lithosphere within the NW European Platform. Similarly, weakening of the lithosphere of southern France can be attributed to the presence of tomographically imaged plumes rising up under the Massif Central (Granet *et al.* 1995; Wilson & Patterson 2001).

The major lateral strength variations that characterize the lithosphere of extra-Alpine Phanerozoic Europe are largely related to its Late Cenozoic thermal perturbation as well as to Mesozoic and Cenozoic rift systems and intervening stable blocks, and not so much to the Caledonian and Variscan orogens and their accreted terranes (Fig. 9b) (Dèzes *et al.* 2004). These lithospheric strength variations (Fig. 10a) are primarily related to variations in the thermal structure of the lithosphere, and therefore, are compatible with inferred variations in the effective elastic thickness (EET) of the lithosphere (see Cloetingh & Burov 1996; Perez-Gussinye & Watts 2005).

The most important strong inliers in the lithosphere of the Alpine foreland lithosphere correspond to the Early Palaeozoic London–Brabant Massif and the Variscan Armorican, Bohemian and West Iberian Massifs. The strong Proterozoic Fenno-Scandian–East European Craton flanks the weak Phanerozoic European lithosphere to the NE whereas the strong Adriatic indenter contrasts with the weak lithosphere of the Mediterranean collision zone.

Crustal seismicity in Europe is largely concentrated on the presently still active Alpine plate boundaries, and particularly on the margins of the Adriatic indenter (Fig. 11). In the Alpine foreland, seismicity is largely concentrated on zones of low lithospheric strength, such as the European

Cenozoic rift system, and areas where pre-existing crustal discontinuities can be reactivated under the presently prevailing NW-directed stress field, such as the South Armorican shear zone (Dèzes *et al.* 2004) and the rifted margin of Norway (Mosar 2003).

The strength maps presented in Figure 10 do not incorporate the effects of spatial variations in composition in crustal and mantle layers. Future work will address the effects of such second order strength perturbations, adopting constraints on the composition of several crustal and mantle layers provided by seismic velocities (Guggisberg *et al.* 1991; Aichroth *et al.* 1992) and crustal and upper mantle xenolith studies (Mengel *et al.* 1991; Wittenberg *et al.* 2000).

Transition from post-rift basin inversion to lithospheric folding due to lithospheric strength reversal in NW Europe

Seismicity and stress-indicators, combined with geodetic and geomorphic observations, demonstrate that the northern Alpine foreland is being actively deformed (Camelbeeck & Meghraoui 1996; Ziegler *et al.* 2002). Localized Cenozoic extension in areas affected by plumes occurs in the Bresse, Eger, and Rhine Graben segments (Wilson & Patterson 2001) of the European Cenozoic rift system. However, seismicity (Fig. 11) (Grünthal *et al.* 1999) and stress-indicator data (Müller *et al.* 1992; Gölke & Coblentz 1996; Tesauro *et al.* 2004) demonstrate that active compressional deformation is also taking place in the Alpine foreland well outside the localized Cenozoic rift regions. Seismicity occurs primarily in areas of crustal thickness contrast between the Cenozoic rifts and their surrounding platform areas, as well as in areas of crustal contrast along the northeastern Atlantic rifted margins. Typically these contrasts occur at pre-existing faults, such as those bounding the Bohemian and Armorican Massifs. GPS measurements also indicate that the highest deformation rates occur in the European Cenozoic rift system where strain rates are on the order of 10^{-16} s^{-1} (Tesauro *et al.* 2004). The simultaneous occurrence of thrust faulting, normal faulting, and strike-slip faulting in the Alpine foreland indicates a stress distribution dominated by heterogeneous upper-crustal structures, including weak zones (Handy & Brun 2004).

Late Neogene vertical motions (Japsen & Chalmers 2000) (Fig. 11) caused rapid uplift in onshore compartments of the rifted North Atlantic margins and simultaneous rapid acceleration of subsidence in adjacent offshore basins. Fission-track studies in southern Norway (Rohrmann *et al.*

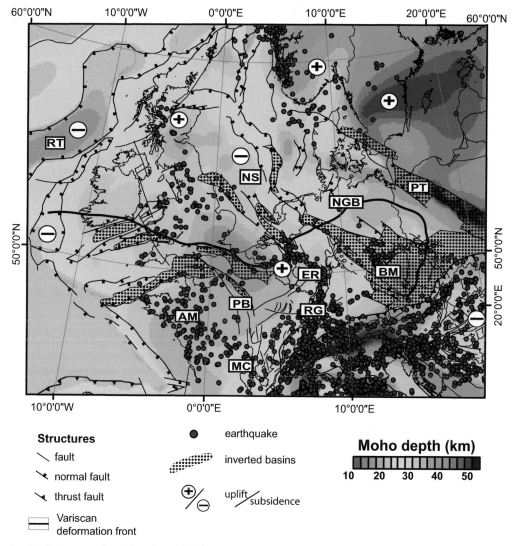

Fig. 11. Seismicity (after Grünthal *et al.* 1999) superimposed on map of depth to Moho (after Dèzes & Ziegler 2004) of NW Europe. Neogene uplift and subsidence anomalies are indicated by circled plus and minus symbols, respectively (cf. Japsen & Chalmers 2000). Also shown are locations of inverted basin structures (modified from Brun & Nalpas 1996). Note concentrations of intraplate seismicity in areas of crustal thickness contrast between the basinal and Palaeozoic Massif areas, as well as in areas of crustal contrast along the NE Atlantic rifted margins. Notable exception is seismicity along neotectonically active Rhine Graben (RG). AM, Armorican Massif; BM, Bohemian Massif; ER, Eifel region; MC, Massif Central; NS, North Sea Basin; NGB, North German Basin; PB, Paris Basin; PT, Polish Trough; RT, Rockall Trough.

1995) and the British Isles (Allen *et al.* 2002) demonstrate onset of uplift as early as Oligocene time. Similarly, quantitative subsidence analysis shows late Neogene acceleration of subsidence in the North Atlantic (Cloetingh *et al.* 1990; Van Wees & Cloetingh 1996).

These vertical motions have been attributed to upper-mantle thermal perturbations and folding (Cloetingh *et al.* 1999; Japsen & Chalmers 2000). Similar motions have also occurred in the foreland closer to the Alpine collision zone, including the North German (Marotta *et al.* 2000) and Paris (Lefort & Agarwal 1996) basins, the Armorican (Bonnet *et al.* 2000; Lagarde *et al.* 2000) and Bohemian Massifs (Achauer 2003, pers. comm.), the Eifel region (Garcia-Castellanos *et al.* 2000), the Massif Central (Granet *et al.* 1995) and Iberia (Cloetingh *et al.* 2002).

The timing and magnitude of these vertical motions reflect the interplay of plate reorganizations (Ziegler *et al.* 2002) and plume activity in the North Atlantic (Bijwaard & Spakman 1999) and western and central Europe (Goes *et al.* 2000*a*, *b*; Ritter *et al.* 2001; Wilson & Patterson 2001). Geochemical and petrological studies show that widespread volcanic activity in the European foreland culminated in the Neogene and formed high topography (Wilson & Patterson 2001). It seems plausible that the volcanism and associated uplift would have weakened the lithospheric mantle over areas considerably wider than the dimension of the plume itself, and thus promoted folding and controlled the wavelength of the resulting folds (see also Burov *et al.* 2007). Although some other folded areas like the Tien Shan in Central Asia are marked by pronounced mantle strength (Cloetingh *et al.* 1999), the fact that the European foreland was folding at shorter wavelengths likely reflects the lithospheric mantle being significantly weaker.

Neogene transition in mode of intraplate deformation

The mode of intraplate deformation changed from Neogene onward. Since early Mesozoic, northwestern Europe has been characterized by the formation of many basinal structures bordered by deep-seated boundary faults (Fig. 11). The evolution of these basins has been marked by repeated reactivation of their fabric. Alpine compression in Late Cretaceous and early Tertiary time resulted in pervasive basin inversion. Inversion ceased in Miocene times and gave way to the current mode of widespread deformation that particularly affects the nonbasinal areas (Ziegler *et al.* 1998).

An additional important factor has been elevation of temperatures in the upper mantle by Neogene plume impingement, as inferred from seismic tomography (Goes *et al.* 2000*a*). These high temperatures would have reduced mantle strength (Garcia-Castellanos *et al.* 2000), in accordance with inferred wavelengths for lithospheric folding (Cloetingh *et al.* 1999). However, this upper-mantle thermal perturbation, which should have a similar weakening effect in both offshore and onshore areas, could not alone explain the cessation of basin reactivation in the North Sea area. Hence, in order to investigate what may have controlled this significant change in the mode of deformation, we explore how lithospheric strength may have changed prior to and during the transition in Neogene time.

Strength reversal in Europe's intraplate lithosphere

The net strength of the lithosphere is controlled both by the geotherm and the depth of the Moho, which determines the relative ratio of mantle and crustal strength (e.g. Watts & Burov 2003). To explore how both may have varied we constructed strength envelopes for lithosphere in compression for two typical sections in the northwestern European foreland lithosphere: an inverted basin in the North Sea (NS), and a typical Palaeozoic massif where no rifted basin formed (Fig. 11). The initial lithospheric thicknesses of the Massif setting are constrained by subsidence modelling of wells from the Paris Basin and adjacent areas (Ziegler *et al.* 2004). The Palaeozoic massifs of western Europe, such as the Bohemian Massif, are characterized by a slightly deepened Moho (Dèzes & Ziegler 2004) and seismicity along their borders (Fig. 11). In contrast, the North Sea is representative of Mesozoic inverted basins in NW Europe with shallower Moho depths and lower seismicity. In the model, initial Mesozoic crustal and lithospheric thickness for the North Sea is considerably lower than for the Palaeozoic Massif setting, because of basin localization during Mesozoic time (Van Wees & Beekman 2000) (Fig. 12a). We forward modelled repeated basin reactivation and inversion in the North Sea and the associated rheological evolution using constraints from subsidence data (Van Wees & Beekman 2000). As in earlier studies, the reactivated basins are marked by zones of weakness, which reduce in particular the brittle strength (Ziegler *et al.* 1995; De Bresser *et al.* 2001; Van Wees & Beekman 2000; Bos & Spiers 2002). Although during inversion, basin strength increases as a consequence of lithospheric thickening, it remains low compared to that of the Palaeozoic Massif setting (Fig. 12b), because of the initial lithospheric thinning.

We assume that these strength profiles were subsequently perturbed by lithospheric heating in the Neogene by mantle plumes. Numerical models (e.g. Burov *et al.* 2007) predict that the lithosphere–plume interaction would cause the lower lithosphere to be assimilated by the underlying mantle and raise its temperatures.

We model this effect by adopting a subcrustal stretching factor of 1.6 for the Palaeozoic Massif setting (see Cloetingh & Van Wees 2005 for a more extensive discussion) (Fig. 12c). As a consequence, strength below the Palaeozoic Massif setting has been reduced to lower values than

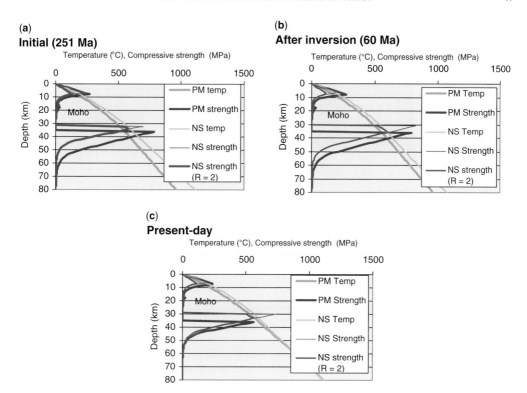

Fig. 12. Strength envelopes characteristic for Palaeozoic Massif (PM) and North Sea Basin (NS) settings (cf. Van Wees & Beekman 2000), adopting a lithospheric-stretching model and rheological parameters before perturbation by plume impingement. (**a**) Compressive-strength curves for early Mesozoic time, showing differentiation between Palaeozoic Massif and North Sea settings. Palaeozoic massifs are marked by moderately higher strength owing to higher lithospheric thickness. Strength differentiation is in agreement with localization of basin deformation in the northwestern European foreland. (**b**) Lithospheric strength after basin extension and inversion. Extended basins most likely require zones of crustal- and mantle-scale weakness for repeated reactivation. During inversion, North Sea strength is at its peak, but still low compared to strength of Palaeozoic massifs. (**c**) Neogene underplating—thermally resetting lithospheric thickness in Palaeozoic Massif and North Sea areas to *c.* 100 km—results in pronounced relative reduction of mantle strength underneath massif areas compared to inverted North Sea Basin. Progressive mantle weakening results in lowest strength underneath Palaeozoic massifs. Marked Neogene reduction of mantle strength underneath Palaeozoic massifs triggers lithospheric folding. Thrust zones are preferentially reactivated in Palaeozoic massifs, which, at their borders, are marked by a concentration of seismicity in Figure 11.

below the North Sea. Thus, plume-related heating reduces the strength in areas characterized by a deep Moho and thick lithosphere prior to the plume impingement (i.e. the Palaeozoic massifs) more than in other areas.

The integrated lithospheric strength of the Palaeozoic Massif and North Sea Basin settings (Fig. 13) is marked by a pronounced Neogene reversal. This reversal can explain both the concentration of intraplate deformation, as reflected by seismicity and GPS data in the massif areas close to the Alpine collision zone, and the cessation of deformation in the basinal areas. Furthermore, the change to a mode of deformation resulting in lithospheric folding in the massif areas rather than inversion appears also to be the consequence of this reversal.

The primary factor in the strength reversal is the large-scale thermal perturbation of Europe's upper mantle caused by plume activity rather than the composition of the crust, except for the depth of the Moho and thickness of the lithosphere, which depend largely on the Mesozoic rift history. Hence, our modelling results are fairly robust in terms of the crustal and mantle rheologies used. Alternative wet and dry dunite mantle rheologies (Carter & Tsenn 1987) result in a relative decrease and increase of the absolute strength values respectively, but the relative difference in strength values is retained (Fig. 13). Permissible relative variations of crustal and lithospheric thickness point to a deeper Moho for the Palaeozoic Massif setting than for the North Sea Basin (Fig. 11). As the

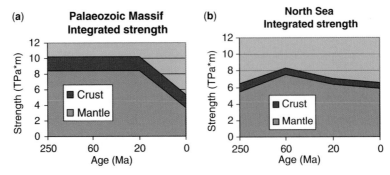

Fig. 13. Temporal evolution of integrated lithospheric strengths. (**a**) Palaeozoic Massif setting. (**b**) North Sea Basin. Strength evolution shows a pronounced Neogene weakening of mantle strength underneath Palaeozoic Massif settings relative to inverted North Sea Basin area, leading to a progressive transition from concentration of deformation in basin areas toward concentration of deformation around massifs in onshore areas, as reflected by seismicity patterns in Figure 11.

Palaeozoic Massif lithosphere is expected to be stronger throughout the Mesozoic than the North Sea Basin lithosphere, it should be marked by a relatively higher lithospheric thickness. With these assumptions the model is fairly robust in the range of uncertainties (Cloetingh & Van Wees 2005). Models adopting zero strength for the continental mantle (e.g. Jackson 2002; see for a discussion also Watts & Burov 2003) are incompatible with cessation of deformation in the weakest, basinal areas, because these are marked by relatively low crustal strength throughout their history (Fig. 13). Intraplate stresses (Cloetingh & Burov 1996), fluids, and shear zones (Handy & Brun 2004) may further reduce the strength of the lithosphere, but do not affect the first-order patterns of the inferred temporal and spatial evolution of lithospheric strength in the European foreland.

Black Sea Basin: compressional reactivation of an extensional basin

The Black Sea (Fig. 14), in which water depths range down to 2.2 km, is underlain by a larger western and a smaller eastern sub-basin that are separated by the Andrusov Ridge. The western basin is floored by oceanic and transitional crust and contains up to 19 km of Cretaceous to Recent sediments. The eastern basin is floored by strongly thinned continental crust and contains up to 12 km of Cretaceous and younger sediments. The Andrusov Ridge is buried beneath 5–6 km thick sediments and is upheld by attenuated continental crust. Significantly, the sedimentary fill of the Black Sea Basin system is characterized by nearly horizontal layering that is only disturbed along its flanks bordering the orogenic systems of the

Balkanides and Pontides in the south, and the Great Caucasus and Crimea in the north and NE.

The Black Sea Basin system is thought to have evolved by Aptian–Albian back-arc rifting that progressed in the western sub-basin to crustal separation and Cenomanian–Coniacian seafloor spreading. During the late Senonian and Palaeocene the Black Sea was subjected to regional compression in conjunction with the evolution of its flanking orogenic belts. During the early Eocene major rifting and volcanism affected the eastern Black Sea Basin and the eastward adjacent Acharat–Trialeti Basin. During the late Eocene and Oligocene the Pontides thrust belt developed along the southern margin of the Black Sea and inversion of the Great Caucasus Trough and the Acharat–Trialeti rift commenced. The present stress regime of the Black Sea area, as deduced from earthquake focal mechanisms, structural and GPS data is compression dominated, reflecting continued collisional interaction of the Arabian and the Eurasian plates that controls on-going crustal shortening in the Great Caucasus. In the absence of intra-basinal deformations, the Pliocene and Quaternary accelerated subsidence of the Black Sea Basin is attributed to stress-induced downward deflection of its lithosphere (Nikishin *et al.* 2001, 2003; Cloetingh *et al.* 2003).

Although there is general agreement that the Black Sea evolved in response to Late Cretaceous and Eocene back-arc extension, the exact timing and kinematics of opening of its western and eastern sub-basins is still being debated (e.g. Robinson *et al.* 1995; Nikishin *et al.* 2001, 2003; Cloetingh *et al.* 2003). This applies particularly to the exact opening timing of the eastern Black Sea for which different interpretations have been advanced varying from Middle- to Late Cretaceous

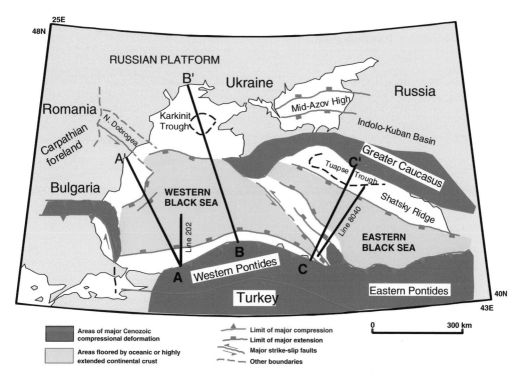

Fig. 14. Regional tectonic map of the Black Sea (Cloetingh *et al.* 2003).

(Finetti *et al.* 1988) to Early Eocene opening (Robinson *et al.* 1995) or a combination thereof (Nikishin *et al.* 2003).

Gravity data show an important difference in the mode of flexural compensation between the western and eastern Black Sea (Spadini *et al.* 1997). The western Black Sea appears to be isostatically under-compensated and in a state of upward flexure, consistent with a deep level of lithospheric necking. By contrast, for the eastern Black Sea gravity data point towards isostatic overcompensation and a downward state of flexure, compatible with a shallow necking level. This is thought to reflect differences in the pre-rift mechanical properties of the lithosphere of the western and eastern Black Sea sub-basins (Cloetingh *et al.* 1995; Spadini *et al.* 1996).

Cloetingh *et al.* (2003) discuss the results of thermo-mechanical modelling of the Black Sea Basin along a number of regional cross-sections through its western and eastern parts, that are constrained by a large integrated geological and geophysical database (see Spadini 1996; Spadini *et al.* 1996, 1997). Below, we address the relationship between the pre-rift finite strength of the lithosphere and geometry of extensional basins and discuss the effects of differences in pre-rift rheology on the Mesozoic–Cenozoic stratigraphy of the

Black Sea Basin system. These findings raise important questions on post-rift tectonics and on intraplate stress transmission into the Black Sea Basin from its margins.

Rheology and sedimentary basin formation

Inferred differences in the mode of basin formation between the western and eastern Black Sea Basins can be largely explained in terms of palaeorheologies (Fig. 15). The pre-rift lithospheric strength of the western Black Sea appears to be primarily controlled by the combined mechanical response of a strong upper crust and strong upper mantle (Spadini *et al.* 1996). The shallow necking level in the eastern Black Sea is compatible with a pre-rift strength controlled by a strong upper crust decoupled from the weak hot underlying mantle. These differences point to important differences in the thermo-tectonic age of the lithosphere of the two sub-basins (Cloetingh & Burov 1996). The inferred lateral variations between the western and eastern Black Sea suggest thermal stabilization of the western Black Sea prior to rifting whilst the lithosphere of the eastern Black Sea was apparently already thinned and thermally destabilized by the time of Eocene rifting. The inferred differences in

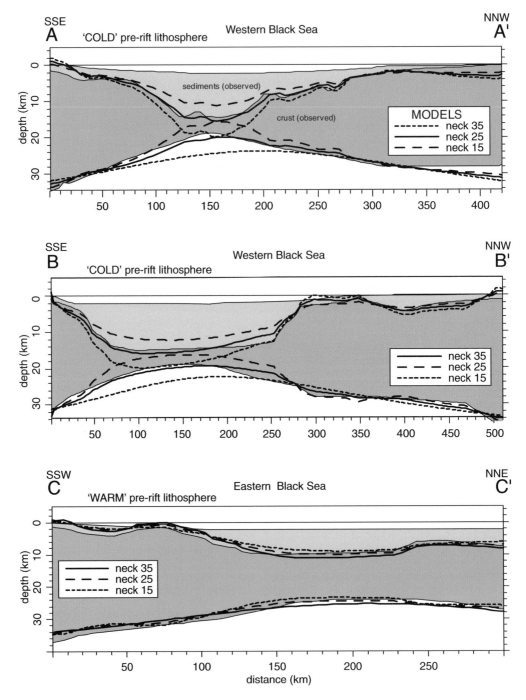

Fig. 15. Crustal scale models for extensional basin formation for the western and eastern Black Sea. See Figure 14 for location of cross-sections. A comparison of predicted and observed Moho depths provides constraints on levels of necking and thermal regime of pre-rift lithosphere. The models support the presence of cold pre-rift lithosphere compatible with a deep level of necking of 25 km in the western Black Sea. In the eastern Black Sea, the models suggest the presence of a warm pre-rift lithosphere with a level of necking of 15 km (Cloetingh *et al.* 2003).

necking level and in the timing of rifting between the western and eastern Black Sea suggest an earlier and more pronounced development of rift shoulders in the western Black Sea basin as compared to the eastern Black Sea (Robinson *et al.* 1995).

In the western Black Sea rifting began during the late Barremian–Aptian and progressed to crustal separation at the transition to the Cenomanian with seafloor spreading ending in the Coniacian (Cloetingh *et al.* 2003). In this deep-marine basin, up to 12.5 km thick sediments accumulated prior to the late middle Miocene Sarmatian sea level fall when it was converted into a relatively small (up to 800 m deep) lake. Late Miocene to Recent sediments attain thicknesses of up to 2.5 km. The eastern Black Sea Basin may have undergone an Aptian–Turonian and a Campanian–Maastrichtian rifting stage prior to its Palaeocene–early Eocene rift-related main subsidence and deepening that was accompanied by little flank uplift and erosion. During the late Eocene, sediment supply from the compressionally active Pontides and Greater Caucasus belts increased and led in the basin centre to the deposition of up to 5 km thick sediments. Also the eastern Black Sea remained a deep-marine basin until the late middle Miocene Sarmatian when it was converted into a lake. When sea level returned to normal in the late Miocene, water depth increased dramatically to 2800 m in both the western and eastern Black Sea Basins, presumably in response to the loading effect of the water (Spadini 1996). By the Quaternary, increased sediment supply led to significant subsidence and sediment accumulation, with a modest decrease in water depth to the present-day value of 2200 m.

Overall uplift of the margins of the Black Sea commenced in middle Miocene times (Nikishin *et al.* 2003). Although the reconstructions by Spadini *et al.* (1997) and Nikishin *et al.* (2003) differ in the assumed maximum depth of the basin, and the assumed palaeobathymetry and sea-level fluctuations, the derived Pliocene–Quaternary subsidence acceleration appears to be robust (Robinson *et al.* 1995; Spadini *et al.* 1997; Nikishin *et al.* 2003).

Constraints on the present-day stress regime are lacking for the central parts of the Black Sea Basin. However, structural geological field studies and earthquake focal mechanisms in areas bordering the Black Sea (see Nikishin *et al.* 2001), as well as GPS data (Reilinger *et al.* 1997) demonstrate that in the collisional setting of the European and Arabian plate the area is subjected to compression.

The collisional Caucasus orogeny commenced during the late Eocene and culminated during Oligocene–Quaternary times. On the other hand, the North Pontides thrust belt was activated during the late Eocene and remained active until the end of the Oligocene (Nikishin *et al.* 2001). Correspondingly, the late Eocene accelerated subsidence of the Black Sea Basin can be attributed to the build-up of a regional compressional stress field (Robinson *et al.* 1995).

The late Eocene–Quaternary Caucasus orogeny, overprinting back-arc extension in the Black Sea, was controlled by the collisional inter-action of the Arabian plate with the southern margin of the East European Craton (Nikishin *et al.* 2001).

Strength evolution and neotectonic reactivation at the basin margins during the post-rift phase

Automated back-stripping analyses and comparison of results with forward models of lithospheric stretching (Van Wees *et al.* 1998) provide estimates of the integrated lithospheric strength at various syn- and post-rift stages (Cloetingh *et al.* 2003). Figure 16 (left) shows a comparison of observed and forward modelled tectonic subsidence for the centre of the Western Black Sea Basin. Automated back-stripping yields a stretching factor β of 6. The modelling fails to predict the pronounced late Neogene subsidence acceleration, documented by the stratigraphic record that may be attributed to late-stage compression. As post-rift cooling of the lithosphere leads in time to a significant increase in its integrated strength, its early post-rift deformation is favoured. Present-day lithospheric strength profiles calculated for the centre and margin of western Black Sea show a pronounced difference. The presence of relatively strong lithosphere in the basin centre and weaker lithosphere at the basin margins favours deformation of the latter during late-stage compression. This may explain why observed compressional structures appear predominantly at the edges of the Black Sea Basin and not in its interior (Fig. 14).

In Figure 16 (right) the observed and forward modelled tectonic subsidence of the centre of the eastern Black Sea Basin are compared, adopting for modelling a stretching factor β of 2.3 that is compatible with the subsidence data and consistent with geophysical constraints. During the first ten million years of post-rift evolution, integrated strengths are low but subsequently increase rapidly owing to cooling of the lithosphere. During the first ten million years after rifting, and in the presence of very weak lithosphere, the strength of which was primarily controlled by the rift-inherited mechanical properties of its upper parts, we expect that this area would be prone

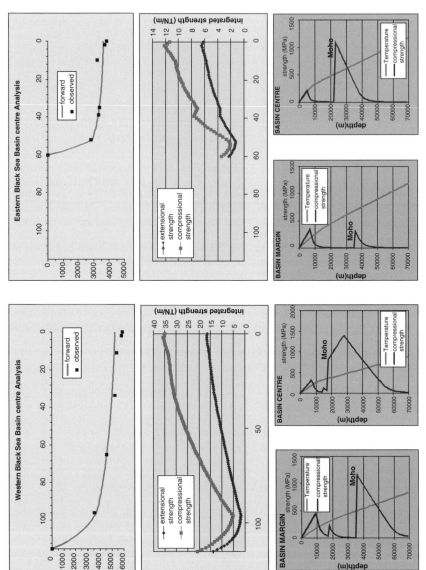

Fig. 16. A comparison of observed and forward modelled tectonic subsidence for the western Black Sea centre (left) and the eastern Black Sea centre (right). Automated back-stripping (top panels) yields an estimate for the stretching factor β of 6 for the western Black Sea and a β of 2.3 for the eastern Black Sea. The observed pronounced acceleration of late Neogene subsidence documented in the stratigraphic record could be an indication of late-stage compression. The middle panels show that for both areas post-rift cooling leads to a significant increase in the predicted integrated strength with time for both compressional and extensional regimes (1 TNm^{-1} = 10^{12} Nm^{-1}). Present-day lithospheric compressional strength profiles calculated for the centre and margin of the western and eastern Black Sea (bottom panels) show a pronounced difference with depth. Temperature profiles (in °C) and Moho depth are given for reference. Note the important role of the actual depth of the Moho in the mechanical decoupling of upper crust and mantle parts of the Black Sea lithosphere (Cloetingh *et al.* 2003).

to early post-rift compressional deformation. However, given the cooling-related progressive increase of the integrated lithospheric strength with time increasingly higher stress levels are required to cause large-scale deformation (Fig. 16). Due to substantial crustal thinning, a strong upper mantle layer is present in the central part of the basin at relatively shallow depths.

Based on the present thermo-mechanical configuration with relatively strong lithosphere in the basin centre and relatively weak lithosphere at the basin margins, we predict that a substantial amount of late-stage shortening induced by orogenic activity in the surrounding areas will be taken up along the basin margins, with only minor deformation occurring in the relatively stiff central parts of the basin. The relative difference in rheological strength of the marginal and central parts of the basin is more pronounced in the eastern than in the western Black Sea. These predictions have to be validated by new data focusing on the neotectonics of the Black Sea. High-resolution shallow seismic profiles and acquisition of stress-indicator data could provide the necessary constraints for such future modelling.

Modelling predictions for basement and surface heat flow in the eastern and western Black Sea (Cloetingh et al. 2003) show markedly different patterns in timing of the rift-related heat flow maximum. The predicted present-day heat flow is considerably lower for the western than for the eastern sub-basin. This is attributed to the presence of more heat producing crustal material in the eastern than in the western Black Sea that is partly floored by oceanic crust. The effects of sedimentary blanketing were taken into account in heat flow modelling (Van Wees & Beekman 2000). Heat flow values vary between 30 mW m^{-2} in the centre of the basins to 70 mW m^{-2} in its Crimean and Caucasus margins (Nikishin et al. 2003). Thermal modelling (Cloetingh et al. 2003) indicates a pronounced effect of thermal blanketing in the western Black Sea that contains up to 19 km thick sediments. As a result its present-day integrated strength is not that much higher than its initial strength. By contrast, the integrated strength of the eastern Black Sea is much higher than the initial strength as the blanketing effect of its up to 12 km thick sedimentary fill is less pronounced and as water depths are greater.

Cloetingh et al. (1999) have made a comparison of theoretical predictions for lithosphere folding of rheologically coupled and decoupled lithosphere, as a function of its thermo-mechanical age with estimates of folding wavelengths documented in continental lithosphere for various representative areas on the globe including the Black Sea. The western Black Sea centre is marked by a thermo-mechanical age of around 100 Ma with rheological modelling indicating mechanical decoupling of the crust and lithospheric mantle (see Fig. 16). These models imply an effective elastic thickness (EET) of at least 40 km (Burov & Diament 1995) and folding wavelengths of 100–200 km for the mantle and 50–100 km for the upper crust (Cloetingh et al. 1999). For the eastern Black Sea, a probably significantly younger thermo-mechanical lithospheric age of 55 Ma, implies an EET of no more than 25 km and indicates mantle folding at wavelengths of c. 100–150 km and a crustal folding wavelength similar to the western Black Sea. A comparison of estimated folding wavelengths with theoretical predictions shows a systematic deviation to larger values. This is characteristic for 'atypical' folding where the large dimension of the pre-existing rift basin during the late-stage compressional phase causes a pronounced increase in the wavelength of the stress-induced down-warp (Cloetingh et al. 1999). This effect has been observed in the North Sea Basin (Van Wees & Cloetingh 1996) and the Pannonian Basin (Horváth & Cloetingh 1996), both of which are characterized by large sediment loads and a wide rift basin. Such a neotectonic compressional reactivation provides an alternative to previous explanations for recent differential motions in the northern Black Sea Basin (Smolyaninova et al. 1996) that were attributed to convective mantle flow. In view of the recent evidence for crustal shortening in the Black Sea region as a consequence of the Arabian–Eurasian plate interaction (Reilinger et al. 1997), an interpretation in terms of an increased late Neogene compressional stress level appears to be more likely. The modelling results indicate that both the basin centre and the margins of the eastern Black Sea are much weaker than those of the western Black Sea (Fig. 16). An important difference is that in the western Black Sea the basin centre and margins have a comparable strength, whereas in the eastern Black Sea the margins are substantially weaker than the basin centre. This may explain why the margins of the eastern Black Sea appear to be more prone to strain localization (i.e. lithospheric folding), whereas the western Black Sea as a whole is more prone to stress transmission.

The Pannonian–Carpathian Basin system: modes of basin (de)formation, lithospheric strength and vertical motions

The Pannonian–Carpathian system (Fig. 17) represents a natural laboratory for models for basin formation in weak back-arc lithosphere. This system, located within the Alpine orogenic belt at the transition between the western European

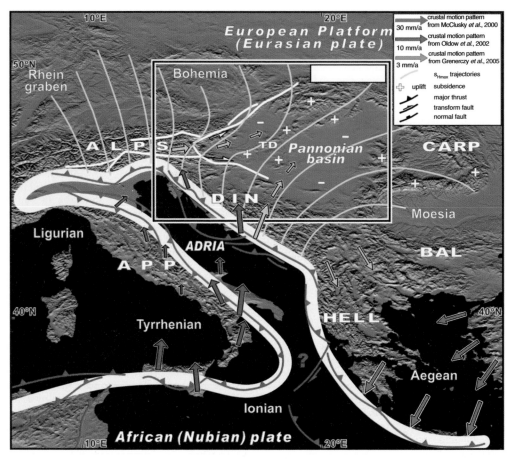

Fig. 17. Topography and present-day tectonic setting in the central Mediterranean region. NNE directed motion and counterclockwise rotation of the Adriatic microplate, outlined by thick pale yellow line, result in collision in the Southern Alps and dextral transpression in the Dinarides. Tectonic stresses and strain are transmitted into the Pannonian Basin, resulting in its on-going structural inversion. Generalized pattern of crustal motions, adopted from GPS studies, are in a fixed Eurasian frame. Note the markedly different scale for the velocity pattern by McClusky *et al.* (2000), Oldow *et al.* (2002) and Grenerczy *et al.* (2005) shown by green, red and blue arrows, respectively. Insert indicates area of detailed study. Structural elements for the Mediterranean, shown in red, are after Facenna *et al.* (2004). APP, Apennines; BAL, Balkanides; CARP, Carpathians; DIN, Dinarides; HELL, Hellenides; TD, Transdanubia (after Bada *et al.* 2007).

lithosphere and the East European Craton, comprises some of the best documented sedimentary basins in the world. The Pannonian Basin evolved from its syn-rift to post-rift phase during early to late Miocene times (*c.* 20–5 Ma), when back-arc extension was coupled with subduction dynamics in the Carpathian orogenic arc system (Royden & Horváth 1988). The lithosphere of the Pannonian Basin is a particularly sensitive recorder of changes in lithospheric stress induced by near-field intraplate and far-field plate boundary processes (Bada *et al.* 2001). High-quality constraints exist on the present-day and palaeostress (Fodor *et al.* 1999; Gerner *et al.* 1999) fields in the lithosphere as a result of earthquake focal mechanism studies, analyses of borehole break-outs and studies of palaeostress field indicator data. A close relationship has been demonstrated between the timing and nature of stress changes in the extensional basin and structural episodes in the surrounding thrust belts, pointing to an intrinsic mechanical coupling between the orogen and its back-arc basin. The Pannonian Basin, the hottest in continental Europe, is thought to have gone through a rapid temporal transition from passive to active rifting during late Miocene times, simultaneously with the climax of compression in the Carpathian arc (Huismans *et al.* 2001).

A crucial element of the dynamics of lithospheric deformation is the mechanics of coupling back-arc deformation in the Pannonian Basin with continental collision and foreland basin evolution along the Carpathian arc. This has been addressed through a combination of dynamic and kinematic modelling studies constrained by integrated basin analysis in the Pannonian sector and by thermochronology, basin modelling and structural field studies in the Carpathian belt. In particular, the inversion events (i.e. late Miocene and late Pliocene–Quaternary) recorded in the Pannonian Basin (Horváth 1995; Fodor et al. 1999) are coeval with the climax of thrusting in the Carpathians (e.g. Săndulescu 1988; Hippolyte et al. 1999) related to continental collision and late-stage out-of-sequence contraction. Horváth & Cloetingh (1996) established the importance of Late Pliocene through Quaternary compression in the Pannonian–Carpathian system, explaining its anomalous Quaternary uplift and subsidence pattern as well as its intraplate seismicity, thus establishing a novel conceptual model for structural reactivation of back-arc basins in orogenic settings. The basin system has reached an advanced stage of evolution with respect to other Mediterranean back-arc basins and its structural inversion has been taking place for the last few million years. Basin inversion is related to changes in the regional stress field (see for a general discussion Ziegler et al. 1995, 2002), from one of tension that controlled basin formation and subsidence, to one of compression resulting in contraction and flexure of the lithosphere associated with differential vertical movements.

Pannonian Basin: stretching models and subsidence analysis

Efforts to quantify the evolution of the Pannonian Basin started in the early 1980s with the application of classical basin analysis techniques. Due to the availability of excellent geological and geophysical constraints, this basin has been a key area for testing stretching models. At the same time, the main characteristics of the Pannonian basin system, such as its extremely high heat flow, the presence of an anomalously thin lithosphere and its position within Alpine orogenic belts, made it particularly suitable and challenging for basin analysis. Research on the Pannonian Basin was triggered by its hydrocarbon potential and addressed local tectonics and regional correlations, as well as studies on its crustal configuration, magmatic activity and related mantle processes.

Sclater et al. (1980) were the first to apply the stretching model of McKenzie (1978) to the intra-Carpathian basins. They found that the development of peripheral basins could be fairly well simulated by the pure shear uniform extension concept with a stretching factor of about two. However, for the more centrally located basins, their considerable thermal subsidence and high heat flow suggested unrealistically high stretching factors (up to five). Thus, they postulated differential extension of the Pannonian lithosphere with moderate crustal stretching (δ factor) and larger stretching of the lithospheric mantle (β factor). Building on this and using a wealth of well data, Royden et al. (1983) introduced the non-uniform stretching concept according to which the magnitude of lithospheric thinning is depth dependent. This concept accounts for a combination of uniform mechanical extension of the lithosphere and thermal attenuation of the lithospheric mantle (Ziegler 1992, 1996; Ziegler & Cloetingh 2004). This is compatible with the subsidence pattern and thermal history of major parts of the Pannonian Basin that suggest a greater attenuation of the lithospheric mantle as compared to the finite extension of the crust. Horváth et al. (1988) further improved this concept by considering radioactive heat generation in the crust, and the thermal blanketing effect of basin-scale sedimentation. By reconstructing the subsidence and thermal history, and by calculating the thermal maturation of organic matter in the central region of the Pannonian Basin (Great Hungarian Plain), a significant step was made in the field of hydrocarbon prospecting by means of basin analysis techniques.

These studies highlighted the difficulties met in explaining basin subsidence and crustal thinning in terms of uniform extension, and pointed towards the applicability of anomalous subcrustal thinning. This issue was central to subsequent investigations involving quantitative subsidence analyses (backstripping) of an extended set of Pannonian Basin wells and cross-sections and their forward modelling (Lankreijer et al. 1995; Sachsenhofer et al. 1997; Juhász et al. 1999; Lenkey 1999). Kinematic modelling, incorporating the concept of necking depth and finite strength of the lithosphere during and after rifting (van Balen et al. 1999), as well as dynamic modelling studies (Huismans et al. 2001), suggested that the transition from passive to active rifting was controlled by the onset of subcrustal flow and small scale convection in the asthenosphere. In order to quantify basin-scale lithospheric deformation, Lenkey (1999) carried out forward modelling applying the concept of non-uniform lithospheric stretching and taking into account the effects of lateral heat flow, flexure and necking of the lithosphere. Calculated crustal thinning factors (δ) indicate large lateral variation of crustal extension in the Pannonian Basin (Fig. 18). This is consistent with the areal pattern

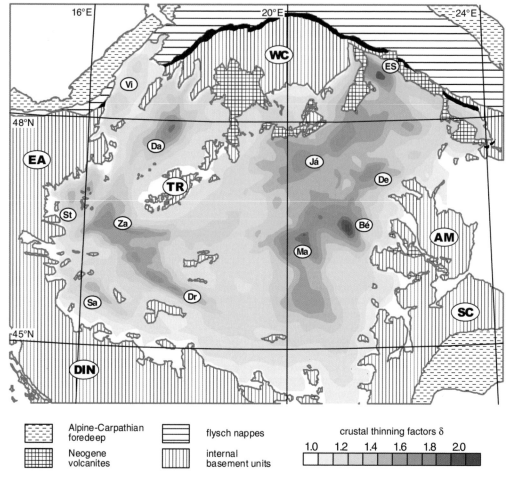

Fig. 18. Crustal thinning factors δ calculated by means of forward modelling for the Pannonian Basin employing the concept of non-uniform stretching complemented by the effects of lateral heat flow and the flexure of the lithosphere (after Lenkey 1999). Note the pronounced lateral variation of crustal extension leading to the formation of deep sub-basins connected by areas of lower level of deformation. AM, Apuseni Mts; DIN, Dinarides; EA, Eastern Alps; TR, Transdanubian Range; SC, WC: Southern and Western Carpathians, respectively. Local depressions of the Pannonian Basin system: Bé, Békés; Da, Danube; De, Derecske; Dr, Drava; ES, East Slovakian; Já, Jászság; Ma, Makó; Sa, Sava; St, Styrian; Vi, Vienna; Za, Zala (Cloetingh *et al.* 2006).

of the depth to the pre-Neogene basement (Horváth *et al.* 2006). The indicated range of crustal thinning factors of 10%–100% crustal extension is in good agreement with the pre-rift palinspastic reconstruction of the Pannonian Basin, and the amount of cumulative shortening in the Carpathian orogen (e.g. Roure *et al.* 1993; Fodor *et al.* 1999).

As a major outcome of basin analysis studies, Royden *et al.* (1983) provided a two-stage subdivision for the evolution of the Pannonian Basin with a syn-rift (tectonic) phase during early to middle Miocene times, and a post-rift (thermal) phase during the late Miocene–Pliocene. However, further development of the stratigraphic database

demonstrated the need to refine this scenario. According to Tari *et al.* (1999), the regional middle Badenian unconformity, marking the termination of the syn-rift stage, is followed by a post-rift phase that is characterized by only minor tectonic activity. Nevertheless, the subsidence history of the Pannonian Basin can be subdivided in three main phases that are reflected in the subsidence curves of selected sub-basins (Fig. 19). The initial syn-rift phase is characterized by rapid tectonic subsidence, starting synchronously at about 20 Ma in the entire Pannonian Basin. This phase of pronounced crustal extension is recorded everywhere in the basin system and was mostly limited to relatively narrow, fault-bounded grabens or sub-basins. During the subsequent post-rift phase much broader areas began to subside, reflecting general down-warping of the lithosphere in response to its thermal subsidence. This is particularly evident in the central parts of the Pannonian Basin, suggesting that in this area syn-rift thermal attenuation of the lithospheric mantle played a greater role than in the marginal areas (e.g. Sclater *et al.* 1980; Royden & Dövényi 1988). The third and final phase of basin evolution is characterized by the gradual structural inversion of the Pannonian Basin system during the late Pliocene–Quaternary. During these times intra-plate compressional stresses gradually built up and caused basin-scale buckling of the Pannonian litho-sphere that was associated with late-stage subsidence anomalies and differential vertical motions (Horváth & Cloetingh 1996). As is evident from the subsi-dence curves (Fig. 19), accelerated late-stage subsi-dence characterized the central depressions of the Little and Great Hungarian Plains (Fig. 19b,c), whereas the peripheral Styrian and East Slovakian sub-basins were uplifted by a few hundred metres after mid-Miocene times (Figs 19d,e) and the Zala Basin during the Pliocene–Quaternary (Fig. 19f). The importance of tectonic stresses both during the rifting (extension) and subsequent inversion phase (compression) is highlighted by this late-stage tec-tonic reactivation, as well as by other episodic inver-sion events in the Pannonian Basin (Horváth 1995; Fodor *et al.* 1999).

For the Carpathian foreland, modelling curves (Fig. 19h–j) indicate an important late Miocene (Sarmatian) phase of basin subsidence that relates to tectonic loading of the Eastern and Southern Carpathian foreland by intra-Carpathian terranes. This phase is coeval with the end of syn-rift subsi-dence of the Pannonian Basin (Horváth & Cloetingh 1996). Subsidence curves for the Transylvanian Basin (Fig. 19g) indicate for the Badenian–Pannonian a subsidence pattern similar to that of the Carpathian foreland, and for the Pliocene–Quaternary a phase of uplifting that correlated with inversion of the Pannonian Basin.

Lithospheric strength in the Pannonian–Carpathian system

The Pannonian–Carpathian system shows remark-able variations in the thermo-mechanical properties of the lithosphere. Lithospheric rigidity varies in space and time, giving rise to important differences in the tectonic behaviour of different parts of the system. As rheology controls the response of the lithosphere to stresses, and thus the formation and deformation of basins and orogens, the characteriz-ation of rheological properties and their temporal

changes has been a major challenge to constrain and quantify tectonic models and scenarios. This is particularly valid for the Pannonian–Carpathian region where tectonic units with different history and rheological properties are in close contact.

Figure 20a displays three strength envelopes for the western, central and eastern part of the Pannonian lithosphere that were constructed on the basis of extrapolated rock mechanic data, incorporating con-straints on crustal and lithospheric structure, and present-day heat flow along the modelled rheological section. These strength profiles show that the average strength of the Pannonian lithosphere is very low (see also Lankreijer 1998), which is mainly due to high heat flow related to upwelling of the asthenosphere beneath the basin system. The Pannonian Basin, the hottest basin of continental Europe, has an extremely low rigidity lithosphere that renders it prone to repeated tectonic reactivation. This is the result of Cretaceous and Palaeogene orogenic phases involv-ing nappe emplacement and crustal accretion, thickening and loading. During this process, the strength of the different Pannonian lithospheric seg-ments gradually decreased, allowing for their ten-sional collapse under high level strain localization that leads to the development of the Pannonian Basin. Another essential feature is the noticeable absence of present-day lithospheric strength in the lithospheric mantle of the Pannonian Basin. Strength appears to be concentrated in the crustal upper 7–12 km of the lithosphere. This finding is in very good agreement with the depth distribution of seismi-city. Earthquake hypocentres are restricted to the uppermost crustal levels, suggesting that brittle deformation of the lithosphere is limited to depth of 5–15 km (Tóth *et al.* 2002).

Figure 20b shows estimates of the total inte-grated strength (TIS) of the Pannonian–Carpathian lithosphere along section A–A'. Rheology calcu-lations suggest significant differences in the mech-anical properties of different tectonic units within the system (Lankreijer *et al.* 1997, 1999). In general, there is a gradual increase of TIS from the centre of the basin towards the basin flanks in the peripheral areas (see also Fig. 20c). The centre of the Pannonian Basin and the Carpathian foreland are the weakest and strongest parts of the system, respectively. The presence of a relatively strong lithosphere in the Transylvanian Basin is due to the absence of large-scale Cenozoic extension that prevails in the Pannonian Basin (Ciulavu *et al.* 2002). The Carpathian arc, particularly its western parts, shows a high level of rigidity apart from the southeastern bend zone where a striking decrease in lithospheric strength is noticed. Calculations for the seismically active Vrancea area indicate the pre-sence of a very weak crust and mantle lithosphere, indicating mechanical decoupling between the

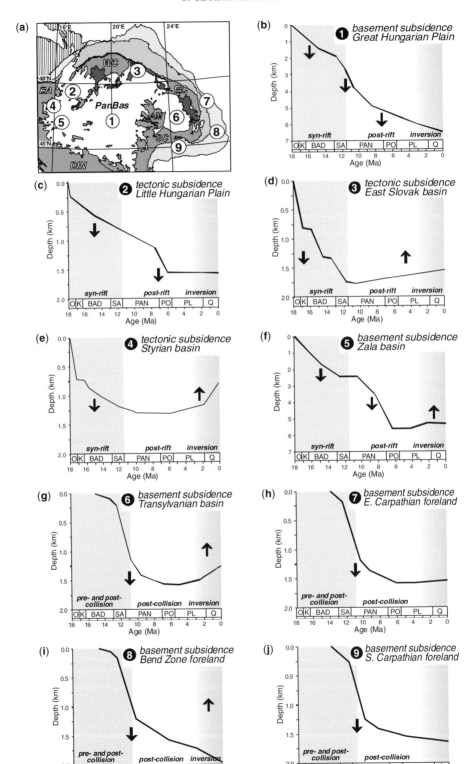

Transylvanian Basin and the Carpathian Orogen. The pronounced contrast in TIS between the Pannonian Basin (characterized by TIS < $2.0 \times 10^{12} \, \text{Nm}^{-1}$) and the Carpathian Orogen and its foreland (characterized by TIS > $3.0 \times 10^{12} \, \text{Nm}^{-1}$) indicates that recent lithospheric deformation is more likely to have been concentrated in the hot and hence weak Pannonian lithosphere than in the surrounding Carpathians.

By conversion of strength predictions to EET values at a regional scale, Lankreijer (1998) mapped the EET distribution for the entire Pannonian–Carpathian system. Calculated EET values are largely consistent with the spatial variation of lithospheric strength of the system. Lower values are characteristic for the weak central part of the Pannonian Basin (5–10 km), whereas EET increases toward the Dinarides and Alps (15–30 km) and particularly toward the Bohemian Massif and Moesian Platform (25–40 km). This trend is in good agreement with EET estimates obtained from flexural studies and forward modelling of extensional basin formation. Systematic differences, however, can occur and may be the consequence of significant horizontal intraplate stresses (e.g. Cloetingh & Burov 1996) or of mechanical decoupling of the upper crust and uppermost mantle that can lead to a considerable reduction of EET values.

The range of calculated EET values reflects the distinct mechanical characteristics and response of the different domains that form part of the Pannonian–Carpathian system to the present-day stress field. These characteristics can be attributed mainly to the memory of the lithosphere. The tectonic and thermal evolution of these domains differed considerably during the Cretaceous–Neogene Alpine build-up of both the outer and intra-Carpathian units and the Neogene extension of the Pannonian Basin, resulting in a wide spectrum of lithospheric strengths. These, in turn, exert a strong control on the complex present-day pattern of ongoing tectonic activity.

Deformation of the Pannonian–Carpathian system

The present-day deformation pattern and related topography development in the Pannonian–Carpathian system is characterized by pronounced spatial and temporal variations in the stress and strain fields (Cloetingh et al. 2006). Horváth & Cloetingh (1996) established the importance of late Pliocene and Quaternary compressional deformation of the Pannonian Basin that explains its anomalous uplift and subsidence, as well as intraplate seismicity. Based on the case study of the Pannonian–Carpathian system, these authors established a novel conceptual model for the structural reactivation of back-arc basins within orogens. At present, the Pannonian Basin has reached an advanced evolutionary stage as compared to other Mediterranean back-arc basins in so far as it has been partially inverted during the last few million years. Inversion of the Pannonian Basin can be related to temporal changes in the regional stress field, from one of tension that controlled its Miocene extensional subsidence, to one of Pliocene–Quaternary compression resulting in deformation, contraction and flexure of the lithosphere associated with differential vertical motions. Therefore, the spatial distribution of uplifting and subsiding areas within the Pannonian Basin can be interpreted as resulting fom the build-up of intraplate compressional stresses, causing large-scale positive and negative deflection of the lithosphere at various scales. This includes basin-scale positive reactivation of Miocene normal faults, and large-scale folding of the system leading to differential uplift and subsidence of anticlinal and synclinal segments of Pannonian crust and lithosphere. Model calculations are in good agreement with the overall topography of the system. Several flat-lying, low-elevation areas (e.g. Great Hungarian Plain, Sava and Drava troughs) subsided continuously from the beginning of basin development during the early Miocene, and contain 300–1000 m thick Quaternary alluvial sequences. By contrast, the periphery of this basin system, as well as the Transdanubian Range, the Transylvanian Basin and the adjacent Carpathian orogen were uplifted and considerably eroded from Miocene–Pliocene times onward (see Fig. 19). Quantitative subsidence analyses confirm that late-stage compressional stresses caused accelerated subsidence of the central parts of the Pannonian Basin (Van Balen et al. 1999) whilst the Styrian Basin (Sachsenhofer et al. 1997), the Vienna and East Slovak Basins (Lankreijer et al.

Fig. 19. (*Continued*) Subsidence curves for selected sub-basins of the Pannonian Basin and Carpathian foreland. Note that after a rapid phase of general subsidence throughout the whole Pannonian basin, the sub-basins show distinct subsidence history from Middle Miocene times on. Arrows indicate generalized vertical movements. Timing of the syn- and post-rift phases is after Royden et al. (1983). Timing of Carpathians collision after Maţenco et al. (2003). For time-scale the central Paratethys stages is used. O, K, Ottnangian and Karpatian, respectively (Early Miocene); BAD, SA, Badenian and Sarmatian, respectively (Middle Miocene); PAN, PO, Pannonian and Pontian, respectively (Late Miocene); PL, Pliocene; Q, Quaternary. AM, Apuseni Mts; DIN, Dinarides; EA, Eastern Alps; PanBas, Pannonian basin; SC, WC, Southern and Western Carpathians, respectively (Cloetingh et al. 2006).

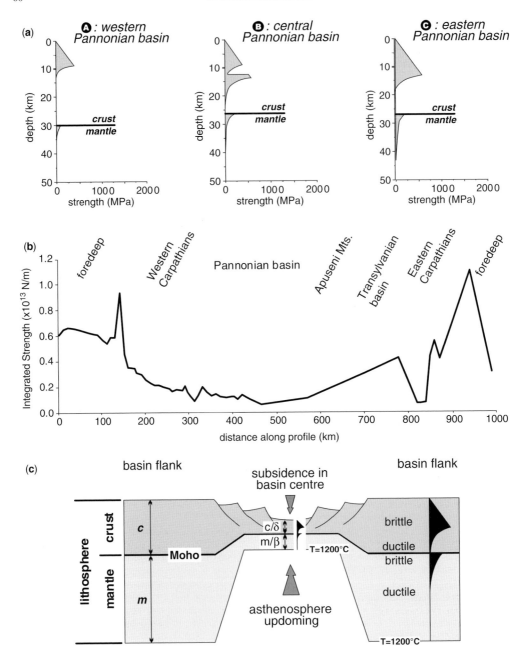

Fig. 20. (**a**) Typical strength envelopes from the western (A), central (B) and eastern (C) part of the Pannonian Basin. For location see Figure 18. For calculation, numerous constraints on the lithospheric structure and petrography, heat flow, strain rate and stress regime have been adopted (see details in Lankreijer *et al.* 1997; Sachsenhofer *et al.* 1997; Lenkey *et al.* 2002). Note the nearly complete absence of mantle strength predicted by the model. (**b**) Total integrated lithospheric strength (TIS, in 10^{13} Nm^{-1}) along a regional profile through the Pannonian–Carpathian system (Lankreijer 1998). (**c**) Schematic cross-section showing the non-uniform stretching of the Pannonian lithosphere and its effect on depth-dependent rheology. The thickness of the crust (c) and mantle lithosphere (m) is reduced by the stretching factors of δ and β, respectively, in the basin centre. The ascending asthenosphere is heating up the system, the isotherms become significantly elevated. As a result, the thinned and hot Pannonian lithosphere become extremely weak and, thus, prone for subsequent tectonic reactivation (Cloetingh *et al.* 2006).

1995) and the Transylvanian Basin (Ciulavu *et al.* 2002), were uplifted by several hundred metres starting in late Mio-Pliocene times (Fig. 19). The mode and degree of coupling of the Carpathians with their foreland controls the Pliocene to Quaternary deformation patterns in their hinterland, and particularly interesting, in the Transylvanian Basin (Ciulavu *et al.* 2002). During their evolution, the Western and Eastern Carpathians were intermittently mechanically coupled with the strong European foreland lithosphere, as evidenced by coeval deformations in both the upper and lower plate (Krzywiec 2001; Maţenco & Bertotti 2000; Oszczypko 2006). In terms of coupled deformation, the Carpathian Bend Zone had two distinct periods during its Cenozoic evolution, i.e. Early–Middle Miocene and late Miocene–Quaternary (see Matenco *et al.* 2007 for a detailed discussion). During the first period, the orogen was decoupled from its Moesian lower plate during the middle Miocene (Badenian) as evidenced by contraction in the upper plate (e.g. Hippolyte *et al.* 1999) and extensional collapse of the western Moesian Platform (Tărăpoancă *et al.* 2003). During the late Miocene, collisional-coupling between the orogenic wedge and the foreland increased and persisted to the present (e.g. Bala *et al.* 2003).

Fission track studies in the Romanian Carpathians demonstrate up to 5 km of erosion that migrated since 12 Ma systematically from their northwestern and southwestern parts towards the Bend area where uplift and erosion was initiated around 4 Ma ago (Sanders *et al.* 1999). This region coincides with the actively deforming Vrancea zone that is associated with considerable seismic activity at crustal levels and in the mantle. These findings can be related to the results of seismic tomography that highlight upwelling of hot mantle material under the Pannonian Basin and progressive detachment of the subducted lithospheric slab that is still ongoing in the Vrancea area (Wortel & Spakman 2000; Wenzel *et al.* 2002). Moreover, in the internal parts of the Carpathians, magmatic activity related to slab detachment decreases systematically in age from 16–14 Ma in their northern parts to 4–0 Ma in the Bend Zone (Nemcok *et al.* 1998). As such it tracks the uplift history of the Carpathians that can be related to isostatic rebound of the lower plate upon slab detachment. These rapid differential motions along the rim of the Pannonian Basin and in the adjacent Carpathians had important implications for the sediment supply to depocentres, as well as for the hydrocarbon habitat (Dicea 1996; Tari *et al.* 1997; Horváth & Tari 1999).

Results of forward basin modelling shows that an increase in the level of compressional tectonic stress during Pliocene–Quaternary times can explain the first-order features of the observed pattern of accelerated subsidence in the centre of the Pannonian Basin and uplift of basins in peripheral areas. Therefore, both observations (see Horváth *et al.* 2006) and modelling results lead to the conclusion that compressional stresses can cause considerable differential vertical motions in the Pannonian–Carpathian back-arc basin orogen system.

In the context of basin inversion, the sources of compression were investigated by means of finite element modelling (Bada *et al.* 1998, 2001). Results suggest that the present stress state of the Pannonian–Carpathian system, and particularly of its western part, is controlled by the interplay between plate boundary and intraplate forces. The former include the counterclockwise rotational northward motion of the Adriatic microplate and its indentation into the Alpine–Dinaric orogen, whereas intraplate buoyancy forces are associated with the elevated topography and related crustal thickness variation of the Alpine–Carpathian–Dinaric belt. Model predictions indicate that uplifted regions surrounding the Pannonian basin system can exert compression of about 40–60 MPa on its thinned lithosphere, comparable to values calculated for far-field tectonic stresses (Bada *et al.* 2001). The analysis of tectonic and gravitational stress sources permitted to estimate the magnitude of maximum horizontal compression, amounting to as much as 100 MPa. These significant compressional stresses are concentrated in the elastic core of the lithosphere, consistent with the ongoing structural inversion of the Pannonian Basin. Such high-level stresses are close to the integrated strength of the system, which may lead to whole lithospheric failure in the form of large-scale folding and related differential vertical motions, and intense brittle deformation in the form of seismoactive faulting.

Conclusions

In this paper we have demonstrated that poly-phase deformation of compressional nature is a common feature in the post-rift evolution of many passive margins and rifts. The compressional mode of deformation in these sedimentary basins, originally formed by extension in an intraplate setting, is characterized by a spectrum of spatial wavelengths spanning several tens of kilometres up to several hundreds of kilometres (Cloetingh *et al.* 1999; Sokoutis *et al.* 2005). Results from numerical and analogue modelling support a key role for lithospheric folding in the compressional reactivation of passive margins and extensional basins. The actual mode of compressional deformation appears to be strongly affected by the evolution of the rheological structure of the underlying lithosphere, the level of the regional intraplate stress field, and the geometry of the rifted basin configuration prior to late-stage compressional reactivation. The interplay of plumes and intraplate compressional deformation can lead to temporal transitions from basin inversion to lithospheric folding (Cloetingh & Van Wees 2005). These compressional modes of post-rift deformation lead to substantial differential vertical motions and late-stage anomalies in subsidence and uplift patterns.

This research was funded through the Netherlands Research Centre for Integrated Solid Earth Science and the EUCOR-URGENT program. Constructive reviews by R. England and R. Gatliff are gratefully appreciated.

References

AICHROTH, B., PRODEHL, C. & THYBO, H. 1992. Crustal structure along the central segment of the EGT from seismic-refraction studies. *Tectonophysics*, **207**, 43–64.

ALLEN, P. A., BENNET, S. D., CUNNINGHAM, M. J. M. *ET AL*. 2002. The post-Variscan thermal and denudational history of Ireland. *In*: DORÉ, A. G., CARTWRIGHT, J. A. STOKER, M. S., TURNER, J. P. & WHITE, N. (eds) *Exhumation of the North Atlantic Margin: Timing, Mechanisms and Implications for Petroleum Exploration*. Geological Society, London, Special Publications, **196**, 371–399.

ANDEWEG, B., DE VICENTE, G., CLOETINGH, S., GINER, J. & MUÑOZ MARTIN, A. 1999. Local stress fields and intraplate deformation of Iberia: variations in spatial and temporal interplay of regional stress sources. *Tectonophysics*, **305**, 153–164.

ARTEMIEVA, I. M. & MOONEY, W. D. 2001. Thermal thickness and evolution of Precambrian lithosphere. A global study. *Journal of Geophysical Research*, **106**, 16 387–16 414.

ARTEMIEVA, I. M., THYBO, H. & KABAN, M. K. 2006. Deep Europe today: Geophysical synthesis of upper mantle structure and lithospheric processes over 3.5 Ga. *In*: GEE, D. & STEPHENSON, R. A. (eds) *European Lithosphere Dynamics*. Geological Society, London, Memoirs, **32**, 11–41.

BABUSKA, V. & PLOMEROVA, J. 1992. The lithosphere in central Europe – seismological and petrological aspects. *Tectonophysics*, **207**, 141–163.

BABUSKA, V. & PLOMEROVA, J. 1993. Lithospheric thickness and velocity anisotropy – seismological and geothermal aspects. *Tectonophysics*, **225**, 79–89.

BABUSKA, V. & PLOMEROVA, J. 2001. Subcrustal lithosphere around the Saxothuringian-Moldanubian Suture Zone – a model derived from anisotropy of seismic wave velocities. *Tectonophysics*, **332**, 185–199.

BADA, G., GERNER, P., CLOETINGH, S. & HORVÁTH, F. 1998. Sources of recent tectonic stress in the Pannonian region: inferences from finite element modelling. *Geophysical Journal International*, **134**, 87–102.

BADA, G., HORVÁTH, F., CLOETINGH, S., COBLENTZ, D. D. & TÓTH, T. 2001. The role of topography induced gravitational stresses in basin inversion: The case study of the Pannonian basin. *Tectonics*, **20**, 343–363.

BADA, G., GRENERCZY, G., TOTH, L. *ET AL*. 2007. *Motion of Adria and ongoing Inversion of the Pannonian Basin: Seismicity, GPS Velocities and Stress Transfer*. Geological Society of America, Special Paper, **425**, 243–262.

BALA, A., RADULIAN, M. & POPESCU, E. 2003. Earthquakes distribution and their focal mechanism in correlation with the active tectonic zones of Romania. *Journal of Geodynamics*, **36**, 129–145.

BAYER, U., SCHECK, M. & RABBEL, W. 1999. An integrated study of the NE German Basin. *Tectonophysics*, **314**, 285–307.

BEEKMAN, F., BULI, J. M., CLOETINGH, S. & SCRUTTON, R. A. 1996. Crustal fault reactivation as initiator of lithospheric folding in the Central Indian Ocean. *In*: BUCHANAN, P. G. & NIEUWLAND, D. A. (eds). *Modern Developments in Structural Interpretation, Validation and Modelling*. Geological Society, London, Special Publications, **99**, 251–263.

BERGERAT, F. 1987. Stress fields in the European platform at the time of Africa–Eurasia collision. *Tectonics*, **6**, 99–132.

BERTOTTI, G., TER VOORDE, M., CLOETINGH, S. & PICOTTI, V. 1997. Thermomechanical evolution of the South Alpine rifted margin (North Italy): constraints on the strength of passive continental margins. *Earth and Planetary Science Letters*, **146**, 181–193.

BERTOTTI, G., PODLACHIKOV, Y. & DAEHLER, A. 2000. Dynamic link between the level of ductile crustal flow and style of normal faulting of brittle crust. *Tectonophysics*, **320**, 195–218.

BIJWAARD, H. & SPAKMAN, W. 1999. Fast kinematic ray tracing of first- and later-arriving global seismic phases. *Geophysical Journal International*, **139**, 359–369.

BLUNDELL, D., FREEMAN, R. & MUELLER, S. (eds) 1992. *A Continent Revealed, The European Geotraverse*. Cambridge University Press, Cambridge.

BOILLOT, G., MOUGENOT, D., GIRARDEAU, J. & WINTERER, E. I. 1989. Rifting processes on the West Galicia Margin, Spain. *In*: TANKARD, A. J. & BALKWILL, H. R. (eds) *Extensional Tectonics and Stratigraphy of the North Atlantic Margins*. American Association of Petroleum Geologists, Memoir, **46**, 363–377.

BONJER, K. P. 1997. Seismicity pattern and style of seismic faulting at the eastern borderfault of the southern Rhine Graben. *Tectonophysics*, **275**, 41–69.

BONNET, S., GUILLOCHEAU, F. & BRUN, J.-P. 1998. Relative uplift measured using river incision: the case of the Armorican basement (France). *Comptes Rendus de l'Academie des Sciences, Earth and Planetary Sciences*, **327**, 245–251.

BONNET, S., GUILLOCHEAU, F., BRUN, J.-P. & VAN DEN DRIESSCHE, J. 2000. Large-scale relief development related to Quaternary tectonic uplift of a Proterozoic-Palaeozoic basement: The Armorican Massif, NW France. *Journal of Geophysical Research*, **105**, 19 273–19 288.

Bos, B. & Spiers, C. J. 2002. Frictional-viscous flow of phyllosilicate-bearing fault rock: Microphysical model and implications for crustal strength profiles. *Journal of Geophysical Research*, **107**, 2028, doi: 10.1029/2001JB000301,2002.

Brun, J.-P. 1999. Narrow rifts versus wide rifts: Inferences for the mechanics of rifting from laboratory experiments. *Philosophical Transactions of the Royal Society of London*, **357**, 695–712.

Brun, J.-P. 2002. Deformation of the continental lithosphere: insights from brittle ductile models. *In*: De Meer, S., Drury, M. R., De Bresser, J. H. P. & Pennock, G. M. (eds) *Deformation Mechanisms, Rheology and Tectonics: Current Status and Future Perspectives.* Geological Society, London, Special Publications, **200**, 355–370.

Brun, J. P. & Beslier, M. O. 1996. Mantle exhumation at passive margins. *Earth and Planetary Science Letters*, **142**, 161–173.

Brun, J. P. & Nalpas, T. 1996. Graben inversion in nature and experiments. *Tectonics*, **15**, 677–687.

Buck, W. R. 1991. Modes of continental lithospheric extension. *Journal of Geophysical Research*, **96**, 20 161–20 178.

Burg, J. P. & Podlachikov, Y. 1999. Lithospheric scale folding: numerical modelling and application to the Himalayan syntaxes. *International Journal of Earth Sciences*, **88**, 190–200.

Burg, J.-P., Van den Driessche, J. & Brun, J.-P. 1994. Syn- to post-thickening extension in the Variscan Belt of Western Europe: modes and structural consequences. *Géologie de la France*, **3**, 33–51.

Burg, J.-P., Sokoutis, D. & Bonini, M. 2002. Model-inspired interpretation of seismic structures in the Central Alps: crustal wedging and buckling at mature stage of collision. *Geology*, **30**, 643–646.

Burov, E. B. & Cloetingh, S. 1997. Erosion and rift dynamics: new thermo-mechanical aspects of post-rift evolution of extensional basins. *Earth and Planetary Science. Letters*, **150**, 7–26.

Burov, E. B. & Diament, M. 1995. The effective elastic thickness of continental lithosphere: What does it really mean? (constraints from rheology, topography and gravity). *Journal of Geophysical Research*, **100**, 3905–3927.

Burov, E. B. & Molnar, P. 1998. Gravity Anomalies over the Ferghana Valley (central Asia) and intracontinental Deformation, *Journal of Geophysical Research*, **103**, 18 137–18 152.

Burov, E. B., Nikishin, A. M., Cloetingh, S. & Lobkovsky, L. I. 1993. Continental lithosphere folding in central Asia (Part II): constraints from gravity and tectonic modelling. *Tectonophysics*, **226**, 73–87.

Burov, E., Guillou-Frottier, L., d'Acremont, E., Le Pourhiet, L. & Cloetingh, S. 2007. Plume head-lithosphere interactions near intra-continental plate boundaries. *Tectonophysics* **434**, 15–38.

Calcagnile, G. & Panza, G. F. 1987. Properties of the lithosphere–asthenosphere system in Europe with a view toward Earth conductivity. *Pure and Applied Geophysics*, **125**, 241–254.

Camelbeeck, T. & Meghraoui, M. 1996. Large earthquakes in Northern Europe more likely than once thought. *Eos, Transactions, American Geophysical Union*, **77**, 405–409.

Carter, N. L. & Tsenn, M. C. 1987. Flow properties of continental lithosphere. *Tectonophysics*, **136**, 27–63.

Chalmers, J. A. & Laursen, K. H. 1995. Labrador Sea: the extent of continental and oceanic crust and the timing of the onset of seafloor spreading. *Marine and Petroleum Geology*, **12**, 205–217.

Ciulavu, D., Dinu, C. & Cloetingh, S. 2002. Late Cenozoic tectonic evolution of the Transylvanian Basin and northeastern part of the Pannonian Basin (Romania): constraints from seismic profiling and numerical modelling. *In*: Cloetingh, S., Horváth, F., Bada, G. & Lankreijer, A. (eds) *Neotectonics and Surface Processes: the Pannonian Basin and Alpine/Carpathian System.* EGU St. Mueller Special Publication Series, **3**, 105–120.

Cloetingh, S. & Burov, E. 1996. Thermomechanical structure of European continental lithosphere: constraints from rheological profiles and EET estimates. *Geophysical Journal International*, **124**, 695–723.

Cloetingh, S. & Kooi, H. 1992. Intraplate stresses and dynamical aspects of rift basins. *Tectonophysics*, **215**, 167–185.

Cloetingh, S. & Van Wees, J.-D. 2005. Strength reversal in Europe's intraplate lithosphere: Transition from basin inversion to lithospheric folding. *Geology*, **33**, 285–288.

Cloetingh, S., McQueen, H. & Lambeck, K. 1985. On a tectonic mechanism for regional sea level fluctuations. *Earth and Planetary Science Letters*, **75**, 157–166.

Cloetingh, S., Gradstein, F., Kooi, H., Grant, A. & Kaminski, M. 1990. Plate reorganization: a cause of rapid late Neogene subsidence and sedimentation around the North Atlantic? *Journal of the Geological Society, London*, **147**, 495–506.

Cloetingh, S., Van Wees, J.-D., Van der Beek, P. A & Spadini, G. 1995. Role of pre-rift rheology in kinematics of basin formation: constraints from thermomechanical modelling of Mediterranean basins and intracratonic rifts. *Marine and Petroleum Geology*, **12**, 793–808.

Cloetingh, S., Burov, E. & Poliakov, A. 1999. Lithosphere folding: primary response to compression? (from Central Asia to Paris Basin). *Tectonics*, **18**, 1064–1083.

Cloetingh, S., Burov, E., Beekman, F., et al. 2002. Lithospheric folding in Iberia. *Tectonics*, **21**, 1041 doi:10.1029/2001TC901031.

Cloetingh, S., Spadini, G., Van Wees, J.-D. & Beekman, F. 2003. Thermo-mechanical modelling of Black Sea Basin (de)formation. *Sedimentary Geology*, **156**, 169–184.

Cloetingh, S., Ziegler, P. A., Beekman, F., et al. 2005. Lithospheric memory, state of stress and rheology: neotectonic controls on Europe's intraplate continental topography. *Quaternary Science Reviews*, **24**, 241–304.

Cloetingh, S., Bada, G., Maţenco, L., Lankreijer, A., Horváth, F. & Dinu, C. 2006. Thermomechanical modelling of the Pannonian-Carpathian system: Modes of tectonic deformation, lithospheric strength and vertical motions. *In*: Gee, D. &

STEPHENSON, R. (eds) *European Lithosphere Dynamics*. Geological Society, London, Memoirs, **32**, 207–221.

COBBOLD, P. R., DAVY, P., GAPAIS, E. A., *ET AL.* 1993. Sedimentary basins and crustal thickening. *Sedimentary Geology*, **86**, 77–89.

CORTI, G., BONINI, M., SOKOUTIS, D., INNOCENTI, F., MANETTI, P., CLOETINGH, S. & MULUGETA, G. 2004. Continental rift architecture and patterns of magma migration: a dynamic analysis based on centrifuge models. *Tectonics*, **23**, TC2012, doi:10.1029/2003TC001561.

CURRAY, J. R. & MOORE, D. G. 1971. Growth of the Bengal deep-sea fan and denudation of the Himalayas. *Geological Society of America Bulletin*, **82**, 563–572.

DAVY, P. & COBBOLD, P. R. 1988. Indentation tectonics in nature and experiments: 1. Experiments scaled for gravity. *Bulletin of the Geological Institutions of the University of Uppsala*, **14**, 129–141.

DAVY, P. & COBBOLD, P. R. 1991. Experiments on shortening of a 4 layer continental lithosphere. *In*: COBBOLD, P. R. (ed.) *Experimental and Numerical Modelling of Continental Deformation. Tectonophysics*, **188**, 1–25.

DE BRESSER, J. H. P., TER HEEGE, J. H. & SPIERS, C. J. 2001. Grain-size reduction by dynamic recrystallization: Can it result in major rheological weakening. *International Journal of Earth Sciences*, **90**, 28–45.

DÈZES, P. & ZIEGLER, P. A. 2004. Moho depth map of western and central Europe. EUCOR-URGENT homepage: http://www.unibas.ch/eucor-urgent

DÈZES, P., SCHMID, S. M. & ZIEGLER, P. A. 2004. Evolution of the European Cenozoic Rift System: Interaction of the Alpine and Pyrenean orogens with their foreland lithosphere. *Tectonophysics*, **389**, 1–33.

DICEA, O. 1996. Tectonic setting and hydrocarbon habitat of the Romanian external Carpathians. *In*: ZIEGLER, P. A. & HORVÁTH, F. (eds) *Peri-Tethys Memoir 2: Structure and prospects of Alpine basins and forelands*. Mémoires du Museum National d'Histoire Naturelle, **170**, 403–425.

DORÉ, A. G., LUNDIN, E. R., BIRKELAND, O., ELIASSEN, P. E. & JENSEN, L. N. 1997. The NE Atlantic margin: implications of late Mesozoic and Cenozoic events for hydrocarbon prospectivity. *Petroleum Geoscience*, **3**, 117–131.

DOUST, H. & OMATSOLA, E. 1989. Niger Delta. *In*: EDWARDS, J. D. & SANTOGROSSI, P. A. (eds) *Divergent Passive Margin Basins*. American Association of Petroleum Geologists Memoir, **48**, 201–238.

DU, Z. J., MICHELINI, A. & PANZA, G. F. 1998. EurID, a regionalized 3-D seismological model of Europe. *Physics of the Earth and Planetary Interiors*, **105**, 31–62.

ELFRINK, N. M. 2001. Quaternary groundwater avulsions: Evidence for large-scale midcontinent folding? *Association of Engineering Geologists News*, **44**, 60.

ESCHER, A. & BEAUMONT, C. 1997. Formation, burial and exhumation of basement nappes at crustal scale: a geometric model based on the Western Swiss Italian Alps. *Journal of Structural Geology*, **19**, 955–974.

FACCENNA, C., PIROMALLO, C., CRESPO-BLAN, A., JOLIVET, L. & ROSSETTI, F. 2004. Lateral slab deformation and the origin of the western Mediterranean arcs. *Tectonics*, **23**, TC1012, doi:10.1029/2002TC001488.

FAVRE, P. & STAMPFLI, G. M. 1992. From rifting to passive margin: the Red Sea, Central Atlantic and Alpine Tethys. *Tectonophysics*, **215**, 69–97.

FINETTI, I., BRICCHI, G., DEL BEN, A., PIPAN, M. & XUAN, Z. 1988. Geophysical study of the Black Sea Basin. *Bollettino di Geofisica Teorica ed Applicata*, **30**, 197–324.

FODOR, L., CSONTOS, L., BADA, G., BENKOVICS, L. & GYÖRFI, I. 1999. Tertiary tectonic evolution of the Carpatho-Pannonian region: a new synthesis of paleostress data. *In*: DURAND, B., JOLIVET, L., HORVÁTH, F. & SÉRANNE, M. (eds) *The Mediterranean Basins: Tertiary Extension within the Alpine Orogen*. Geological Society, London, Special Publications, **156**, 295–334.

FROITZHEIM, N. & MANATSCHAL, G. 1996. Kinematics of Jurassic rifting, mantle exhumation, and passive margin formation in the Austroalpine and Penninic nappes (eastern Switzerland). *Geological Society of America Bulletin*, **108**, 1120–1133.

GARCIA-CASTELLANOS, D. 2002. Interplay between lithospheric flexure and river transport in foreland basins. *Basin Research*, **14**, 89–104.

GARCIA-CASTELLANOS, D., CLOETINGH, S. A. P. L. & VAN BALEN, R. T. 2000. Modeling the Middle Pleistocene uplift in the Ardennes–Rhenish Massif: thermo-mechanical weakening under the Eifel? *Global and Planetary Change*, **27**, 39–52.

GARCIA-CASTELLANOS, D., VERGÉS, J., GASPAR-ESCRIBANO, J. M. & CLOETINGH, S. 2003. Interplay between tectonics, climate and fluvial transport during the Cenozoic evolution of the Ebro Basin (NE Iberia). *Journal of Geophysical Research*, **108**, 2347.

GERBAULT, M., BUROV, E., POLIAKOV, A. N. B. & DAIGNIERES, M. 1999. Do faults trigger folding in the lithosphere? *Geophysical Research Letters*, **26**, 271–274.

GERNER, P., BADA, G., DÖVÉNYI, P., MÜLLER, B., ONCESCU, M. C., CLOETINGH, S. & HORVÁTH, F. 1999. Recent tectonic stress and crustal deformation in and around the Pannonian basin: data and models. *In*: DURAND, B., JOLIVET, L., HORVÁTH, F. & SÉRANNE, M. (eds) *The Mediterranean Basins: Tertiary Extension within the Alpine Orogen*. Geological Society, London, Special Publications, **156**, 269–294.

GOES, S., GOVERS, R. & VACHER, P. 2000a. Shallow upper mantle temperatures under Europe from P and S wave tomography. *Journal of Geophysical Research*, **105**, 11 153–11 169.

GOES, S., LOOHUIS, J. J. P., WORTEL, M. J. R. & GOVERS, R. 2000b. The effect of plate stresses and shallow mantle temperatures on tectonics of northwestern Europe. *Global and Planetary Change*, **27**, 23–39.

GÖLKE, M. & COBLENZ, D. D. 1996. Origin of the European regional stress field. *Tectonophysics*, **266**, 11–24.

GRANET, M., WILSON, M. & ACHAUER, U. 1995. Imaging a mantle plume beneath the French Massif

Central. *Earth and Planetary Science Letters*, **136**, 281–296.

GRENERCZY, G., SELLA, G., STEIN, S. & KENYERES, A. 2005. Tectonic implications of the GPS velocity field in the northern Adriatic region. *Geophysical Research Letters*, **32**, 1–4.

GRÜNTHAL, G. and the GSHAP Region 3 Working Group 1999. Seismic hazard assessment for central, north and northwest Europe: GSHAP Region 3. *Annali di Geofisica*, **42**, 999–1011.

GUGGISBERG, B., KAMINSKI, W. & PRODEHL, C. 1991. Crustal structure of the Fennoscandian Shield: a traveltime interpretation of the long-range Fennolora seismic refraction profile. *Tectonophysics*, **195**, 105–137.

GUILLOCHEAU, F., ROBIN, C., ALLEMAND, P. *ET AL.* 2000. Meso-Cenozoic geodynamic evolution of the Paris basin: 3D stratigraphic constraints. *Geodynamica Acta*, **13**, 189–246.

HANDY, M. R. & BRUN, J.-P. 2004. Seismicity, structure and strength of the continental lithosphere. *Earth and Planetary Science Letters*, **223**, 427–441.

HIPPOLYTE, J.-C., BADESCU, D. & CONSTANTIN, P. 1999. Evolution of the transport direction of the Carpathian belt during its collision with the east European Platform. *Tectonics*, **18**, 1120–1138.

HORVÁTH, F. 1995. Phases of compression during the evolution of the Pannonian basin and its bearing on hydrocarbon exploration. *Marine and Petroleum Geology*, **12**, 837–844.

HORVÁTH, F. & CLOETINGH, S. 1996. Stress-induced late-stage subsidence anomalies in the Pannonian basin. *Tectonophysics*, **266**, 287–300.

HORVÁTH, F. & TARI, G. 1999. IBS Pannonian basin project: a review of the main results and their bearings on hydrocarbon exploration. *In*: DURAND, B., JOLIVET, L., HORVÁTH, F. & SÉRANNE, M. (eds) *The Mediterranean Basins: Tertiary Extension within the Alpine Orogen*. Geological Society, London, Special Publications, **156**, 195–213.

HORVÁTH, F., SZALAY, Á. & ROYDEN, L. H. 1988. Subsidence, thermal and maturation history of the Great Hungarian Plain. *In*: ROYDEN, L. H. & HORVÁTH, F. (eds) *The Pannonian Basin: A Case Study in Basin Evolution*. American Association of Petroleum Geologists Memoir, **45**, 355–372.

HORVÁTH, F., BADA, G., SZAFIÁN, P., TARI, G., ÁDÁM, A. & CLOETINGH, S. 2006. Formation and deformation of the Pannonian basin: Constraints from observational data. *In*: GEE, D. & STEPHENSON, R. (eds) *European Lithosphere Dynamics*. Geological Society, London, Memoirs, **32**, 191–206.

HUISMANS, R., PODLADCHIKOV, Y. & CLOETINGH, S. 2001. Dynamic modeling of the transition from passive to active rifting, application to the Pannonian basin. *Tectonics*, **20**, 1021–1039.

JACKSON, J. A. 2002. Strength of the continental lithosphere: Time to abandon the jelly sandwich. *GSA Today*, **12**, 4–9.

JANSSEN, M. E. 1996. *Intraplate Deformation in Africa as a Consequence of Plate Boundary Changes*. Ph.D. thesis, Vrije Universiteit, Amsterdam.

JANSSEN, M. E., STEPHENSON, R. A. & CLOETINGH, S. 1995. Temporal and spatial correlations between changes in plate motions and the evolution of rifted basins in Africa. *Geological Society of America Bulletin*, **107**, 1317–1332.

JAPSEN, P. & CHALMERS, J. A. 2000. Neogene uplift and tectonics around the North Atlantic: Overview. *Global and Planetary Change*, **24**, 165–173.

JUHÁSZ, E., PHILLIPS, L., MÜLLER, P., RICKETTS, B., TÓTH-MAKK, Á., LANTOS, M. & KOVÁCS, L. 1999. Late Neogene sedimentary facies and sequences in the Pannonian Basin, Hungary. *In*: DURAND, B., JOLIVET, L., HORVÁTH, F. & SÉRANNE, M. (eds) *The Mediterranean Basins: Tertiary Extension within the Alpine Orogen*. Geological Society, London, Special Publications, **156**, 335–356.

KAIKKONEN, P., MOISO, K. & HEEREMANS, M. 2000. Thermomechanical lithospheric structure of the central Fennoscandian Shield. *Physics of the Earth and Planetary Interiors*, **119**, 209–235.

KIRBY, R. H. 1983. Rheology of the lithosphere. *Reviews of Geophysics and Space Physics*, **21**, 1458–1487.

KIRBY, R. H. 1985. Rock mechanic observations pertinent to the rheology of the continental lithosphere and the localization of strain along shear zones. *Tectonophysics*, **119**, 1–27.

KRZYWIEC, P. 2001. Contrasting tectonic and sedimentary history of the central and eastern parts of the Polish Carpathian Foredeep basin; results of seismic data interpretation. *Marine and Petroleum Geology*, **18**, 13–38.

KUSZNIR, N. J. & PARK, R. G. 1987. The extensional strength of the continental lithosphere; its dependence on geothermal gradient, and crustal composition and thickness. *In*: COWARD, M. P., DEWEY, J. F. & HANCOCK, P. L. (eds) *Continental Extension Tectonics*. Geological Society, London, Special Publications, **28**, 35–52.

LAGARDE, J.-L., BAIZE, S., AMORESE, D., DELCAILLAU, B. & FONT, M. 2000. Active tectonics, seismicity and geomorphology with special reference to Normandy (France). *Journal of Quaternary Science*, **15**, 745–758.

LANKREIJER, A. 1998. *Rheology and Basement Control on Extensional Basin Evolution in Central and Eastern Europe: Variscan and Alpine-Carpathian-Pannonian Tectonics*. Ph.D. thesis, Vrije Universiteit, Amsterdam

LANKREIJER, A., KOVAČ, M., CLOETINGH, S., PITOŇÁK, P., HLÔŠKA, M. & BIERMANN, C. 1995. Quantitative subsidence analysis and forward modelling of the Vienna and Danube basins: thin-skinned versus thick-skinned extension. *Tectonophysics*, **252**, 433–451.

LANKREIJER, A., MOCANU, V. & CLOETINGH, S. 1997. Lateral variations in lithospheric strength in the Romanian Carpathians, constraints on basin evolution. *Tectonophysics*, **272**, 433–451.

LANKREIJER, A., BIELIK, M., CLOETINGH, S. & MAJCIN, D. 1999. Rheology predictions across the western Carpathians, Bohemian massif, and the Pannonian basin: Implications for tectonic scenarios. *Tectonics*, **18**, 1139–1153.

LEFORT, J.-P. & AGARWAL, P. 1996. Gravity evidence for an Alpine buckling of the crust beneath the Paris Basin. *Tectonophysics*, **258**, 1–14.

LENKEY, L. 1999. *Geothermics of the Pannonian basin and its bearing on the tectonics of basin evolution.* Ph.D. thesis. Vrije Universiteit, Amsterdam.

LENKEY, L., DÖVÉNYI, P., HORVÁTH, F. & CLOETINGH, S. 2002. Geothermics of the Pannonian basin and its bearing on the neotectonics. *In*: CLOETINGH, S., HORVÁTH, F., BADA, G. & LANKREIJER, A. (eds) *Neotectonics and Surface Processes: the Pannonian Basin and Alpine/Carpathian System.* EGU Stephan Mueller Special Publication Series, Katlenburg-Lindau, Germany, **3**, 29–40.

LENOTRE, N., THIERRY, P., BLANCHIN, R. & BROCHARD, G. 1999. Current vertical movement demonstrated by comparative leveling in Brittany (France). *Tectonophysics*, **301**, 333–344.

LETOUZEY, J. 1986. Cenozoic paleo-stress pattern in the Alpine foreland and structural interpretation in a platform basin. *Tectonophysics*, **132**, 215–231.

LISTER, G., ETHERIDGE, M. & SYMONDS, P. 1991. Detachment models for the formation of passive margins. *Tectonics*, **10**, 1038–1064.

LUNDIN, E. & DORE, A. G. 2002. Mid-Cenozoic post-breakup deformation in the "passive" margins bordering the Norwegian-Greenland Sea. *Marine and Petroleum Geology*, **19**, 79–93.

MAROTTA, A. M., BAYER, U. & THYBO, H. 2000. The legacy of the NE German Basin – Reactivation by compressional buckling. *Terra Nova*, **12**, 132–140.

MARTINOD, J. & DAVY, P. 1992. Periodic instabilities during compression or extension of the lithosphere: 1. Deformation modes from an analytical perturbation method. *Journal of Geophysical Research*, **97**, 1999–2014.

MARTINOD, J. & DAVY, P. 1994. Periodic instabilities during compression of the lithosphere: 2. Analogue experiments. *Journal of Geophysical Research*, **99**, 12 057–12 069.

MARTINOD, J. & MOLNAR, P. 1995. Lithospheric folding in the Indian Ocean and the rheology of the oceanic plate. *Bulletin de la Société Géologique de France*, **166**, 813–821.

MAȚENCO, L. & BERTOTTI, G. 2000. Tertiary tectonic evolution of the external East Carpathians (Romania). *Tectonophysics*, **316**, 255–286.

MAȚENCO, L., BERTOTTI, G., CLOETINGH, S. & DINU, C. 2003. Subsidence analysis and tectonic evolution of the external Carpathian–Moesian Platform region during Neogene times. *Sedimentary Geology*, **156**, 71–94.

MAȚENCO, L., BERTOTTI, G., LEEVER, K., CLOETINGH, S., SCHMID, S. M., TARAPOANCA, M. & DINU, C. 2007. Large scale deformation in a locked collisional boundary: interplay between subsidence and uplift, intraplate stress and inherited lithospheric structure in the late stage of the SE Carpathians evolution. *Tectonics*, **26** TC4011, doi:10.1029/2006TC001951.

MCCLUSKY, S., BALASSANIAN, S., BARKA, A. *ET AL.* 2000. Global Positioning System constraints on plate kinematics and dynamics in the eastern Mediterranean and Caucasus, *Journal of Geophysical Research*, **105**, 5695–5719.

MCKENZIE, D. P. 1978. Some remarks on the development of sedimentary basins. *Earth and Planetary Science Letters*, **40**, 25–32.

MENGEL, K., SACHS, P. M., STOSCH, H. G., WÖRNER, G. & LOOK, G. 1991. Crustal xenoliths from Cenozoic volcanic fields of West Germany: implication for structure and composition of the continental crust. *Tectonophysics*, **195**, 271–289.

MEYER, W. & STETS, J. 1998. Junge Tektonik in Rheinischen Schiefergebirge und ihre Quantifizierung. *Zeitschrift der Deutsches Geologisches Gesellschaft*, **149**, 359–379.

MOISIO, K., KAIKKONEN, P. & BEEKMAN, F. 2000. Rheological structure and dynamical response of the DSS profile BALTIC in the SE Fennoscandian shield. *Tectonophysics*, **320**, 175–194.

MONTESI, L. G. J. & ZUBER, M. T. 2003. Spacing of faults at the scale of the lithosphere and localization instability: 2. Application to the Central Indian Basin. *Journal of Geophysical Research*, **108**, 2111, doi:10.1029/2002JB001924.

MOSAR, J. 2003. Scandinavia's North Atlantic passive margin. *Journal of Geophysical Research*, **108**, 2630.

MÜLLER, B., ZOBACK, M.-L., FUCHS, K., MASTIN, L.G., GREGERSEN, S., PAVONI, N., STEPHANSSON, O. & LJUNGGREN, C. 1992. Regional patterns of tectonic stress in Europe. *Journal of Geophysical Research*, **97**, 11 783–11 803.

NEMCOK, M., POSPISIL, L., LEXA, J. & DONELICK, R. A. 1998. Tertiary subduction and slab break-off model of the Carpathian–Pannonian region. *Tectonophysics*, **295**, 307–340.

NIKISHIN, A. M., CLOETINGH, S., LOBKOVSKY, L. & BUROV, E. B. 1993. Continental lithosphere folding in Central Asia (Part I): constraints from geological observations. *Tectonophysics*, **226**, 59–72.

NIKISHIN, A. M., ZIEGLER, P. A., PANOV, D. I. *ET AL.* 2001. Mesozoic and Cainozoic evolution of the Scythian Platform–Black Sea–Caucasus domain. *In*: ZIEGLER, P. A., CAVAZZA, W., ROBERTSON, A. H. F. & CRASQUIN-SOLEAU, S. (eds) *Peri-Tethys Memoire 6: Peri-Tethyan Rift/Wrench Basins and Passive Margins.* Mémoirs du Museum National d'Histoire Naturelle, Paris, **186**, 295–346.

NIKISHIN, A. M., KOROTAEV, M. V., ERSHOV, A. V. & BRUNET, M.-F. 2003. The Black Sea Basin: tectonic history and Neogene-Quaternary rapid subsidence modelling. *Sedimentary Geology*, **156**, 1–10.

NIVIÈRE, B. & WINTER, T. 2000. Pleistocene northwards fold propagation of the Jura within the southern Rhine Graben: seismotectonic implications. *Global and Planetary Change*, **27**, 263–288.

OLDOW, J. S., FERRANTI, L., LEWIS, D.S. *ET AL.* 2002. Active fragmentation of Adria, the north African promontory, central Mediterranean orogen, *Geology*, **30**, 779–782.

OSZCZYPKO, N. 2006. Late Jurassic–Miocene evolution of the Outer Carpathian fold-and-thrust belt and its foredeep basin (Western Carpathians, Poland). *Geology Quarterly*, **50**, 169–194.

PANZA, G. F. 1983. Lateral variations in the European lithosphere and seismic activity. *Physics of the Earth and Planetary Interiors*, **33**, 194–197.

PÉREZ-GUSSINYÉ, M. & WATTS, A. B. 2005. The long-term strength of Europe and its implications for plate forming processes. *Nature*, **436**, doi:10.1038/nature03854.

PFIFFNER, O. A., ELLIS, S. & BEAUMONT, C. 2000. Collision tectonics in the Swiss Alps: insight from geodynamic modeling. *Tectonics*, **19**, 1065–1094.

PHILIP, H. 1987. Plio-Quaternary evolution of the stress field in Mediterranean zones of subduction and collision. *Annals of Geophysics*, **5B**, 301–320.

PIQUE, A. & LAVILLE, E. 1995. L'ouverture initiale de l'Atlantique central. *Bulletin de la Société Géologique de France*, **166**, 725–738.

PLOMEROVA, J., KOUBA, D. & BABUSKA, V. 2002. Mapping the lithosphere-asthenosphere boundary through changes in surface-wave anisotropy. *Tectonophysics*, **358**, 175–185.

RAMBERG, H. 1980. Diapirism and gravity collapse in the Scandinavian Caledonides. *Journal of the Geological Society, London*, **137**, 261–270.

RANALLI, G. 1995. *Rheology of the Earth*. 2nd edn. Chapman and Hall, London.

RANALLI, G. 1997. Rheology of the lithosphere in space and time. *In*: BURG, J. P. & FORD, M. (eds) *Orogeny Through Time*. Geological Society, London, Special Publications, **121**, 19–37.

RANALLI, G. & MURPHY, D. C. 1987. Rheological stratification of the lithosphere. *Tectonophysics*, **132**, 281–295.

REILINGER, R. E., MCCLUSKY, S. C., ORAL, M. B. ET AL. 1997. Global positioning system measurements of present-day crustal movements in the Arabia-Africa-Eurasia plate collision zone. *Journal of Geophysical Research*, **102**, 9983–9999.

RITTER, J. R. R., ACHAUER, U. & CHRISTENSEN, U. R. 2000. The teleseismic tomography experiment in the Eifel region, central Europe: design and first results. *Seismological Research Letters*, **71**, 437–443.

RITTER, J. R. R., JORDAN, M., CHRISTENSEN, U. R. & ACHAUER, U. 2001. A mantle plume below the Eifel volcanic fields, Germany. *Earth and Planetary Science Letters*, **186**, 7–14.

ROBIN, C., ALLEMAND, P., BUROV, E., DOIN, M. P., GUILLOCHEAU, F., DROMART, G. & GARCIA, J. P. 2003. Vertical movements of the Paris Basin (Triassic-Pleistocene): from 3D stratigraphic database to numerical models. *In*: NIEUWLAND, D. A. (ed.) *New Insights in Structural Interpretation and Modelling*. Geological Society, London, Special Publications, **212**, 225–250.

ROBINSON, A., SPADINI, G., CLOETINGH, S. & RUDAT, J. 1995. Stratigraphic evolution of the Black Sea: inferences from basin modelling. *Marine and Petroleum Geology*, **12**, 821–836.

ROHRMAN, M., VAN DER BEEK, P. A., ANDRIESSEN, P. A. M. & CLOETINGH, S. 1995. Meso-Cenozoic morphotectonic evolution of Southern Norway: Neogene domal uplift inferred from apatite fissiontrack thermochronology. *Tectonics*, **14**, 704–718.

ROURE, F., ROCA, E. & SASSI, W. 1993. The Neogene evolution of the outer Carpathian flysch units (Poland, Ukraine and Romania): kinematics of a foreland/fold-and-thrust belt system. *Sedimentary Geology*, **86**, 177–201.

ROYDEN, L. H. & KEEN, 1980. Rifting processes and thermal evolution of the continental margin of eastern Canada determined from subsidence curves. *Earth and Planetary Science Letters*, **51**, 343–361.

ROYDEN, L. H. & DÖVÉNYI, P. 1988. Variations in extensional styles at depth across the Pannonian basin system. *In*: ROYDEN, L. H. & HORVÁTH, F. (eds) *The Pannonian Basin: A Case Study in Basin Evolution*. American Association of Petroleum Geologist Memoir, **45**, 235–255.

ROYDEN, L. H. & HORVÁTH, F. (eds) 1988. *The Pannonian Basin, A Study in Basin Evolution*. American Association of Petroleum Geologists Memoir, **45**.

ROYDEN, L. H., HORVÁTH, F., NAGYMAROSY, A. & STEGENA, L. 1983. Evolution of the Pannonian Basin System. 2. Subsidence and thermal history. *Tectonics*, **2**, 91–137.

SACHSENHOFER, R. F., LANKREIJER, A., CLOETINGH, S. & EBNER, F. 1997. Subsidence analysis and quantitative basin modelling in the Styrian basin (Pannonian Basin System, Austria). *Tectonophysics*, **272**, 175–196.

SANDERS, C. A. E., ANDRIESSEN, P. A. M. & CLOETINGH, S. A. P. L. 1999. Life cycle of the East Carpathian orogen: Erosion history of a doubly vergent critical wedge assessed by fission track thermochronology. *Journal of Geophysical Research*, **104**, 29 095–29 112.

SĂNDULESCU, M. 1988. Cenozoic tectonic history of the Carpathians. *In*: ROYDEN, L. H. & HORVÁTH, F. (eds) *The Pannonian Basin, A Study in Basin Evolution*. American Association of Petroleum Geologists Memoir, **45**, 17–25.

SCLATER, J. J. G. & CHRISTIE, P. A. F. 1980. Continental stretching: an explanation for the post mid-Cretaceous subsidence of the central North Sea basin. *Journal of Geophysical Research*, **85**, 3711–3739.

SCLATER, J., ROYDEN, L., HORVÁTH, F., BURCHFIEL, B., SEMKEN, S. & STEGENA, L. 1980. The formation of the intra-Carpathian basins as determined from subsidence data. *Earth and Planetary Science Letters*, **51**, 139–162.

SHUDOFSKY, G. N., CLOETINGH, S., STEIN, S. & WORTEL, M. J. R. 1987. Unusually deep earthquakes in east Africa: constraints on the thermo-mechanical structure of a continental rift system. *Geophysical Research Letters*, **14**, 741–744.

SMOLYANINOVA, E. I., MIKHAILOV, V. O. & LYAKHOVSKY, V. A. 1996. Numerical modelling of regional neotectonic movements in the northern Black Sea. *Tectonophysics*, **266**, 221–231.

SOKOUTIS, D., BONINI, M., MEDVEDEV, S., BOCCALETTI, M., TALBOT, C. J. & KOYI, H. 2000. Indentation of a continent with a built-in thickness change: Experiment and nature. *Tectonophysics*, **320**, 243–270.

SOKOUTIS, D., BURG, J.-P., BONINI, M., CORTI, G. & CLOETINGH, S. 2005. Lithospheric-scale structures from the perspective of analogue continental collision. *Tectonophysics*, **406**, 1–15.

SPADINI, G. 1996. *Lithospheric deformation and vertical motions in back-arc Mediterranean basins: The Black Sea and the Tyrrhenian Sea*. Ph.D. Thesis. Vrije Universiteit, Amsterdam.

SPADINI, G., ROBINSON, A. & CLOETINGH, S. 1996. Western versus eastern Black Sea tectonic evolution: pre-rift lithospheric controls on basin formation. *Tectonophysics*, **266**, 139–154.

SPADINI, G., ROBINSON, A. & CLOETINGH, S. 1997. Thermo-mechanical modelling of Black Sea Basin formation, subsidence and sedimentation. *In*: ROBINSON, A. (ed.) *Regional and Petroleum Geology of the Black Sea and Surrounding Areas.* American Association of Petroleum Geologists Memoir, **68**, 19–38.

STECKLER, M. S. & WATTS, A. B. 1982. Subsidence history and tectonic evolution of Atlantic-type continental margins. *In*: SCRUTTON, R. A. (ed.) *Dynamics of Passive Margins.* AGU Geodynamics Series, **6**, 184–196.

STEPHENSON, R. A. 1989. Beyond first-order thermal subsidence models for sedimentary basins? *In*: CROSS, T. A. (ed.) *Quantitative Dynamic Stratigraphy.* Prentice-Hall, Englewood Cliffs, NJ, 113–125.

STEPHENSON, R. A. & CLOETINGH, S. 1991. Some examples and mechanical aspects of continental lithospheric folding, *Tectonophysics*, **188**, 27–37.

SUHADOLC, P. & PANZA, G. F. 1989. Physical properties of the lithosphere–asthenosphere system in Europe from geophysical data. *In*: BORIANI, A., BONAFEDE, M., PICCARDO, G. B. & VAI, G. B. (eds) *The Lithosphere in Italy — Advances in Earth Science Research.* Accademia Nazionale dei Lincei, Roma, **80**, 15–40.

TĂRĂPOANCĂ, M., BERTOTTI, G., MAŢENCO, L., DINU, C. & CLOETINGH, S. 2003. Architecture of the Focsani depression: A 13 km deep basin in the Carpathians bend zone (Romania). *Tectonics*, **22**, 1074, doi:10.1029/2002TC001486.

TARI, G., DICEA, O., FAULKERSON, J., GEORGIEV, G., POPOV, S., STEFANESCU, M. & WEIR, G. 1997. Cimmerian and Alpine stratigraphy and structural evolution of the Moesian platform (Romania/Bulgaria). *In*: ROBINSON, A. G. (ed.) *Regional and Petroleum Geology of the Black Sea and Surrounding Regions.* American Association of Petroleum Geologists Memoir, **68**, 63–90.

TARI, G., DÖVÉNYI, P., DUNKL, I. *ET AL.* 1999. Lithospheric structure of the Pannonian basin derived from seismic, gravity and geothermal data. *In*: DURAND, B., JOLIVET, L., HORVÁTH, F. & SÉRANNE, M. (eds) *The Mediterranean Basins: Tertiary Extension within the Alpine Orogen.* Geological Society, London, Special Publications, **156**, 215–250.

TER VOORDE, M. & CLOETINGH, S. 1996. Numerical modelling of extension in faulted crust: effects of localized and regional deformation on basin stratigraphy. *In*: BUCHANAN, P. G. & NIEUWLAND, D. A. (eds) *Modern Developments in Structural Interpretation, Validation and Modelling.* Geological Society, London, Special Publications, **99**, 283–296.

TER VOORDE, M., REVNAS, E. R., FAERSETH, R. & CLOETINGH, S. 1997. Tectonic modelling of the Middle Jurassic syn-rift stratigraphy in the Oseberg-Brage area, Southern Viking Graben. *Basin Research*, **9**, 133–150.

TER VOORDE, M., VAN BALEN, R. T., BERTOTTI, G. & CLOETINGH, S. 1998. The influence of a stratified rheology on the flexural response of the lithosphere to (un-)loading by extensional faulting. *Geophysical Journal International*, **134**, 721–735.

TER VOORDE, M., DE BRUIJNE, K., ANDRIESSEN, P. & CLOETINGH, S. 2004. Thermal consequences of thrust faulting: simultaneous versus successive fault activation and exhumation. *Earth and Planetary Science Letters*, **223**, 395–413.

TESAURO, M., HOLLENSTEIN, C., EGLI, R., GEIGER, A. & KAHLE, H.-G. 2004. CGPS and broad-scale deformation across the Rhine Graben and the Alps. *International Journal of Earth Sciences*, **94**, 525–537.

TÓTH, L., MÓNUS, P., ZSÍROS, T. & KISZELY, M. 2002. Seismicity in the Pannonian Region – earthquake data. *In*: CLOETINGH, S., HORVÁTH, F., BADA, G. & LANKREIJER, A. (eds) *Neotectonics and Surface Processes: the Pannonian Basin and Alpine/Carpathian System.* EGU Stephan Mueller Special Publication Series, Katlenburg-Lindau, Germany, **3**, 9–28.

VAN BALEN, R. T., PODLADCHIKOV, Y. & CLOETINGH, S. 1998. A new multi-layered model for intraplate stress-induced differential subsidence of faulted lithosphere, applied to rifted basins. *Tectonics*, **17**, 938–954.

VAN BALEN, R., LENKEY, L., HORVÁTH, F. & CLOETINGH, S. 1999. Two-dimensional modelling of stratigraphy and compaction-driven fluid flow in the Pannonian basin. *In*: DURAND, B., JOLIVET, L., HORVÁTH, F. & SÉRANNE, M. (eds) *The Mediterranean Basins: Tertiary Extension within the Alpine Orogen.* Geological Society, London, Special Publications, **156**, 391–414.

VAN BALEN, R. T., HOUTGAST, R. F., VAN DER WATEREN, F. M., VANDENBERGHE, J. & BOGAART, P. W. 2000. Sediment budget and tectonic evolution of the Meuse catchment in the Ardennes and the Roer Valley Rift System. *Global and Planetary Change*, **27**, 113–129.

VAN VLIET-LANOË, B., LAURENT, M., EVERAERTS, M., MANSY, J.-L. & MANBY, G. 2000. Evolution Neogene et quarternaire de la Somme, une flexuration tectonique active. *Comptes Rendus de l'Academie des Sciences, Earth and Planetary Sciences*, **331**, 151–158.

VAN WEES, J.-D. 1994. *Tectonic modelling of basin deformation and inversion dynamics: the role of pre-existing faults and continental lithosphere rheology in basin evolution.* Ph.D. thesis. Vrije Universiteit, Amsterdam.

VAN WEES, J.-D. & BEEKMAN, F. 2000. Lithosphere rheology during intraplate basin extension and inversion: Inferences from automated modelling of four basins in western Europe. *Tectonophysics*, **320**, 219–242.

VAN WEES, J.-D. & CLOETINGH, S. 1996. 3D flexure and intraplate compression in the North Sea basin. *Tectonophysics*, **266**, 343–359.

VAN WEES, J.-D. & STEPHENSON, R. A. 2000. Quantitative modelling of of basin and rheological evolution of the Iberian Basin (Central Spain): Implications for lithosphere dynamics of intraplate extension and inversion. *Tectonophysics*, **252**, 163–178.

VAN WEES, J.-D., STEPHENSON, R. A., STOVBA, S. M. & SHYMANOVSKY, V. A. 1996. Tectonic variation in the Dniepr-Donets Basin from automated modelling and backstripped subsidence curves. *Tectonophysics*, **268**, 257–280.

VAN WEES, J.-D., ARCHE, A., BEIJDORFF, C. G., LOPEZ-GOMEZ, J. & CLOETINGH, S. 1998. Temporal and spatial variations in tectonic subsidence in the Iberian basin (eastern Spain): inferences from automated forward modelling of high-resolution stratigraphy. (Permian-Mesozoic). *Tectonophysics*, **300**, 285–310.

VAUCHEZ, A., TOMMASI, A. & BARRUOL, G. 1998. Rheological heterogeneity, mechanical anisotropy and deformation of the continental lithosphere. *Tectonophysics*, **296**, 61–86.

WATTS, A. B. 2001. *Isostasy and Flexure of the Lithosphere*. Cambridge University Press, Cambridge.

WATTS, A. B. & BUROV, E. B. 2003. Lithospheric strength and its relationship to the elastic and seismogenic layer thickness. *Earth and Planetary Science Letters*, **213**, 113–131.

WENZEL, F., SPERNER, B., LORENZ, F. & MOCANU, V. 2002. Geodynamics, tomographic images and seismicity of the Vrancea region (SE-Carpathians, Romania). *In*: CLOETINGH, S., HORVÁTH, F., BADA, G. & LANKREIJER, A. (eds) *Neotectonics and Surface Processes: the Pannonian Basin and Alpine/Carpathian System*. EGU Stephan Mueller Special Publication Series, Katlenburg-Lindau, Germany **3**, 95–104.

WERNICKE, B. 1985. Uniform-sense normal simple shear of the continental lithosphere. *Canadian Journal of Earth Sciences*, **22**, 108–125.

WERNICKE, B. 1990. The fluid crustal layer and its implication for continental dynamics. *In*: SALISBURY, M. H. & FOUNTAIN, D. M. (eds) *Exposed Cross-Sections of the Continental Crust*. Kluwer Academic Publishing, Dordrecht, 509–544.

WERNICKE, B. & TILKE, P. G. 1989. Extensional tectonics framework of the U.S. Central Atlantic passive margins. *In*: TANKARD, A. J. & BALKWILL, H. R. (eds) *Extensional Tectonic and Stratigraphy of the North Atlantic Margins*. American Association of Petroleum Geologists, Memoir, **46**, 7–21.

WILSON, M. 1993. Geochemical signature of oceanic and continental basalts: a key to mantle dynamics. *Journal of the Geological Society, London*, **150**, 977–990.

WILSON, M. & PATTERSON, R. 2001. Intraplate magmatism related to short-wavelength convective instabilities in the upper mantle: Evidence from the Tertiary-Quaternary volcanic province of western and central Europe. *Geological Society of America Special Paper*, **352**, 37–58.

WITTENBERG, A., VELLMER, C., KERN, H. & MENGEL, K. 2000. The Variscan lower continental crust: evidence for crustal delamination from geochemical and petrological investigations. *In*: FRANKE, W., HAAK, V., ONCKEN, O. & TANNER, D. (eds) *Orogenic Processes: Quantification and Modelling in the Variscan Belt*. Geological Society, London, Special Publications, **179**, 401–414.

WORRALL, D. M. & SNELSON, S. 1989. Evolution of the northern Gulf of Mexico, with emphasis on Cenozoic growth faulting and the role of salt. *In*: BALLY, A. W. & PALMER, A. R. (eds) *The Geology of North America – An Overview*, The Geology of North America, A, Geological Society of America, Boulder, CO, 97–138.

WORTEL, R. & SPAKMAN, W. 2000. Subduction and slab detachment in the Mediterranean–Carpathian region. *Science*, **290**, 1910–1917.

ZIEGLER, P. A. (ed.) 1988. Evolution of the Arctic-North Atlantic and the western Tethys. *American Association of Petroleum Geologists Memoir*, **43**.

ZIEGLER, P. A. 1989a. Evolution of the North Atlantic; an overview. *American Association of Petroleum Geologists Memoir*, **46**, 111–129.

ZIEGLER, P. A. 1989b. Evolution of Laurussia. *A Study in Late Palaeozoic Plate Tectonics*. Kluver Academic Publishers, Dordrecht.

ZIEGLER, P. A. 1990. Collision related intraplate compressional deformations in western and central Europe. *Journal of Geodynamics*, **11**, 357–388.

ZIEGLER, P. A. 1992. Geodynamics of rifting and implications for hydrocarbon habitat. *Tectonophysics*, **215**, 221–253.

ZIEGLER, P. A. 1996. Geodynamic processes governing development of rifted basins. *In*: ROURE, F., ELLOUZ, N., SHEIN, V. S. & SKVORTSOV, L. (eds) *Geodynamic Evolution of Sedimentary Basins*. Editions Technip, Paris, 19–67.

ZIEGLER, P. A. & CLOETINGH, S. 2004. Dynamic processes controlling evolution of rifted basins. *Earth Science Reviews*, **64**, 1–50.

ZIEGLER, P. A. & DÈZES, P. 2005. Evolution of the lithosphere in the area of the Rhine Rift System. *In*: BEHRMANN, J. H., GRANET, M., SCHMID, S. & ZIEGLER, P. A. (eds) *EUCOR-URGENT Special Issue. International Journal of Earth Sciences*, **94**, 594–614.

ZIEGLER, P. A., CLOETINGH, S. & VAN WEES, J.-D. 1995. Dynamics of intraplate compressional deformation: the Alpine foreland and other examples. *Tectonophysics*, **252**, 7–59.

ZIEGLER, P. A., VAN WEES, J.-D. & CLOETINGH, S. 1998. Mechanical controls on collision-related compressional intraplate deformation. *Tectonophysics*, **300**, 103–129.

ZIEGLER, P. A., CLOETINGH, S., GUIRAUD, R. & STAMPFLI, G. M. 2001. Peri-Tethyan platforms: constraints on dynamics of rifting and basin inversion. *In*: ZIEGLER, P. A., CAVAZZA, W., ROBERTSON, A. H. F. & CRASQUIN-SOLEAU, S. (eds) *Peri-Tethys Memoir 6: Peri-Tethyan Rift/Wrench Basins and Passive margins*. Mémoirs du Museum national d'Histoire naturelle, Paris, **186**, 9–49.

ZIEGLER, P. A., BERTOTTI, G. & CLOETINGH, S. 2002. Dynamic processes controlling foreland development—the role of mechanical (de)coupling of orogenic wedges and forelands. *In*: BERTOTTI, G., SCHULMANN, K. & CLOETINGH, S. (eds) *Continental Collision and the Tectono-Sedimentary Evolution of Forelands*. European Geosciences Union, Stephan Mueller Special Publication Series, Katlenburg-Lindau, Germany, **1**, 17–56.

ZIEGLER, P. A., SCHUMACHER, M. E., DÈZES, P., VAN WEES, J.-D. & CLOETINGH, S. 2004.

Post-Variscan evolution of the lithosphere in the Rhine Graben area: constraints from subsidence modelling. *In*: WILSON, M., NEUMANN, E.-R., DAVIES, G. R., TIMMERMAN, M. J., HEEREMANS, M. & LARSEN, B. T. (eds) *Permo-Carboniferous Magmatism and Rifting in Europe*. Geological Society, London, Special Publications, **223**, 289–317.

ZOBACK, M. D., STEPHENSON, R. A., CLOETINGH, S. *ET AL.* 1993, Stresses in the lithosphere and sedimentary basin formation. *Tectonophysics*, **226**, 1–13.

ZUBER, M.T. 1987. Compression of oceanic lithosphere: an analysis of intraplate deformation in the Central Indian Basin. *Journal of Geophysical Research*, **92**, 4817–4825.

Present-day stresses, seismicity and Neogene-to-Recent tectonics of Australia's 'passive' margins: intraplate deformation controlled by plate boundary forces

RICHARD R. HILLIS[1], MIKE SANDIFORD[2], SCOTT D. REYNOLDS[1,3]
& MARK C. QUIGLEY[2]

[1]*Australian School of Petroleum, University of Adelaide, SA 5005, Australia,*
(e-mail: richard.hillis@adelaide.edu.au)

[2]*School of Earth Sciences, University of Melbourne, Victoria 3010, Australia*

[3]*Present address: Schlumberger Oilfield Services, Abu Dhabi, United Arab Emirates*

Abstract: Neogene-to-Recent deformation is widespread on and adjacent to Australia's 'passive' margins. Elevated historical seismic activity and relatively high levels of Neogene-to-Recent tectonic activity are recognized in the Flinders and Mount Lofty Ranges, the SE Australian Passive Margin, SW Western Australia and the North West Shelf. In all cases the orientation of palaeostresses inferred from Neogene-to-Recent structures is consistent with independent determinations of the orientation of the present-day stress field.

Present-day stress orientations (and neotectonic palaeostress trends) vary across the Australian continent. Plate-scale stress modelling that incorporates the complex nature of the convergent plate boundary of the Indo-Australian Plate (with segments of continent–continent collision, continent–arc collision and subduction) indicates that present-day stress orientations in the Australian continent are consistent with a first-order control by plate-boundary forces. The consistency between the present-day, plate-boundary-sourced stress orientations and the record of deformation deduced from neotectonic structures implicates plate boundary forces in the ongoing intraplate deformation of the Australian continent.

Deformation rates inferred from seismicity and neotectonics (as high as $10^{-16}\ s^{-1}$) are faster than seismic strain rates in many other 'stable' intraplate regions, suggestive of unusually high stress levels imposed on the Australian intraplate environment from plate boundary interactions many thousands of kilometres distant. The spatial overlap of neotectonic structures and zones of concentrated historical seismicity with ancient fault zones and/or regions of enhanced crustal heat flow indicates that patterns of active deformation in Australia are in part, governed, by prior tectonic structuring and are also related to structural and thermal weakening of continental crust. Neogene-to-Recent intraplate deformation within the Australian continent has had profound and under-recognized effects on hydrocarbon occurrence, both by amplifying some hydrocarbon-hosting structures and by inducing leakage from pre-existing traps due to fault reactivation or tilting.

The term 'passive margin' describes a region of extended continental crust, located adjacent to a divergent plate boundary at the time of initiation of seafloor spreading, but now located in an intraplate setting, and thus considered to be tectonically 'passive'. However, as demonstrated in this volume, many passive margins are subject to ongoing intraplate deformation and there has been much debate about the drivers for such behaviour. Intraplate deformation may be generated by plate boundary forces that are transmitted into the plate interiors, with deformation localized in zones of intraplate weakness (e.g. Ziegler *et al.* 1998; Sandiford *et al.* 2004). Alternatively, there may be within-plate drivers for intraplate deformation such as tractions imparted from the mantle below deforming regions (e.g. Gurnis *et al.* 1998; Müller *et al.* 2000) or hotspot-related processes (e.g. Brodie & White 1994). This debate has been particularly active with respect to the North Atlantic passive margin which has seen significant Cenozoic deformation and uplift. In this region, debate has centred on the relative importance of deformation associated with the Iceland mantle plume versus deformation associated with compressional stresses transmitted from plate boundaries (Mid Atlantic Ridge and Alpine collisional zone), and perhaps to a lesser extent, glacially-related processes (see summary in Doré *et al.* 2002). It is instructive to analyse the Neogene-to-Recent deformation of Australia's passive margins in the context of this debate on the drivers of intraplate deformation.

From: JOHNSON, H., DORÉ, A. G., GATLIFF, R. W., HOLDSWORTH, R., LUNDIN, E. R. & RITCHIE, J. D. (eds)
The Nature and Origin of Compression in Passive Margins. Geological Society, London, Special Publications,
306, 71–90. DOI: 10.1144/SP306.3   0305-8719/08/$15.00 © The Geological Society of London 2008.

Structural and geomorphological expressions of Neogene-to-Recent intraplate deformation have been recognized within parts of the Australian continent (Sandiford 2003*b*; Twidale & Bourne 2004; Clark & Bodorkos 2004; Célérier *et al.* 2005; Quigley *et al.* 2006, 2007). This neotectonic record affords an opportunity to investigate whether present-day intraplate stresses as determined from techniques such as earthquake focal mechanism solutions and borehole break-outs in well-bores (Hillis & Reynolds 2000) are consistent with the longer-term geological record, and to assess whether both intraplate stresses and neotectonic deformation are consistent with a first-order control by plate boundary forces. The variation of present-day stress orientations and neotectonic structural trends across the Australian continent provides a more robust test of the consistency of inferred stresses and neotectonic structures than is possible in continental areas where there is little variation in present-day stress orientation.

In this paper, we summarize and compare present-day intraplate stresses, seismicity and neotectonic deformation in four regions of the Australian continent, focusing on its passive margins, in order to evaluate the extent to which

neotectonic deformation can be accounted for in terms of the boundary forces acting on the plate. We argue that plate boundary forces exert the first-order control on the present-day intraplate stress field and on the neotectonic, intraplate deformation of Australia and thus that plate boundary forces are effectively transmitted thousands of kilometres into the plate's interior where they are responsible for intraplate deformation. We also discuss the implications for the controls on intraplate deformation of the Australian continent and for hydrocarbon occurrence.

Intraplate stress field of Australia and plate boundary forces

The Australian continent is situated within the interior of the composite Indo-Australian Plate (Figs 1 & 2). Hillis & Reynolds (2003) described present-day maximum horizontal stress orientations within the Australian continent using earthquake focal mechanism solutions (29% of the data), borehole break-outs and drilling-induced tensile fractures in hydrocarbon exploration wells (44% and 7% of the data respectively) and hydraulic

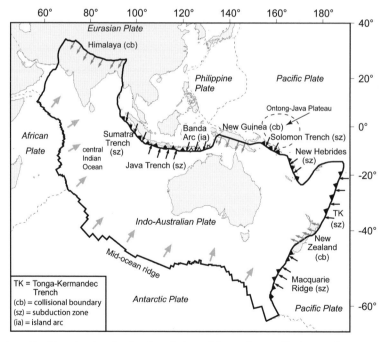

Fig. 1. Indo-Australian Plate showing the plate boundaries and forces discussed in the text. Large grey arrows indicate the mid-ocean ridge push force, small grey arrows indicate resisting continent–continent collisional forces, and small black arrows indicate slab pull forces. Solid triangles indicate the direction of subduction and open triangles delineate the Banda Arc. Modified after Reynolds *et al.* (2003).

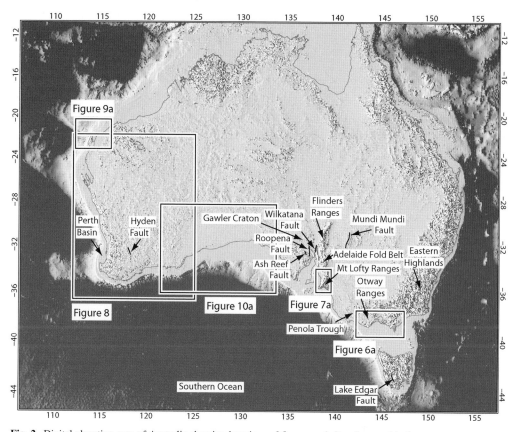

Fig. 2. Digital elevation map of Australia showing locations of figures and sites discussed in the text.

fracture tests, largely undertaken for coal mining purposes (18% of the data). Some 549 stress orientation measurements are available for the Australian continent, 331 of which are considered to be reliable (Fig. 3a). These data were derived independently of the information related to Neogene-to-Recent structures within the Australian continent presented herein. The stress data contain no orientations based on neotectonic structures, although elsewhere this is a recognized source of such information (Zoback 1992). The independence of these datasets is, of course, significant given that we compare present-day stress orientations and neotectonic deformation. The orientation of present-day maximum horizontal stress inferred from *in-situ* stress data is consistent within given regions of the Australian continent (e.g. individual sedimentary basins) but varies from region-to-region throughout the continent (Fig. 3). Present-day maximum horizontal stress is oriented east–west in western Australia. The east–west orientation rotates to NE–SW moving eastwards along the northern Australian margin and in

central Australia. The east–west orientation rotates to NW–SE moving eastwards along the southern Australian margin. Regional stress orientations in the Australian continent are not affected to a first-order by tectonic province, crustal thickness, heat flow, regional structural trends, geological age or by the depth at which orientations are sampled. Numerous workers (e.g. Coblentz *et al.* 1998; Reynolds *et al.* 2002; Sandiford *et al.* 2004) have thus sought an explanation for present-day intraplate stress trajectories in terms of plate boundary forces generated at the margins of the Indo-Australian Plate (Fig. 1).

The NE boundary of the Indo-Australian Plate exhibits a uniquely complex and laterally varying set of convergent tectonic styles. Continental collision is occurring along the Himalayan, New Guinea and New Zealand segments of the plate boundary (Fig. 1). Oceanic parts of the Indo-Australian Plate are being subducted at the Sumatra–Java and Solomon–New Hebrides Trenches, and the Pacific Plate is being subducted under the Indo-Australian Plate at the

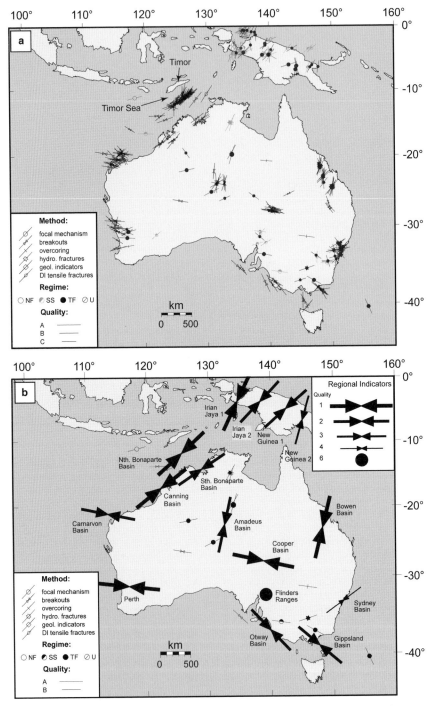

Fig. 3. Australian Stress Map. (**a**) Orientations of the bars indicate orientations of present-day maximum horizontal stress using the techniques indicated in the key. The length of the bar represents the quality (reliability) of the inferred stress orientation. Only reliable, A-C quality data are included. D and E quality data are omitted (from Hillis & Reynolds 2003).(**b**) Mean stress orientations within Australian stress provinces. The size of the arrow indicates the consistency of stress orientations within the province. Isolated A- and B-quality data that do not lie within the defined stress provinces are also shown (from Hillis & Reynolds 2003).

Tonga–Kermadec Trench. The rotation of stress orientation from east–west to NE–SW along the northern margin of Australia results in stress trajectories aligning orthogonal to the collisional New Guinea segment of the NE convergent boundary of the Indo-Australian plate. The rotation of stress orientation from east–west to NW–SE along the southern margin of Australia results in stress trajectories aligning orthogonal to the collisional New Zealand segment of the plate boundary. Qualitatively this suggests that these collisional plate boundary segments exert an important control on intraplate stresses.

Coblentz et al. (1998) and Reynolds et al. (2002) undertook two-dimensional, elastic finite element analysis of the intraplate stress field of the Indo-Australian Plate based on the forces applied to the plate boundaries (Fig. 4). In their first model, Coblentz et al. (1998) ignored the complexity of the NE convergent boundary of the Indo-Australian Plate and balanced the ridge push force associated with the SW plate boundary equally along the length of the convergent NE boundary. This model predicts maximum horizontal stresses that are consistent throughout the plate and parallel to the direction of absolute plate motion (i.e. NNE-oriented). This simple model is broadly similar to successful models of the intraplate stress field of continental areas such as

western Europe (Gölke & Coblentz 1996) and South America (Coblentz & Richardson 1996), where the present-day maximum horizontal stress orientation is indeed consistent and parallel to the direction of absolute plate motion. However, it does not match stress observations within the Australian continent.

In subsequent models, Coblentz et al. (1998) balanced (focused) the ridge push force associated with the SW boundary of the Indo-Australian Plate against the collisional segments of the NE boundary (i.e. Himalayas, New Guinea and New Zealand) and successfully reproduced the broad, continental-scale rotations in maximum horizontal stress orientation across the Australian continent described above. Reynolds et al. (2003) statistically compared the intraplate stresses predicted by plate boundary force models of the Indo-Australian Plate (permitting different forces along the NE boundary segments) with the observed stress data. The best-fitting model provides an excellent fit to the observed stress data (Fig. 4). This indicates that despite the fact that the present-day maximum horizontal stress orientation within the Australian continent is not parallel to the direction of absolute plate motion, it is consistent with a first-order control by plate boundary forces, provided the complexity of the NE convergent boundary of the Indo-Australian Plate is taken into account.

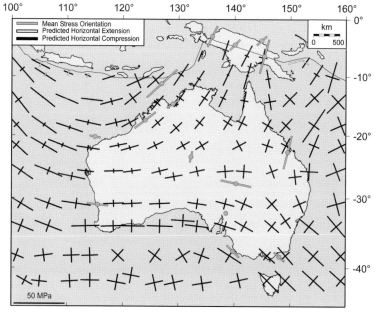

Fig. 4. Plate boundary force stress model that provides the best fit to observed stress data for the Australian continent (from Reynolds et al. 2003).

Seismicity and present-day stress of Australia

Australia shows a relatively high level of seismicity for a continent remote from plate boundaries (Fig. 5). In terms of individual earthquakes, large (M *c.* 6.8), surface rupturing earthquakes have occurred at Meckering (1968) and Tennant Creek (1988). In 1989, the M5.6 Newcastle earthquake resulted in 13 fatalities. In a comparison of seismic activity rates in stable continental regions (SCRs), Johnston (1994) showed that Australia was amongst the most active of SCRs, together with China and North America. Estimated activity rates in Australia are significantly higher than northern Europe, cratonic South America and Africa. India is the most seismically active SCR (Johnson 1994). Calculations of seismic strain rates from activity rates in SCRs are highly uncertain given the incompleteness of the historical databases from which they are derived. They do, however,

provide one view of the 'instantaneous' intraplate deformation field and its variability. On the basis of the activity rates, Johnston (1994) deduced a bulk seismogenic strain rate for the Australian continent of *c.* 10^{-17} s^{-1}, about four times faster than northern Europe and about four times slower than India. Sandiford *et al.* (2004) and Célérier *et al.* (2005) used a similar approach to derive seismogenic strain rates in the most active parts of south-central Australia which are of the order 10^{-16} s^{-1}; a rate that on the geological time scale should produce significant deformation.

Earthquake epicentral locations define four distinct zones of enhanced seismicity across the Australian continent (Fig. 5). (1) The SE Seismic Zone, extending in a coastal belt from central New South Wales through the eastern half of Victoria into Tasmania, including the passive margin bordering the Tasman Sea and the most SE part of the passive margin bordering the Southern Ocean. (2) The Flinders Seismic Zone,

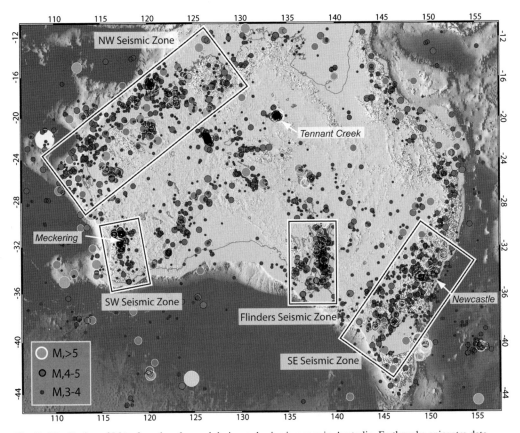

Fig. 5. Distribution of M > 3 earthquakes and designated seismic zones in Australia. Earthquake epicentre data courtesy of Geoscience Australia. Magnitude measures are based on local magnitudes (ML) for M < 5.5 and surface magnitude (Ms) for M > 5.5. The locations of notable Australian earthquakes including the 1968 Ms 6.8 Meckering earthquake; 1988 Ms 6.8 Tennant Creek earthquake, and 1989 Ms 5.6 Newcastle earthquake are shown.

extending from the Flinders and Mount Lofty Ranges to the eastern Gawler Craton. (3) The SW Seismic Zone of SW Western Australia which extends to the southern part of Western Australian Indian Ocean passive margin. (4) The NW Seismic Zone located mainly on the NW Shelf, the passive margin bordering the Indian Ocean and Timor Sea.

Present-day maximum horizontal stress is oriented NW–SE throughout the SE Australian passive margin, albeit rotating slightly from 125°N in the South Australian Otway Basin to 135°N in the Victorian Otway Basin to 140°N in the Gippsland Basin (Fig. 6; Nelson *et al.* 2006). Allen *et al.* (2005) calculated a composite fault plane solution using four eastern Victorian earthquakes (immediately north of the Gippsland Basin) with the solution indicating a reverse fault mechanism with present-day maximum horizontal stress oriented 145°N.

Earthquake focal mechanism solutions in the Flinders Seismic Zone indicate strike-slip and reverse mechanisms with a broadly east–west oriented present-day maximum horizontal stress orientation, but with some scatter in orientations (Fig. 7; Hillis & Reynolds 2000, 2003). Clark & Leonard (2003) inverted six earthquake focal mechanisms from the Flinders Ranges in a composite solution indicating that the maximum principal stress is sub-horizontal and oriented 082°N.

Present-day maximum horizontal stress in the SW Seismic Zone is oriented east–west (Hillis & Reynolds 2003; Fig. 8). Borehole break-outs in the Perth Basin (Fig. 2) indicate an east–west oriented present-day maximum horizontal stress (Fig. 8; Reynolds & Hillis 2000). Shallow (3–10 m depth) overcoring-based stress measurements were undertaken near the epicentres of the 1968 Meckering and 1970 Calingiri earthquakes and both the overcoring measurements and the focal mechanism solutions for those events indicate east–west oriented present-day maximum horizontal stress (Denham *et al.* 1979). Clark & Leonard (2003) inverted five earthquake focal mechanisms from the area, including the Meckering and Calingiri events, in a composite solution indicating that the maximum principal stress is horizontal and oriented 275°N with a pure compression focal mechanism.

There is extensive present-day stress data from the NW Seismic Zone in the form of borehole break-outs analysed in petroleum exploration wells in the Carnarvon Basin. Regional present-day maximum horizontal stress in the Carnarvon Basin is oriented *c.* 100°N (Hillis & Reynolds 2003; Fig. 3). The original interpretation of break-outs in the Carnarvon Basin was based on caliper logs interpreted by Mildren (1997). The stress directions

inferred from caliper logs in individual wells in the Carnarvon Basin show significant scatter, albeit with a mean direction of *c.* 101°N across the basin (standard deviation of 35°; Hillis & Reynolds 2003). Image logs permit more confident interpretation of borehole break-outs than caliper logs, and permit the recognition of drilling-induced tensile fractures, which also indicate the direction of present-day horizontal stress. Recent, unpublished analysis of a large database of image logs indicates a consistent present-day maximum horizontal stress direction of *c.* 105°N across the Carnarvon Basin. Present-day maximum horizontal stress orientation in the Timor Sea (Fig. 3) is well constrained from analysis of borehole break-outs and drilling-induced tensile fractures on caliper and image logs from the area (Hillis & Reynolds 2003). The mean present-day maximum horizontal stress direction in the area is 047°N.

Neotectonics of Australia

Australia is often considered to be a tectonically stable continental region where ancient land surfaces predominate (Twidale & Bourne 1975; Ollier 1978). This is true for much of the continent, but, as discussed above, Neogene-to-Recent tectonic activity is documented in many areas of Australia. A large number of prehistoric fault scarps have been identified onshore in Australia, testifying to a rich record of ongoing earthquake activity (Clark & McCue 2003 and discussed further below). Several important conclusions and implications have been drawn from the studies of these features. Importantly, all documented onshore Quaternary faults involve either purely dip-slip or oblique-slip reverse movement. No Quaternary strike-slip or normal faults have been found. Fault kinematic data derived from fault plane and slickenline orientations from the Flinders Seismic Zone indicate a roughly east–west oriented palaeomaximum horizontal stress orientation, consistent with the orientation derived from historical seismicity (Sandiford 2003a; Quigley *et al.* 2006; Fig. 7).

Estimates of prehistoric SE Australian earthquake magnitudes (M), based on fault rupture lengths, single-event displacements and inferred ranges of hypocentral rupture depth, range from M = 5.8 to 7.2 (Clark & McCue 2003; Quigley *et al.* 2006). These data are consistent with estimates for the largest recorded Australian earthquakes (Meeberiee, WA 1941, M = 7.3; Meckering, WA 1968, M = 6.8; Tennant Creek, NT 1988; M = 6.8). Quaternary fault slip rates derived from cumulative displacements of Pliocene and Quaternary sediments range from

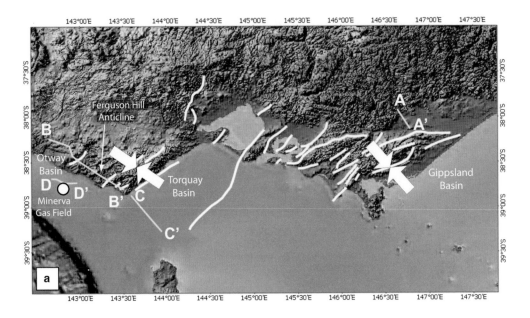

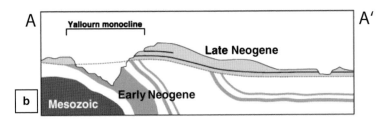

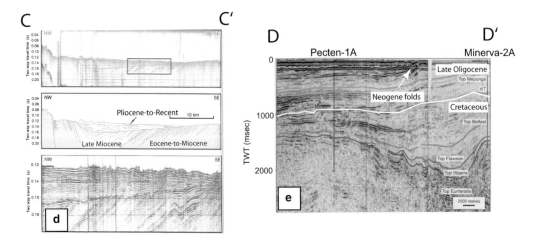

$20–150 \text{ mMa}^{-1}$, suggesting surprisingly high rates of deformation for an intraplate setting (Sandiford 2003a; Quigley et al. 2006). However, the long-term slip rates determined from individual fault exposures have proved more difficult to assess because of the tendency of intracontinental faulting to cluster in time and space (Crone et al. 1997, 2003). For example, faults in the Wilkatana area of the central Flinders Ranges appear to have incurred upwards of 15 m of cumulative slip since c. 67 000 years ago (Quigley et al. 2006), much higher than any reasonable long-term average. Estimates of the recurrence interval of surface-rupturing earthquakes from Quaternary faults range from 1 per 22 000 years to ≥ 1 per 83 000 years, although estimations of these rates are also limited by the sporadic nature of intracontinental faulting (Quigley et al. 2006).

Exposed Quaternary faults commonly occur along previously established geological boundaries and/or zones of crustal weakness (Fig. 2), including lithotectonic boundaries (e.g. Wilkatana and Roopena/Ash Reef Faults at the boundary between the Adelaide Fold Belt and Gawler Craton), ancient fault zones (e.g. Mundi Mundi Fault, Lake Edgar Fault) and range fronts (Flinders and Mt Lofty Ranges). Finally, it appears that earthquake activity may have resulted in upwards of several hundreds of metres of cumulative surface uplift in some parts of SE Australia, such as in the Flinders, Mt Lofty and Otway Ranges (Bourman & Lindsay 1989; Tokarev et al. 1999; Sandiford 2003a; Quigley et al. 2006) and Eastern Highlands (Fig. 2), indicating a profound relationship between intraplate deformation and landscape evolution.

Neogene deformation of Australia's passive margins

In the following sections, we summarize evidence of Neogene-to-Recent tectonic activity in the SE passive margin (Otway, Torquay and Gippsland Basin), the Flinders and Mount Lofty Ranges, onshore SW Western Australia, and the NW Australian passive margin (Carnarvon Basin and Timor Sea). These areas where Neogene-to-Recent tectonic activity can most easily be observed correspond with the areas of elevated historical seismic activity described above, suggesting that deformation is continuing to the present-day. We also compare Neogene-to-Recent structural trends to the present-day stress field.

SE Australian passive margin: Otway, Torquay and Gippsland Basins

There is extensive evidence for Miocene–Recent deformation on Australia's SE passive margin. Figure 6a shows the major Neogene faults of the area as interpreted by Dickinson et al. (2002). The Minerva Gas Field of the offshore Otway Basin is located on a NE-trending inversion anticline which records a major period of Miocene–Recent compression (Schneider et al. 2004; Sharp & Wood 2004; Fig. 6e). Similar, NE-trending Miocene–Recent anticlines occur onshore such as the Ferguson Hill anticline (Port Campbell Embayment 1 : 100 000 Geological Map Sheet; Fig. 6c). These structures lie just to the west of the Otway Ranges on which strandlines indicate c. 200 m of uplift since early-mid Pliocene (Sandiford 2003a, b; Sandiford et al. 2004). In the Torquay Basin, folding and faulting affects the entire section up to the upper Miocene and up to 400 m of Miocene section has been eroded from anticlinal crests (Fig. 6d). Deformation and erosion must postdate the upper Miocene because that section is conformable and uniformly affected by deformation (Dickinson et al. 2002). A very pronounced Miocene–Pliocene angular unconformity is apparent in the basin (Fig. 6d). On shallow seismic records near the shoreline, faulting is evident within the Pliocene, indicating that deformation continued into the Pliocene (Dickinson et al. 2002). The Miocene–Recent structures of the Torquay Basin broadly strike NE–SW but

---

Fig. 6. Compilation of present-day stress and neotectonic data for the SE Australian margin. (**a**) Map shows neotectonic fault scarps interpreted by Dickinson et al. (2002) superimposed on digital elevation data. Block arrows indicate mean regional present-day maximum horizontal stress orientations from Hillis & Reynolds (2003). Map also shows locations of cross-sections in (b)–(e). (**b**) Cross-section of the Yallourn monocline, showing strong deformation of early Neogene sediments and mild deformation of late Neogene sediments (from Barton 1981). (**c**) Cross-section showing deformation of Neogene sediments at Ferguson Hill (Port Campbell Embayment 1 : 100 000 Geological Map Sheet). (**d**) Seismic data and interpretation from the Torquay Basin, showing strong deformation of late Miocene strata and mild deformation and folding of unconformably overlying Pliocene–Recent strata (from Dickinson et al. 2001). (**e**) Seismic profile through the Minerva Gas Field in the Otway Basin. Deformation of late Oligocene strata indicates Miocene or younger folding. Drilling-induced tensile fractures in the Minerva-1 and Minerva-2A wells indicate NW–SE-oriented present-day maximum horizontal stress (Nelson et al. 2006), orthogonal to and consistent with the orientation of the Miocene–Recent anticlines observed in the profile (Sharp & Wood 2004).

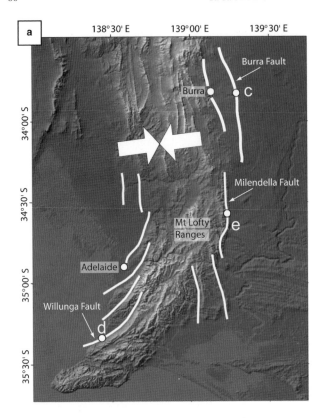

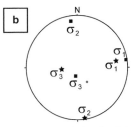

★ Principal stresses from focal-plane
  solutions (Clark and Leonard, 2003)

■ Principal stresses from Quaternary
  faults (Quigley *et al.* 2006)

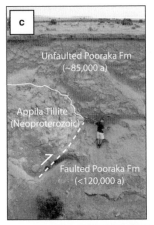

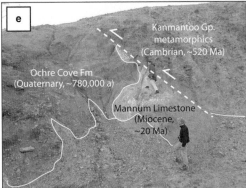

Fig. 7. Compilation of present-day stress and neotectonic data for the southern Flinders and Mount Lofty Ranges.
(**a**) Map shows neotectonic fault scarps interpreted by Sandiford (2003*b*) and Quigley *et al.* (2006) superimposed on
digital elevation data. Block arrows denote mean regional present-day maximum horizontal stress orientation from
Hillis & Reynolds (2003). Map also shows locations of field photos/sketches in (c)–(e). (**b**) Comparison of principal
compressive stresses derived from eight focal-plane solutions of Flinders Ranges earthquakes for the interval 1977–
1991 (Clark & Leonard 2003) and from field measurements of the Wilkatana, Burra, and Mundi Mundi Faults (Quigley
et al. 2006). Stress magnitudes are defined such that compressive stresses are positive and $\sigma_1 > \sigma_2 > \sigma_3$. Note
similarity in stresses derived from historical and neotectonic datasets (from Quigley *et al.* 2006). (**c**) Burra Fault
locality, showing a reverse fault that displaces Neoproterozoic basement rock over late Quaternary sediment (Pooraka
Formation). View looking north (from Quigley *et al.* 2006). (**d**) Willunga Fault locality, showing a *c.*120 ka BP
wave-cut platform in the uplifted hanging wall of the Willunga Fault situated roughly 4–5 m above present sea level,
indicating post *c.*120 ka uplift. Steeply dipping Oligo-Miocene strata further testify to Neogene deformation. View
looking south (from Sandiford 2003*b*). (**e**) Milendella Fault locality, showing metamorphic basement rocks thrust over
Quaternary sedimentary rocks. View looking south (from Sandiford 2003*b*).

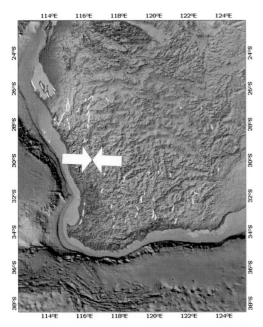

Fig. 8. Compilation of present-day stress and neotectonic data for SW Western Australia. Map shows neotectonic fault scarps interpreted by Clark (2005) superimposed on digital elevation data. Block arrows indicate mean regional present-day maximum horizontal stress orientation from Hillis & Reynolds (2003).

have not been mapped in detail nor are present-day stress orientations available for the Torquay Basin.

Miocene–Recent compression is also witnessed in the coalfields of the onshore Gippsland Basin, for example in the NE–SW-striking Yallourn monocline where a major angular unconformity separates Pliocene from Miocene (Barton 1981; Fig. 6b). Regionally, throughout the onshore Gippsland Basin, Neogene-to-Recent monoclines and reverse faults strike NE–SW to east–west and river channels cut across present-day uplifted structures, suggesting that uplift continued into the middle Pleistocene (Holdgate et al. 2003).

Offshore in the Gippsland Basin, where the predominant inherited structural trend is ESE, only east–west to NE–SW striking faults have been reactivated in compression (Power et al. 2003). The neotectonic structures of the Otway and Gippsland Basins are consistent with the previously described reverse faulting present-day stress regime with maximum horizontal stress oriented NW–SE.

Flinders and Mount Lofty ranges

The Quaternary tectonic record of the Flinders and Mount Lofty ranges is dominated by north- to NE-striking, range-bounding reverse faults

recording approximately east–west shortening (Sandiford 2003b; Sandiford et al. 2004; Célérier et al. 2005; Quigley et al. 2006). Figure 7 shows neotectonic scarps of the Mount Lofty Ranges as interpreted by Sandiford (2003b) and Quigley et al. (2006). The associated faults are largely buried beneath alluvial fans, but are occasionally exposed in coastal and river sections. At Sellicks Beach canyons provide sections from the hanging wall to the footwall of the Willunga Fault (Fig. 7d). Reverse fault motion is indicated by steep east-dipping fault traces in the hanging-wall sequence close to the main fault trace. Tilting of the Oligocene to lower Miocene section indicates post-early Miocene deformation (Sandiford 2003b). The Milendella Fault is part of the eastern range-bounding fault system of the Mount Lofty Ranges, strikes north–south and comprises a west-dipping thrust which juxtaposes Cambrian metamorphic rocks in the hanging wall against Miocene and Quaternary rocks in the footwall (Fig. 7e). Further north in the Flinders Ranges, the Burra, Wilkatana and Paralana Faults all thrust Proterozoic basement over Quaternary deposits (Célérier et al. 2005; Quigley et al. 2006; Fig. 7c). Field measurements of fault orientations and slickenlines on the Wilkatana, Burra and Mundi Mundi Faults yield a maximum principal palaeostress orientation similar to inferred present-day stresses derived from historical earthquake focal mechanisms (Quigley et al. 2006; Fig. 7b).

SW Western Australia

The evidence of neotectonic activity in onshore SW Western Australia is less dramatic than in the Flinders and Mount Lofty ranges of South Australia. Topography is more subdued and we are not aware of sections through neotectonically-active faults, although trenching of the Hyden Fault scarp (Fig. 2) has revealed evidence of repeated Quaternary displacement (Clark et al. 2008). However, recent analysis of digital elevation data has revealed numerous faults scarps (Clark 2005; Fig. 8). The fault scarps strike north–south across the entire region. Most scarps where a displacement sense could be determined from the digital elevation data suggest reverse displacement on the underlying fault (Clark 2005). Nineteen of the features have been verified by ground-truthing and range in apparent age from less than a thousand years to many tens of thousands of years (Clark 2005). The north–south striking reverse fault scarps of SW Western Australia are consistent with the previously described reverse faulting present-day stress regime with maximum horizontal stress oriented east–west as inferred from historical earthquake focal mechanisms, overcoring and borehole breakouts.

NW Australian passive margin:
Carnarvon Basin and Timor Sea

The North West Cape (Fig. 9) is a peninsula formed by the Cape Range anticline, the NNE-strike of

which is parallel to the coastline of the peninsula (the onshore anticlinal trace shown on Fig. 9a). The Rough Range (Fig. 9b) and Giralia anticlines are parallel to the Cape Range anticline and are also both apparent on the digital elevation data for

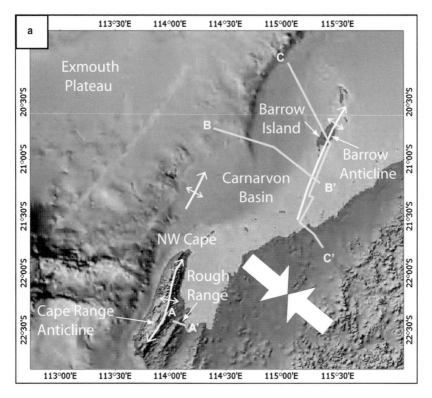

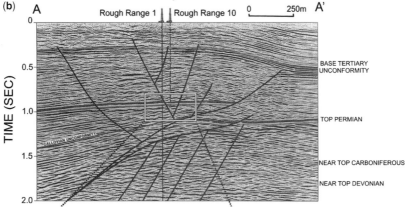

Fig. 9. Compilation of present-day stress and neotectonic data for the NW Australian margin. (**a**) Map shows anticlines with major growth during the Miocene as interpreted by Barber (1988) superimposed on digital elevation data. Block arrows indicate mean regional present-day maximum horizontal stress orientations from Hillis & Reynolds (2003). Fold axes strike orthogonally to the present-day maximum horizontal stress orientation. Map also shows locations of cross-sections in (b)–(d). (**b**) Seismic section through the Rough Range anticline showing deformation of base Tertiary and younger (undated) reflectors (from Malcolm *et al.* 1991).

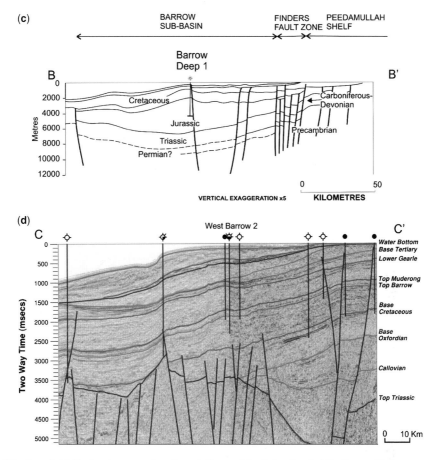

Fig. 9. (*Continued*) (**c**) Regional cross-section through Barrow Island showing that the Barrow Deep was a Jurassic depocentre subsequently inverted and uplifted in Cenozoic times (from Williams & Poynton 1985). (**d**) Seismic section through Barrow Island showing the inverted Jurassic depocentre with the base Tertiary almost exhumed to the surface above the depocentre (from Hearty *et al.* 2002).

the area. Several islands in the Carnarvon Basin also overlie anticlines, the largest of these being Barrow Island which is located along the crest of the Barrow anticline where broad inversion is clear (Fig. 9c, d). The Barrow Island inverted anticline follows the same NNE-trend as the anticlines of North West Cape. Figure 9 shows the Cape Range, Barrow and a third NNE-trending anticlinal structure as mapped by Barber (1988) with major growth dated as 'Miocene'. The anticlines are generally asymmetric because they have developed as fault propagation folds above reversely reactivated normal faults (Hocking 1988).

Although reverse reactivation of older normal faults, and the associated growth of fault propagation anticlines, is generally dated as Miocene in the Carnarvon Basin (e.g. Barber 1988; Hearty *et al.* 2002), little detailed dating on the age

of their growth has been published. Emerged Pleistocene marine terraces on the Cape Range anticline indicate that deformation continued after the Miocene (Van De Graff *et al.* 1976). Indeed, the deeper water Exmouth Plateau was significantly folded and uplifted during this 'Miocene' event (Barber 1988) and doming of the present-day seabed suggests that deformation continues to the present-day. There is also evidence from onlap and facies variation in the Palaeogene and Cretaceous that indicates that some anticlines have been present since those times (Hocking 1988). That deformation continues to the present-day in the Pilbara Craton adjacent to the Carnarvon Basin is demonstrated by neotectonic fracture systems in granite pavements that cut aboriginal petroglyphs (Clark & Bodorkos 2004). The ESE-oriented maximum horizontal palaeostress direction implied by the NNE-trending anticlines and inverted normal faults of the Carnarvon Basin is consistent with the previously described ESE orientation of the present-day maximum horizontal stress inferred from borehole break-outs and drilling-induced tensile fractures in petroleum exploration wells in the region.

At the other end of the NW Australian passive margin, the Timor Sea region of the margin is in collision with the Indonesian Banda Island Arc (Fig. 1), with the former passive margin being deformed in this active collision zone. The island of Timor (Fig. 3) comprises material accreted from the Australian Plate and the 2000 m deep Timor Trench to the south of Timor is an underfilled foreland basin on the Australian side of the collision zone. The Timor Sea is underlain by Australian passive margin south of the Timor Trough. Neogene-to-Recent fault reactivation is common in the Timor Sea with many faults reaching the seabed. The style of neotectonic faulting is unlike that observed elsewhere in Australia and is dominated by steeply-dipping, NE–SW to ENE–WSW-striking faults on which there is apparent Neogene-to-Recent normal displacement (Keep *et al.* 1998; Harrowfield & Keep 2005). There has been considerable debate regarding whether the regional system is one of normal faulting (e.g. Woods 1988) or whether the observed normal fault displacement occurs within an overall left-lateral wrench system (Nelson 1989; Shuster *et al.* 1998). The observed normal displacement on NE–SW-striking faults is consistent with the previously described NE–SW maximum horizontal stress orientation in the region if the vertical stress is the maximum principal stress (normal fault regime) and consistent with left-lateral motion on steeply dipping ENE–WSW striking faults if the maximum horizontal stress is the maximum principal stress (strike-slip fault regime).

Controls on intraplate deformation

Much of the contemporary debate concerning the sources of stress responsible for intraplate deformation is concerned with distinguishing stress transmitted from distant plate boundary interactions versus more local, within-plate sources, such as tractions imparted from the mantle at the base of deforming regions or hotspot-related processes. In most continental areas such as western Europe, South America and stable North America, the present-day maximum horizontal stress orientation is constant over thousands of kilometres and broadly parallels the direction of absolute plate velocity (Zoback 1992; Richardson 1992; Gölke & Coblentz 1996). This observation has led many

investigators to conclude that plate boundary forces are the principal control on the character of the intraplate stress field (Zoback 1992; Richardson 1992; Gölke & Coblentz 1996). In contrast to these other plates, stress orientations in the Australian continent vary significantly and do not generally parallel the NNE direction of absolute plate motion (Figs 1 & 2). In the context of the neotectonic deformation of the Australian continent, it is not possible to preclude the role of relatively local, within-plate sources of stress in driving deformation in each of the widely separated regions we have described. However, as outlined above, the pattern of tectonic stress distribution derived from present-day stress data points to a long wavelength control that is now well understood in terms of a complex set of plate-boundary interactions (Coblentz *et al.* 1998; Reynolds *et al.* 2003). The relatively high levels of active seismicity further point to relatively high stress magnitudes and suggest that at geological time scales we would expect a permanent record in terms of neotectonic structures. There is indeed such a record in each of the four main seismogenic zones of Australia. Further, the orientations of the neotectonic structures accord with the pattern of present day stress and, where neotectonic structures are exposed or revealed in seismic sections, their style is consistent with present-day stress orientations. Together, these observations provide a strong case that the ongoing intraplate deformation field of the Australian continent is a primary response to distant plate boundary interactions. In support of this argument, the late Miocene onset of the Australian stress field in SE Australia, as indicated by structural and sedimentological studies, temporally coincides with significant changes in the nature of the Indo-Australian plate boundary zones (Fig. 1). These changes include: (1) the onset of transpression and mountain building in New Zealand relating to increased Pacific–Australian Plate convergence (Sutherland 1996; Walcott 1998); (2) the onset of compressional deformation and uplift along the Macquarie Ridge (Duncan & Varne 1988; Massell *et al.* 2000); (3) the onset of transpressional deformation and uplift in New Guinea (Hill & Hall 2003; Packham 1996); (4) collision between the Ontong Java Plateau and the Solomon Arc (Petterson *et al.* 1997; Wessel & Kroenke 2000); (5) the onset of deformation in the central Indian Ocean (Cochran 1990; Krishna *et al.* 2001); and (6) major normal faulting in the Himalayan–Tibetan orogen (Harrison *et al.* 1992; Pan & Kidd 1992).

The seismically and neotectonically active regions discussed above contrast markedly with the eastern part of the Great Australian Bight passive margin which borders the Southern Ocean (Figs 2 & 10). This area has amongst the lowest

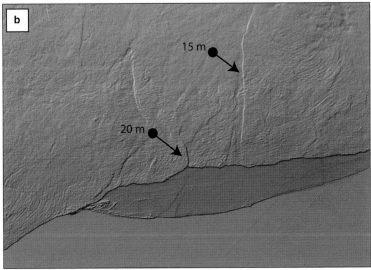

Fig. 10. Digital elevation data for southern central Australia and the Nullarbor Plain. The 15 Ma gently seaward-dipping depositional surface that forms the Nullarbor Plain is cut only by minor north–south trending faults with maximum displacements of c.1 m Ma^{-1}. Arrows denote location of maximum fault scarp height measurements. The seismicity of the area is amongst the lowest in Australia (Fig. 5).

seismic activity rates of any part of the continent (Fig. 5). Further, the Nullarbor Plain (Figs 2 & 10) provides extraordinary testimony to the long-term tectonic stability of this margin. This plain is defined by a vast marine limestone terrace more than 1000 km long and, at its widest, 300 km wide, which was exposed at c. 15 Ma by gentle long wavelength uplift of the southwestern part of the Australian continent (e.g. De Broekert & Sandiford 2005; Fig. 10). The almost total absence of subsequent fluvial processes on the plain has preserved virtually intact the 15 Ma gently seaward-dipping depositional surface. Digital elevation data clearly reveal a number of small displacement, linear north–south trending faults across the western and central part of the plain (Fig. 10b), showing that the maximum fault displacements accumulated over 15 Ma are everywhere less than a few tens of metres (or no more than about 1 m per million years). Much of the eastern part of the plain has been unaffected by faulting during this time. Although there are no present-day stress data for this area, the orientation of these small displacement faults is consistent with the east–west orientation of the present-day stress field inferred for the area from plate-boundary force modelling (Fig. 2).

The localization of seismicity and associated, longer-term neotectonic deformation into discrete regions within the Australian continent suggests that there are additional controls governing the spatial distribution of intraplate 'failure'. A high strength lithosphere is required to transfer tectonic stress over thousands of kilometres in intraplate regions. High differential stresses determined for the Gippsland and Cooper–Eromanga Basins (Nelson & Hillis 2005; Reynolds *et al.* 2006) demonstrate the high strength of the upper crust in Australia (cf. Zoback *et al.* 1993). We suggest three possible broad causes of the localization of deformation into discrete regions:

- favourable orientation of passive margins with respect to present-day stresses;
- overpressuring of faults (pore pressure in excess of hydrostatic; Turner & Williams 2004) so that faults are easier to reactivate, and;
- thermal weakening of the crust (associated with high concentrations of heat producing elements; e.g. McClaren *et al.* 2002) that allowed for focusing of deformation into anomalously weak zones.

In all the cases discussed here (except the Timor Sea), tectonic activity is confined to linear belts many hundreds of kilometres in length, aligned at a high angle to the present-day maximum horizontal stress (e.g. SE, Flinders and SW Seismic Zones). Deformation of the Australian 'passive' margins thus appears to be concentrated in areas where the margins are almost orthogonal to the present-day maximum horizontal stress (Fig. 3). Deformation in the Timor Sea reflects the interaction of plate boundary-derived forces and lithospheric flexure resulting from formation of the Timor Trough (Veevers & Powell 1984; O'Brien *et al.* 1999). The inactive Great Australian Bight margin is aligned parallel to the prevailing maximum horizontal stress. The style of neotectonic deformation observed is thus likely to be influenced by the orientation of pre-existing zones of weakness in the margin (inherited faults) with respect to the present-day stress field. This is supported by neotectonic studies that suggested young faults locally reactivated ancient faults and/or shear zones (Crone *et al.* 2003; Quigley *et al.* 2006).

Overpressures have been demonstrated in the deeper parts of the Carnarvon (van Ruth *et al.* 2004) and Gippsland Basins (Nelson *et al.* 2006). Overpressure reduces the effective normal stress that resists shear failure. The extent of deformation on Australia's passive margins may at least in part reflect the development of overpressure in these basinal settings. However, active seismicity and neotectonic structures extend well onshore, into

terranes exposing crystalline basement, beyond the likely limits of significant overpressuring. In the case of the Flinders Ranges, the high concentrations of heat-producing elements in the crust suggest a likely role for thermal weakening in the localization of deformation (Neumann *et al.* 2000; Célérier *et al.* 2005). Using numerical models, Célérier *et al.* (2005) illustrate how high concentrations of heat producing elements in the crust, as reflected in high present-day heat flows, lead to rheological weakening and localization of deformation.

This study demonstrates that the 'passive' margins bounding the Australian continent are not seismically or tectonically passive. Rather, these margins have been actively deformed from the Neogene to Recent in response to stresses transmitted from plate boundaries into the interior of the Indo-Australian Plate.

Implications for the distribution of hydrocarbons

Neogene-to-Recent intraplate deformation within the Australian continent has had profound and under-recognized effects on hydrocarbon occurrence. On the positive side, neotectonic activity has amplified some hydrocarbon-hosting, four-way dip closed structures, including:

- NNE-trending anticlines of the Carnarvon Basin which have seen Neogene-to-Recent growth including the Barrow Island oilfield located within the Barrow Island inverted anticline (Fig. 9), the giant Scarborough Gas Field located on the Exmouth Plateau (deep-water Carnarvon Basin), and Rough Range, a small oil field located on one of the folds of Australia's NW Cape and the first Australian field to flow oil to the surface.
- Minerva Gas Field of the offshore Otway Basin which is located on an inversion anticline with Neogene-to-Recent growth (Fig. 6).
- Inversion anticline traps of the Gippsland Basin, although there is significant variation in the timing of inversion structures across the Gippsland Basin with some fields such as Barracouta and Flying Fish subject to deformation that continues to the present-day and others such as Turrum subject to little post-mid-Miocene deformation (Dickinson *et al.* 2001; Power *et al.* 2003).

However, in general the effects of Neogene-to-Recent tectonism have been detrimental to hydrocarbon occurrence. For example, the lack of exploration success in the Torquay and eastern Otway Basins has been ascribed to wells targeting structures formed during Neogene-to-Recent inversion which most likely post-dates the main episode of hydrocarbon generation and migration (Trupp *et al.* 1994; Dickinson *et al.* 2001; Green *et al.* 2004). Older structures in such settings may have filled with hydrocarbons but may be prone to seal breach during more recent deformation. Neogene-to-Recent fault reactivation post-charge has been linked to seal breach in both the Penola Trough (Fig. 2) of the Otway Basin (Lyon *et al.* 2005) and in the Timor Sea (O'Brien & Woods 1995). Indeed, the prediction of fault orientations likely to be reactivated within the present-day stress field has been incorporated into prospect ranking in the Timor Sea, with a recognition that traps bound by faults likely to have reactivated face an enhanced risk of seal breach (Mildren *et al.* 2002; Rogers *et al.* 2008).

Even gentle tilting of pre-existing hydrocarbon-filled structures may change the spill point, leading to partial trap breach without rupturing of the seal. There is, however, the possibility of updip accumulations from breached/spilled accumulations that have received relatively little attention in the Australian context. In general, in Australian basins subject to Neogene-to-Recent tectonism, it is necessary to ascertain in detail the timing of filling of hydrocarbon of traps with respect to deformation. Structures must have formed prior to filling. However, structures that have formed prior to deformation and are hydrocarbon-filled are potentially subject to breach due to fault reactivation or tilting. Gentle anticlinal growth may enhance pre-existing structures without beaching them. Neogene-to-Recent deformation has generally been detrimental to hydrocarbon occurrence and in this context, older structures, not subject to Neogene-to-Recent deformation have lower attendant risk.

The authors acknowledge and appreciate funding for this research from the Australian Research Council. Bob Holdsworth and Emma Nelson are thanked for constructive comments in review.

References

ALLEN, T. I., GIBSON, G. & CULL, J. P. 2005. Stress-field constraints from recent intraplate seismicity in south-eastern Australia. *Australian Journal of Earth Sciences*, **52**, 217–229.

BARBER, P. M. 1988. The Exmouth Plateau deep water frontier: a case history. *In*: PURCELL, P. G. & PURCELL, R. R. (eds) *North West Shelf Australia.* Proceedings of the Petroleum Exploration Society of Australia Symposium, Perth, Western Australia, 173–186.

BARTON, C. M. 1981. Regional stress and structure in relation to brown coal open cuts of the Latrobe Valley, Victoria. *Journal of the Geological Society of Australia*, **28**, 333–339.

BOURMAN, R. P. & LINDSAY, J. M. 1989. Timing, extent and character of late Cainozoic faulting along the eastern margin of the Mount Lofty Ranges, South Australia. *Transactions of the Royal Society of South Australia*, **113**, 63–67.

BRODIE, J. & WHITE, N. J. 1994. Sedimentary basin inversion caused by igneous underplating: Northwest European continental shelf. *Geology*, **22**, 147–150.

CÉLÉRIER, J., SANDIFORD, M., HANSEN, D. L. & QUIGLEY, M. 2005. Modes of active intraplate deformation, Flinders Ranges, Australia. *Tectonics*, **20**.

CLARK, D. 2005. A preliminary seismicity model for southwest Western Australia based on neotectonic data. *Australian Earthquake Engineering Society Conference*, Albury, Earthquake Engineering in Australia. Paper 22. http://www.aees.org.au/Proceedings/2005_Papers/22_ClarkD.pdf.

CLARK, D. J. & BODORKOS, S. 2004. Fracture systems in granite pavement of the eastern Pilbara Craton, Western Australia; indicators of neotectonic activity? *Australian Journal of Earth Sciences*, **51**, 831–846.

CLARK, D. J., DENTITH, M., WYRWOLL, K.-H., LU, Y., DENT, V. & FEATHERSTONE, W. 2008. Hyden Fault Scarp, Western Australia: palaeoseismic evidence for repeated Quaternary displacement in an intracratonic setting. *Australian Journal of Earth Sciences*, **55**, 379–395.

CLARK, D. J. & LEONARD, M. 2003. Principal stress orientations from multiple focal-plane solutions: new insight into the Australian intraplate stress field. *In*: HILLIS, R. R. & MÜLLER, R. D. (eds) *Evolution and Dynamics of the Australian Plate.* Geological Society of Australia, Special Publication, **22**, 91–105.

CLARK, D. J. & McCUE, K. 2003. Australian palaeoseismology: towards a better basis for seismic hazard estimation. *Annals of Geophysics*, **46**, 1087–1105.

COBLENTZ, D. D. & RICHARDSON, R. M. 1996. Analysis of the South American intraplate stress field. *Journal of Geophysical Research*, **101**(B4), 8643–8658.

COBLENTZ, D. D., ZHOU, S., HILLIS, R. R., RICHARDSON, R. M. & SANDIFORD, M. 1998. Topography, boundary forces, and the Indo-Australian intraplate stress field. *Journal of Geophysical Research*, **103**, 919–931.

COCHRAN, J. R. 1990. Himalayan uplift, sea level, and the record of Bengal Fan sedimentation at the ODP Leg 116 sites. *Proceedings of the Ocean Drilling Program*, Scientific Results 116, 397–414.

CRONE, A. J., MACHETTE, M. N. & BOWMAN, J. R. 1997. Episodic nature of earthquake activity in stable continental regions revealed by palaeoseismicity studies of Australian and North American Quaternary faults. *Australian Journal of Earth Sciences*, **44**, 203–214.

CRONE, A. J., DE MARTINI, P. M., MACHETTE, M. N., OKUMURA, K. & PRESCOTT, J. R. 2003. Palaeoseismicity of two historically quiescent faults in Australia - implications for fault behaviour in stable continental regions. *Bulletin of the Seismological Society of America*, **93**, 1913–1934.

DE BROEKERT, P. & SANDIFORD, M. 2005. Buried inset-valleys in the eastern Yilgarn Craton, Western

Australia: geomorphology, age and allogenic control. *Journal of Geology*, **113**, 471–493.

DENHAM, D., ALEXANDER, L. G. & WOROTNICKI, G. 1979. Stresses in the Australian crust: evidence from earthquakes and in-situ stress measurements. *BMR Journal of Australian Geology and Geophysics*, **4**, 289–295.

DICKINSON, J. A., WALLACE, M. W., HOLDGATE, G. R., DANIELS, J., GALLAGHER, S. J. & THOMAS, L. 2001. Neogene tectonics in SE Australia: implications for petroleum systems. *Australian Petroleum Production and Exploration Association Journal*, **41**, 37–52.

DICKINSON, J. A., WALLACE, M. W., HOLDGATE, G. R., GALLAGHER, S. J. & THOMAS, L. 2002. Origin and timing of the Miocene-Pliocene unconformity in Southeast Australia. *Journal of Sedimentary Research*, **72**, 288–303.

DORÉ, A. G., CARTWRIGHT, J. A., STOKER, M. S., TURNER, J. P. & WHITE, N. J. 2002. Exhumation of the North Atlantic margin: introduction and background. *In*: DORÉ, A. G., CARTWRIGHT, J. A., STOKER, M. S., TURNER, J. P. & WHITE, N. J. (eds) *Exhumation of the North Atlantic Margin: Timing, Mechanisms and Implications for Petroleum Exploration.* Geological Society, London, Special Publications, **196**, 1–12.

DUNCAN, R. A. & VARNE, R. 1988. The age and distribution of the igneous rocks of Macquarie Island. *Papers and Proceedings of the Royal Society of Tasmania* 122, Part 1, 45–50.

GÖLKE, M. & COBLENTZ, D. 1996. Origins of the European regional stress field. *Tectonophysics*, **266**, 11–24.

GREEN, P. F., CROWHURST, P. V. & DUDDY, I. R. 2004. Integration of the AFTA and (U-Th)/He thermochronology to enhance the resolution and precision of thermal history reconstruction in the Anglesea-1 well, Otway Basin, SE Australia. *In*: BOULT, P. J., JOHNS, D. R. & LAND, S. C. (eds) *Eastern Australasian Basins Symposium II*, Petroleum Exploration Society of Australia, Special Publication, South Australia, 117–131.

GURNIS, M., MÜLLER, R. D. & MORESI, L. 1998. Cretaceous vertical motion of Australia and the Australian-Antarctic discordance. *Science*, **279**, 1499–1504.

HARRISON, T. M., COPELAND, P., KIDD, W. & YIN, A. 1992. Raising Tibet. *Science*, **255**, 5052, 1663–1670.

HARROWFIELD, M. & KEEP, M. 2005. Tectonic modification of the Australian North-West Shelf: episodic rejuvenation of long-lived basin division. *Basin Research*, **17**, 225–239.

HEARTY, D. J., ELLIS, G. K. & WEBSTER, K. A. 2002. Geological history of the western Barrow Sub-basin: implications for hydrocarbon entrapment at Woollybutt and surrounding oil and gas fields. *In*: KEEP, M. & MOSS, S. J. (eds) *The Sedimentary Basins of Western Australia 3.* Proceedings of the Petroleum Exploration Society of Australia Symposium, Perth, Western Australia, 2002, 577–598.

HILL, K. & HALL, R. 2003. Mesozoic-Cenozoic evolution of Australia's New Guinea margin in a West Pacific context. Geological Society of America, Special Paper, **372**, 265–290.

HILLIS, R. R. & REYNOLDS, S. D. 2000. The Australian Stress Map. *Journal of the Geological Society of London*, **157**, 915–921.

HILLIS, R. R. & REYNOLDS, S. D. 2003. In situ stress field of Australia. *In*: HILLIS, R. R. & MÜLLER, R. D. (eds) *Evolution and Dynamics of the Australian Plate*. Geological Society of Australia, Special Publication, **22**, 49–58.

HOCKING, R. M. 1988. Regional geology of the northern Carnarvon Basin. *In*: PURCELL, P. G. & PURCELL, R. R. (eds) *North West Shelf Australia*. Proceedings of the Petroleum Exploration Society of Australia Symposium, Perth, Western Australia, 1988, 97–114.

HOLDGATE, G. R., WALLACE, M. W., GALLAGHER, S. J., SMITH, A. J., KEENE, J. B., MOORE, D. & SHAFIK, S. 2003. Plio-Pleistocene tectonics and eustacy in the Gippsland Basin, southeast Australia; evidence from magnetic imagery and marine geological data. *Australian Journal of Earth Sciences*, **50**, 403–426.

JOHNSTON, A. C. 1994. Seismotectonic interpretations and conclusions from the stable continental region seismicity database. *The Earthquakes of Stable Continental Regions*. Electric Power Research Institute, Report TR-102261-1, 4-1-4-102.

KEEP, M., POWELL, C. M. & BAILLIE, P. W. 1998. Neogene Deformation of the North West Shelf, Australia. *In*: PURCELL, P. G. & PURCELL, R. R. (eds) *The Sedimentary Basins of Western Australia 2*. Proceedings of the Petroleum Exploration Society of Australia Symposium, Perth, Western Australia, 1988, 81–91.

KRISHNA, K. S., BULL, J. M. & SCRUTTON, R. A. 2001. Evidence for multiphase folding of the central Indian Ocean lithosphere. *Geology* 29, **8**, 715–718.

LYON, P. J., BOULT, P. J., WATSON, M. & HILLIS, R. R. 2005. A systematic fault seal evaluation of the Ladbroke Grove and Pyrus traps of the Penola Trough, Otway Basin. *Australian Petroleum Production and Exploration Association Journal*, **45**, 459–476.

MALCOLM, R. J., POTT, M. C. & DELFOS, E. 1991. A new tectono-stratigraphic synthesis of the North West Cape area. *Australian Petroleum Exploration Association Journal*, **31**, 154–176.

MASSELL, C., COFFIN, M. F., MANN, P. *ET AL.* 2000. Neotectonics of the Macquarie Ridge Complex, Australia-Pacific plate boundary. *Journal of Geophysical Research, B, Solid Earth and Planets 105*, **6**, 13457–13480.

MCLAREN, S., DUNLAP, W. J., SANDIFORD, M. & MCDOUGALL, I. 2002. Thermochronology of high heat-producing crust at Mount Painter, South Australia: Implications for tectonic reactivation of continental interiors. *Tectonics* 21, doi:10.1029/2000TC001275.

MILDREN, S. D. 1997. *The Contemporary Stress Field of Australia's North West Shelf and Collision Related Tectonism*. Ph.D. thesis, Department of Geology and Geophysics, The University of Adelaide, Australia.

MILDREN, S. D., HILLIS, R. R. & KALDI, J. 2002. Calibrating predictions of fault seal reactivation in the Timor Sea. *Australian Petroleum Production and Exploration Association Journal*, **42**, 187–202.

MÜLLER, R. D., LIM, V. S. L. & ISERN, A. R. 2000. Late Tertiary tectonic subsidence on the northeast

Australian passive margin: response to dynamic topography? *Marine Geology*, **162**, 337–352.

NELSON, A. W. 1989. Jabiru field – Horst, sub-horst or inverted graben? *Australian Petroleum Exploration Association Journal*, **29**, 176–194.

NELSON, E. J. & HILLIS, R. R. 2005. In situ stresses of the West Tuna area, Gippsland Basin. *Australian Journal of Earth Sciences*, **52**, 299–313.

NELSON, E. J., HILLIS, R. R., REYNOLDS, S. D. & MILDREN, S. D. 2006. Present-day state-of-stress of southeast Australia. *Australian Petroleum Production and Exploration Association Journal*, **46**, 283–305.

NEUMANN, N., SANDIFORD, M. & FODEN, J. 2000. Regional geochemistry and continental heat flow: Implications for the origin of the South Australian heat flow anomaly. *Earth and Planetary Science Letters*, **183**, 170–120.

O'BRIEN, G. W. & WOODS, E. P. 1995. Hydrocarbon related diagenetic zones (HRDZs) in the Vulcan Sub-basin, Timor Sea; recognition and exploration implications. *Australian Petroleum Exploration Association Journal*, **35**, 220–252.

O'BRIEN, G. W., MORSE, M., WILSON, D., QUAIFE, P., COLWELL, J., HIGGINS, R. & FOSTER, C. B. 1999. Margin -scale, basement-involved compartmentalisation of Australia's North West Shelf: a primary control in basin-scale rift, depositional and reactivation histories. *Australian Petroleum Production and Exploration Association Journal*, **39**, 40–63.

OLLIER, C. D. 1978. Tectonics and geomorphology of the Eastern Highlands. In: DAVIES, J. L. & WILLIAMS, M. A. (eds) *Landform Evolution in Australia*, ANU Press, 5–47.

PACKHAM, G. 1996. Cenozoic SE Asia; reconstructing its aggregation and reorganization. In: HALL, R. & BLUNDELL, D. J. (eds) *Tectonic Evolution of Southeast Asia*. Geological Society London, Special Publications, **106**, 123–152.

PAN, Y. & KIDD, W. S. F. 1992. Nyainqentanglha shear zone; a late Miocene extensional detachment in the southern Tibetan Plateau. *Geology*, **20**, 9, 775–778.

PETTERSON, M. G., NEAL, C. R., MAHONEY, J. J., KROENKE, L. W., SAUNDERS, A. D., BABBS, T. L., DUNCAN, R. A., TOLIA, D. & McGRAIL, B. 1997. Structure and deformation of north and central Malaita, Solomon Islands; tectonic implications for the Ontong Java Plateau–Solomon arc collision, and for the fate of oceanic plateaus. *Tectonophysics*, **283**, 1–4, 1–33.

POWER, M. R., HILL, K. C. & HOFFMAN, N. 2003. Structural inheritance, stress rotation, overprinting and compressional reactivation in the Gippsland Basin-Tuna 3D seismic dataset. *Australian Petroleum Production and Exploration Association Journal*, **43**, 197–221.

QUIGLEY, M., CUPPER, M. & SANDIFORD, M. 2006. Quaternary faults of southern Australia: palaeoseismicity, slip rates and origin. *Australian Journal of Earth Sciences*, **53**, 285–301.

QUIGLEY, M., SANDIFORD, M., FIFIELD, K. & ALIMANOVIC, A. 2007. Bedrock erosion and relief production in the northern Flinders Ranges, Australia.

Earth Surface Processes and Landforms, **32**, doi: 10.1002/esp.1459.

REYNOLDS, S. D. & HILLIS, R. R. 2000. The in situ stress field of the Perth Basin, Australia. *Geophysical Research Letters*, **27**, 3421–3424.

REYNOLDS, S. D., COBLENTZ, D. & HILLIS, R. R. 2002. Tectonic forces controlling the regional intraplate stress field in continental Australia: results from new finite-element modelling. *Geophysical Research Letters*, **107**(B7).

REYNOLDS, S. D., COBLENTZ, D. & HILLIS, R. R. 2003. Influences of plate-boundary forces on the regional intraplate stress field of continental Australia. In: HILLIS, R. R. & MÜLLER, R. D. (eds) *Evolution and Dynamics of the Australian Plate*. Geological Society of Australia, Special Publication, **22**, 59–70.

REYNOLDS, S. D., MILDREN, S. D., HILLIS, R. R. & MEYER, J. J. 2006. Constraining stress magnitudes using petroleum exploration data in the Cooper-Eromanga Basins, Australia. *Tectonophysics*, **415**, 123–140.

RICHARDSON, R. M. 1992. Ridge forces, absolute plate motions, and the intraplate stress field. *Journal of Geophysical Research*, **97**, 11739–11748.

ROGERS, C., VAN RUTH, P. J. & HILLIS, R. R. 2008. Fault reactivation in the Port Campbell Embayment with respect to carbon dioxide sequestration, Otway Basin, Australia. *Geological Society London, Special Publication*, **306**, 201–214.

SANDIFORD, M. 2003a. Geomorphic constraints on the late Neogene tectonics of the Otway Ranges. *Australian Journal of Earth Sciences*, **50**, 69–80.

SANDIFORD, M. 2003b. Neotectonics of southeastern Australia: linking the Quaternary faulting record with seismicity and in situ stress. In: HILLIS, R. R. & MÜLLER, D. R. (eds) *Evolution and Dynamics of the Australian Plate*. Geological Society of Australia, Special Publication, **22**, 107–119.

SANDIFORD, M., WALLACE, M. W. & COBLENTZ, D. 2004. Origin of the in situ stress field in southeastern Australia. *Basin Research*, **16**, 325–338.

SCHNEIDER, C. L., HILL, K. C. & HOFFMAN, N. 2004. Compressional growth of the Minerva anticline, Otway Basin, Southeast Australia-evidence of oblique rifting. *Australian Petroleum Production and Exploration Association Journal*, **44**, 463–480.

SHARP, N. C. & WOOD, G. R. 2004. Casino Gas Field, offshore Otway Basin, Victoria-the appraisal story and some stratigraphic enlightenment. In: BOULT, P. J., JOHNS, D. R. & LAND, S. C. (eds) *Eastern Australasian Basins Symposium II*, Petroleum Exploration Society of Australia, Special Publication, South Australia, 1–11.

SHUSTER, M. W., EATON, S., WAKEFIELD, L. L. & KOOSTERMAN, H. J. 1998. Neogene tectonics, greater Timor Sea, offshore Australia: implications for trap risk. *Australian Petroleum Production and Exploration Association Journal*, **38**, 351–379.

SUTHERLAND, R. 1996. Transpressional development of the Australia-Pacific boundary through southern South Island, New Zealand; constraints from Miocene-Pliocene sediments, Waiho-1 borehole, South Westland, New Zealand. *Journal of Geology and Geophysics* 39, **2**, 251–264.

TOKAREV, V., SANDIFORD, M. & GOSTIN, V. 1999. Landscape evolution in the Mount Lofty Ranges: implications for regolith development. *In*: TAYLOR, G. & PAIN, C. (eds) *New Approaches to an Old Continent, 3rd Australian Regolith Conference Proceedings, Regolith '98.* Cooperative Research Centre for Landscape Evolution and Mineral Exploration, 127–134.

TRUPP, M. A., SPENCE, K. W. & GIDDING, M. J. 1994. Hydrocarbon prospectivity of the Torquay Sub-basin, offshore Victoria. *Australian Petroleum Exploration Association Journal*, **34**, 479–494.

TURNER, J. P. & WILLIAMS, G. A. 2004. Sedimentary basin inversion and intra-plate shortening. *Earth Science Reviews*, **65**, 277–304.

TWIDALE, C. R. & BOURNE, J. A. 1975. Geomorphological evolution of part of the eastern Mount Lofty Ranges, South Australia. *Transactions of the Royal Society of South Australia*, **99**, 197–210.

TWIDALE, C. R. & BOURNE, J. A. 2004. Neotectonism in Australia: its expressions and implications. *Geomorphologie: relief, processus, environnement*, **3**, 179–194.

VAN DE GRAFF, W. J. E., DENMANN, P. D. & HOCKING, R. M. 1976. Emerged Pleistocene marine terraces on Cape Range, Western Australia. *Geological Survey of Western Australia.* Annual Report for 1975, 62–70.

VAN RUTH, P., HILLIS, R. R. & TINGATE, P. 2004. The origin of overpressure in the Carnarvon Basin, Western Australia: implications for pore pressure prediction. *Petroleum Geoscience*, **10**, 247–257.

VEEVERS, J. J. & POWELL, C. MCA. 1984. Dextral shear within the eastern Indo-Australian plate. *In*: VEEVERS, J. J. (eds) *Phanerozoic Earth History of Australia.* Claredon Press, Oxford, 102–103.

WALCOTT, R. I. 1998. Modes of oblique compression: late Cainozoic tectonics of the South Island of New Zealand. *Reviews of Geophysics* **36**, 1–26.

WESSEL, P. & KROENKE, L. 2000. Ontong Java Plateau and late Neogene changes in Pacific Plate motion. *Journal of Geophysical Research, B, Solid Earth and Planets* **105**, 12, 28, 255–28, 277.

WILLIAMS, A. F. & POYNTON, D. J. 1985. The geology and evolution of the South Pepper hydrocarbon accumulation. *Australian Petroleum Exploration Association Journal*, **25**, 235–247.

WOODS, E. P. 1988. Extensional structures of the Jabiru Terrace, Vulcan Sub-basin. *In*: PURCELL, P. G. & PURCELL, R. R. (eds) *North West Shelf Australia.* Proceedings of the Petroleum Exploration Society of Australia Symposium, Perth, Western Australia, 1988, 311–330.

ZIEGLER, P. A., VAN WEES, J. & CLOETINGH, S. 1998. Mechanical controls on collision related compressional intraplate deformation. *Tectonophysics*, **300**, 103–129.

ZOBACK, M. D., APEL, R., BAUMGÄRTNER, J., *ET AL.* 1993. Upper-crustal strength inferred from stress measurements to 6 km depth in the KTB borehole. *Letters to Nature*, **365**, 633–635.

ZOBACK, M. L. 1992. First- and second-order patterns of stress in the lithosphere: the world stress map project. *Journal of Geophysical Research*, **97**, 11703–11728.

Evidence for kilometre-scale Neogene exhumation driven by compressional deformation in the Irish Sea basin system

SIMON P. HOLFORD[1], PAUL F. GREEN[2], JONATHAN P. TURNER[3],
GARETH A. WILLIAMS[4], RICHARD R. HILLIS[1],
DAVID R. TAPPIN[4] & IAN R. DUDDY[2]

[1]*Australian School of Petroleum, University of Adelaide, Adelaide, South Australia 5005,
Australia (e-mail: simon.holford@adelaide.edu.au)*

[2]*Geotrack International Pty Ltd, 37 Melville Road, West Brunswick, Victoria 3055, Australia*

[3]*School of Geography, Earth & Environmental Sciences, University of Birmingham,
Edgbaston, Birmingham B15 2TT, UK*

[4]*British Geological Survey, Keyworth, Nottingham NG12 5GG, UK*

Abstract: Large tracts of the NW European continental shelf and Atlantic margin have experienced kilometre-scale exhumation during the Cenozoic, the timing and causes of which are debated. There is particular uncertainty about the exhumation history of the Irish Sea basin system, Western UK, which has been suggested to be a focal point of Cenozoic exhumation across the NW European continental shelf. Many studies have attributed the exhumation of this region to processes associated with the early Palaeogene initiation of the Iceland Plume, whilst the magnitude and causes of Neogene exhumation have attracted little attention. However, the sedimentary basins of the southern Irish Sea contain a mid–late Cenozoic sedimentary succession up to 1.5 km in thickness, the analysis of which should permit the contributions of Palaeogene and Neogene events to the Cenozoic exhumation of this region to be separated. In this paper, an analysis of the palaeothermal, mechanical and structural properties of the Cenozoic succession is presented with the aim of quantifying the timing and magnitude of Neogene exhumation, and identifying its ultimate causes. Synthesis of an extensive apatite fission-track analysis (AFTA), vitrinite reflectance (VR) and compaction (sonic velocity and density log-derived porosities) database shows that the preserved Cenozoic sediments in the southern Irish Sea were more deeply buried by up to 1.5 km of additional section prior to exhumation which began between 20 and 15 Ma. Maximum burial depths of the preserved sedimentary succession in the St George's Channel Basin were reached during mid–late Cenozoic times meaning that no evidence for early Palaeogene exhumation is preserved whereas AFTA data from the Mochras borehole (onshore NW Wales) show that early Palaeogene cooling (i.e. exhumation) at this location was not significant. Seismic reflection data indicate that compressional shortening was the principal driving mechanism for the Neogene exhumation of the southern Irish Sea. Coeval Neogene shortening and exhumation is observed in several sedimentary basins around the British Isles, including those along the UK Atlantic margin. This suggests that the forces responsible for the deformation and exhumation of the margin may also be responsible for the generation of kilometre-scale exhumation in an intraplate sedimentary basin system located >1000 km from the most proximal plate boundary. The results presented here show that compressional deformation has made an important contribution to the Neogene exhumation of the NW European continental shelf.

The NE Atlantic margin and large portions of the surrounding continental hinterlands have experienced substantial uplift and erosion (exhumation) during the Neogene which has profoundly influenced the distribution and morphology of the present-day landmasses (Doré *et al.* 1999) and exerted a critical control on prospectivity in many petroliferous sedimentary basins across this region (Doré *et al.* 2002a). At present the exact causes of this exhumation are poorly constrained (e.g. Rohrman & van der Beek 1996; Stuevold &

Eldholm 1996; Japsen & Chalmers 2000; Doré *et al.* 2002b; Japsen *et al.* 2005, 2006; Praeg *et al.* 2005). Suggested tectonic causes of this exhumation are varied, and include compressional deformation induced by Atlantic ridge-push and Alpine collisional forces (Cloetingh *et al.* 1990; Lundin & Doré 2002), lithospheric flexure (Redfield *et al.* 2005), and dynamic uplift supported by the Iceland mantle plume (Mackay *et al.* 2005), asthenospheric diapirism (Rohrman & van der Beek 1996) or evolving patterns of mantle

From: JOHNSON, H., DORÉ, A. G., GATLIFF, R. W., HOLDSWORTH, R., LUNDIN, E. R. & RITCHIE, J. D. (eds)
The Nature and Origin of Compression in Passive Margins. Geological Society, London, Special Publications,
306, 91–119. DOI: 10.1144/SP306.4   0305-8719/08/$15.00 © The Geological Society of London 2008.

convection following continental breakup (Praeg *et al.* 2005). A significant problem in determining the origin of the uplift lies in separating the effects of Neogene exhumation from those of earlier events, in the late Mesozoic and Palaeogene (Japsen & Chalmers 2000; Japsen *et al.* 2005; Holford *et al.* 2005a).

In recent years, considerable attention has been paid to the late Mesozoic–Cenozoic uplift and exhumation histories of the British Isles (Roberts 1989; Lewis *et al.* 1992; Brodie & White 1994; Cope 1994; Hillis 1995; Japsen 1997; White & Lovell 1997; Rowley & White 1998; Green *et al.* 2002; Ware & Turner 2002; Bott & Bott 2004; Holford *et al.* 2005b). A great deal of this discussion has been presented in terms of Palaeogene uplift, which has been assumed to represent the dominant exhumation episode. Consequently, the magnitude and timing of late Cenozoic/Neogene exhumation across this region is poorly resolved (Praeg *et al.* 2005; Stoker *et al.* 2005). This imbalance is typified by studies of the exhumation history of the Irish Sea basin system. Numerous workers have cited this suite of intraplate sedimentary basins as the locus of Cenozoic exhumation across the British Isles, and indeed, the NW European continental shelf (Lewis *et al.* 1992; Chadwick *et al.* 1994; Brodie & White 1995; White & Lovell 1997; Jones *et al.* 2002). Many workers have suggested that the main phase of exhumation in the Irish Sea occurred during early Palaeogene times, with the uplift caused by the isostatic response to magmatic underplating of the lower crust, associated with the initiation of the Iceland Plume (Brodie & White 1994; White & Lovell 1997; Rowley & White 1998; Al-Kindi *et al.* 2003; Tiley *et al.* 2004). Much of this research has focused on the East Irish Sea Basin (EISB), where early applications of apatite fission-track analysis (AFTA®) revealed that samples close to the seabed today had resided at elevated palaeotemperatures in excess of 100 °C prior to early Palaeogene (65–60 Ma) cooling. This cooling was interpreted in terms of the removal of a thick (up to 3 km) cover of Mesozoic sediments (Lewis *et al.* 1992). Subsequent work in this basin, aided by both a substantially enlarged dataset and methodological advances, has demonstrated the importance of advective fluid-related heating and periods of elevated basal heat flow, implying that the elevated palaeotemperatures recorded by AFTA cannot be interpreted in terms of heating due solely to deeper burial (Green *et al.* 1997; Green 2002; Holford *et al.* 2005a). Since the youngest pre-Quaternary sediments in the EISB are Lower Jurassic in age (Jackson & Mulholland 1993) minimal stratigraphic constraints can be placed upon the timing and magnitude of late Mesozoic–Cenozoic exhumation; the

top Mesozoic unconformity in this basin is in all likelihood a composite feature which records at least three separate pulses of uplift and erosion (Holford 2006).

Given the existence of a thick sequence of Cenozoic sedimentary rocks in the basins of the southern Irish Sea, it is perhaps surprising that relatively few studies have exploited this in order to provide insights into the exhumation history of the wider region. The Cardigan Bay Basin (CBB) contains *c.* 0.5 km of Oligocene–Miocene sediments, whereas a *c.* 1.5 km thick succession of Eocene–Oligocene sediments can be found in the contiguous St George's Channel Basin (SGCB) (Tappin *et al.* 1994) (Fig. 1). The analysis of the burial and exhumation history of these Cenozoic sediments should permit the effects of late Cenozoic exhumation to be separated from those of earlier events. The principal aims of this paper, therefore, are to assess whether the Cenozoic sedimentary succession in the southern Irish Sea has been more deeply buried in the past, and if so, to determine when the exhumation occurred and what its underlying causes were. A diverse range of techniques have been employed to address these issues. Palaeothermal (AFTA and vitrinite reflectance (VR)) and compaction (sonic velocity and density log-derived porosities) data are used to quantify the amounts by which the Cenozoic (and underlying Mesozoic) rocks of the CBB and SGCB have been more deeply buried prior to exhumation. AFTA data combined with stratigraphical constraints have been used to determine the timing of exhumation (cf. Green *et al.* 2002). Finally, a dense grid of high resolution, well-calibrated 2D seismic reflection data is used to assess the structural properties of the Cenozoic fill of the SGCB.

Our investigations reveal that the preserved Cenozoic rocks in the southern Irish Sea have been more deeply buried by up to 1–1.5 km of additional sedimentary section, prior to exhumation which began between 25 and 15 Ma (based on a regional synthesis of AFTA data). Seismic reflection data show that the principal cause of this exhumation episode was the compressional shortening and resultant thickening and uplift of the Cenozoic sedimentary fill of these basins. Given that this compression and exhumation is coeval with intense Neogene compressional deformation observed along the Atlantic margin and in the Alpine foreland, it is likely to be a function of compressional stresses generated by both Atlantic ridge-push and Alpine lithospheric shortening. This paper therefore provides a good example of kilometre-scale exhumation across a continental interior setting which can, at least in part, be attributed to plate boundary forces.

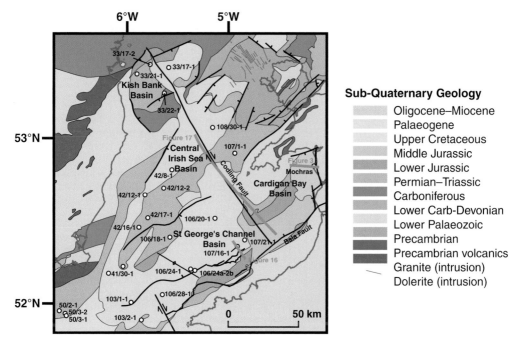

Fig. 1. Pre-Pleistocene solid geology of the southern Irish Sea basin system. Map courtesy of the British Geological Survey.

The Mesozoic–Cenozoic geological record in the southern Irish Sea

The Irish Sea basin system comprises a suite of mostly offshore extensional sedimentary basins which was initiated during the Permian–Triassic (Coward 1995), largely exploiting pre-existing Precambrian, Caledonian and Variscan structural trends (Tappin *et al.* 1994; Welch & Turner 2000). Interspersed periods of rifting, thermal subsidence and uplift have resulted in a variable post-Palaeozoic stratigraphic record across this region (Tappin *et al.* 1994). In this paper, the southern Irish Sea basin system refers to the en-echelon CBB and SGCB (Fig. 1). These basins are flanked by the neighbouring Central Irish Sea Basin to the NW, the burial and exhumation of which has previously been studied in detail by Duncan *et al.* (1998) and Green *et al.* (2001*a*).

Although the principal concern of this contribution is the Cenozoic sedimentary succession preserved in the southern Irish Sea area, the CBB and SGCB also contain considerable thicknesses of Mesozoic sediments. The Mochras borehole, which penetrated the sedimentary fill of the CBB, encountered the thickest known sequence of Lower Jurassic sediments in the British Isles at 1305 m (Woodland 1971; Hallam 1992). The

contiguous SGCB contains an even thicker Jurassic succession, with seismic reflection data indicating that greater than 5 km of Jurassic rocks, and possibly even Lower Cretaceous deposits, are preserved in the deepest parts of the basin (Tappin *et al.* 1994; Welch & Turner 2000). This is in marked contrast to the stratigraphy of the more northerly EISB where, with the exception of several Lower Jurassic outliers, the youngest preserved pre-Quaternary rocks are generally Late Triassic (Mercia Mudstone Group) in age (Jackson *et al.* 1995).

The Mesozoic rocks of the CBB and SGCB are overlain, commonly with marked unconformity, by Cenozoic sediments which attain a thickness of 0.52 km in the CBB at Mochras, and locally exceed 1.5 km in the SGCB (Tappin *et al.* 1994; Williams *et al.* 2005). The Cenozoic succession at Mochras comprises interbedded mudstones and siltstones with subordinate lignites and several thick conglomeratic units towards the base (Fig. 2) (Woodland 1971; O'Sullivan 1979), and has been assigned a middle Oligocene to lower Miocene age by Herbert-Smith (1979) on the basis of palynological data. The Cenozoic sediments of the SGCB are penetrated by four wells which encountered Eocene–Oligocene sands, silts, clays and lignites that show a marked similarity to those samples in the Mochras borehole (Tappin *et al.* 1994). The

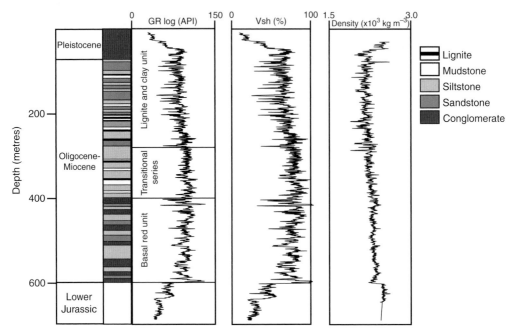

Fig. 2. Log of the Cenozoic sediments in the Mochras borehole, after Tappin *et al.* (1994). The lithostratigraphical units were erected by O'Sullivan (1979) on the basis of sonic, density and gamma ray logs, where breaks occur at depths of 280 and 405 m.

sediments from both basins are indicative of deposition in non-marine, alluvial-dominated environments (Dobson & Whittington 1987; Tappin *et al.* 1994). In terms of its relation to regional fault systems, Williams *et al.* (2005) interpreted the SGCB as a large transtensional basin located at a releasing stepover on a major NW–SE trending Mesozoic–Cenozoic strike-slip fault system

comprising the Codling and Sticklepath Faults. Dextral displacements along this fault system also led to the formation of Eocene–Oligocene transtensional basins containing similar deposits in SW England, Central Irish Sea Basin and Northern Ireland (Izatt *et al.* 2001; Cunningham *et al.* 2004; Ziegler 2004). In the southern Irish Sea, the transfer of displacement between the Sticklepath and

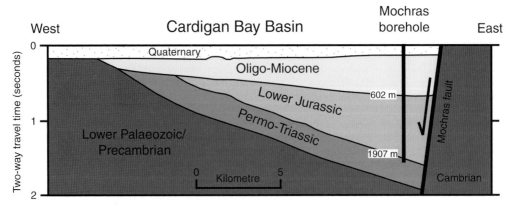

Fig. 3. Approximately east–west trending cross-section through the Cardigan Bay Basin based on the interpretation of a BGS seismic reflection profile, extended to the Mochras Fault. Modified after Tappin *et al.* (1994).

Codling faults was accommodated by normal movements along the Mochras–St George's Channel–Bala fault system (Turner 1997; Holford et al. 2005b; Williams et al. 2005). The CBB has the form of a southeasterly deepening half-graben downfaulted against the Lower Palaeozoic Welsh Massif following normal displacements along the Mochras Fault (Tappin et al. 1994) (Fig. 3).

The provenance of the Cenozoic deposits of the southern Irish Sea is uncertain. Lower Palaeozoic clasts are found in the base of the Mochras borehole (Tappin et al. 1994), although these may record more local footwall uplift and erosion in NW Wales rather than more regional uplift and exhumation across Wales (Holford et al. 2005a; Holford 2006). Fission-track studies in northern England demonstrate considerable exhumation across this region which began between 65 and 55 Ma (Green 2002, 2005). The proposal by Dobson & Whittington (1987) that the Cenozoic sediments of the southern Irish Sea were deposited on the floodplain of a highly sinuous southwesterly flowing river system is consistent with the suggestion of a northeasterly sediment source.

Methods used to reconstruct magnitudes and timing of exhumation

Most techniques available for the estimation of exhumation in sedimentary basins utilise 'point' measurements (i.e. local estimates for an individual well or borehole) of vertical rock displacement relative to a specified frame of reference (Corcoran & Doré 2005). In this study the main frames of reference used to estimate exhumation are thermal (e.g. apatite fission-track analysis and vitrinite reflectance and compactional (e.g. formation density and sonic velocity from wireline log data).

Compaction-driven porosity reduction is an effective and widely used measure of former burial depths in sedimentary basins (Hillis 1991, 1995; Japsen 2000; Ware & Turner 2002). The term compaction refers to the three-dimensional reduction in sediment volume which occurs as a result of mechanical and thermochemical processes during burial (Giles et al. 1998; Corcoran & Doré 2005). Compaction is generally expressed by the reduction of porosity with burial depth, although it is important to note that porosity reduction can also be caused by increases in solid volume (i.e. by cementation) in addition to volume strains (Giles et al. 1998). In order to estimate the magnitude of exhumation at a well or borehole using compaction data, it is first necessary to establish a reference porosity–depth curve (i.e. one in which the entire succession is presently at its maximum

burial depth, and pressure is hydrostatic (Japsen et al. 2002)). This is usually constructed from 'normally buried', unexhumed parts of a basin, or if the entire basin has been affected by exhumation, then a reference trend from a different, unexhumed basin can be used, as long as the reference trend has been constructed for a sufficiently similar lithology (Corcoran & Doré 2005). Sedimentary successions in exhumed basins will exhibit anomalously low porosities with respect to their present-day burial depth.

Studies of maximum burial depths conducted in the thermal reference frame exploit the progressive increase of temperature with depth within the lithosphere. Sedimentary units are progressively heated during burial and begin to cool at the initiation of exhumation (Green et al. 2002). AFTA and VR provide quantitative constraints upon the temperatures attained by a rock sample at a palaeothermal maximum, prior to the onset of cooling (Green et al. 2002). The analysis of AFTA and VR samples over a range of depths in an exploration well or borehole reveals the variation of maximum palaeotemperature with depth. The form of the palaeotemperature profile characterizing a particular palaeothermal episode can provide vital information on the likely mechanisms of heating and cooling; heating caused solely by deeper burial should result in an approximately linear palaeotemperature profile with a similar value to the present-day geothermal gradient (e.g. Duddy et al. 1994; Green et al. 2002). The extrapolation of a fitted palaeogeothermal gradient, above an appropriate unconformity and to an assumed palaeosurface temperature, provides an estimate of the amount by which the rock succession preserved beneath that unconformity was more deeply buried prior to exhumation. Using maximum likelihood theory, the ranges of values for both the palaeogeothermal gradient and thickness of additional sedimentary section which are consistent with the measured palaeotemperature constraints can be defined within 95% confidence limits (Bray et al. 1992).

Of the multitude of techniques available for reconstructing the exhumation histories of sedimentary basins (e.g. Corcoran & Doré 2005), AFTA is perhaps the most useful because it can provide an independent estimate of the time at which a rock sample began to cool from its maximum palaeotemperature, or a subsequent palaeotemperature peak. If the cooling can be attributed to exhumation AFTA can consequently be used to constrain the timing of the onset of exhumation (Green et al. 2002). Since AFTA only provides information on the temperature–time history of a rock sample below a critical temperature limit of $>110–120\,°C$ (i.e. the temperature at which at which all tracks are 'totally annealed' such that track lengths are reduced to zero) (Green *et al.* 1986, 2002), AFTA data are especially useful in conjunction with VR data which allows estimation of higher maximum palaeotemperatures (Duddy *et al.* 1994). Given that the key aspects of the thermal history which control the development of the AFTA parameters (i.e. the track length distribution and fission-track age) are the maximum palaeotemperature of the sample, and the time at which cooling from that temperature began, the approach adopted in this study focuses on constraining these key parameters, rather than attempting to constrain the entire thermal history of each apatite sample (Green *et al.* 2002). Wherever possible, AFTA data from each sample have been interpreted in terms of two or three episodes of heating and cooling, using assumed heating and cooling rates. Our modelling approach also makes full quantitative allowance for the important effects of chlorine content on the annealing kinetics of fission tracks in apatite (Green *et al.* 1986, 2005). Full descriptions of the analytical and interpretative procedures by which thermal history solutions are derived from AFTA and VR data are provided by Green *et al.* (2001*b*, 2002).

All techniques available for the estimation of exhumation in sedimentary basins are subject to various uncertainties (Corcoran & Doré 2005). These are magnified in regions such as the Irish Sea basin system which have experienced complex geological histories characterized by repeated cycles of burial and exhumation (Green *et al.* 2002; Holford *et al.* 2005*b*). The diverse approach adopted in this study combines both palaeothermal and compactional proxies to reconstruct former burial depths and when integrated with seismic data, has the advantage of improving the precision of estimates of the timing and magnitude of exhumation. If the estimates from the independent techniques show a high degree of consistency, this serves to validate the use of methods such as AFTA, VR and compaction analyses as valuable tools for reconstructing the burial and exhumation histories of sedimentary basins.

Mesozoic–Cenozoic burial and exhumation at Mochras, Cardigan Bay Basin

In this section, palaeothermal (AFTA and VR) and compaction (density log-derived porosities) data are used to estimate the amounts by which the preserved Lower Jurassic and Oligocene–Miocene successions penetrated by the Mochras borehole in the Cardigan Bay Basin have been more deeply buried prior to exhumation, whilst AFTA and stratigraphic observations are used to constrain the

timing of exhumation at this location. The Mochras borehole is located only *c.* 50 km to the SW of the deeply eroded EISB, where post-Triassic sediments are largely absent, such that the preserved stratigraphic record cannot be used to constrain the timing and separate the effects of late Mesozoic–Cenozoic exhumation. Many studies have assumed that the main phase of exhumation to have affected the EISB and NW Wales began during early Palaeogene times (e.g. Brodie & White 1994; Cope 1994; Rowley & White 1998). The preservation of a thick Lower Jurassic (*c.* 1.3 km) and Cenozoic (*c.* 0.52 km) sedimentary record at Mochras should provide valuable insights into the exhumation history of the wider region by enabling the effects of Neogene exhumation to be separated from those of earlier events. A more complete analysis of the Mesozoic–Cenozoic burial and exhumation history of the Mochras borehole is presented in Holford *et al.* (2005*a*).

A palaeothermal dataset comprising four AFTA samples and 24 VR samples was first used to constrain the thermal history of the Mochras borehole. Of the AFTA samples analysed, the most precise thermal history solution was provided by the deepest sample, GC399-13, obtained from a suite of Triassic sandstones (deposited between 220–205 Ma; Woodland 1971) located near the base of the borehole (1910–1931 m). This AFTA sample yielded a pooled fission-track age (indicating that the apatite grains all come from a single age population; Galbraith & Laslett 1993) of 108.0 ± 9.4 Ma (Holford *et al.* 2005*a*). The present-day temperature at this depth (*c.* 55 °C) (Holford *et al.* 2005*a*) is below the temperature range over which most annealing of fission-tracks occurs (*c.* 60–120 °C; Green *et al.* 1986), and hence the fission-track age of sample GC399-13 is immediately diagnostic of cooling from maximum palaeotemperatures at some time during the late Mesozoic. In order to extract more detailed thermal history information from an AFTA sample, measured track length distributions and fission-track ages are compared against the track length distributions and fission-track ages predicted for a range of thermal history scenarios, using a kinetic annealing model that makes full quantitative allowance for the influence of chlorine content on annealing rates (e.g. Green *et al.* 2002). This process is illustrated in Figure 4 for sample GC399-13. The best fit to the measured data is clearly provided by a thermal history solution involving two discrete episodes of heating and cooling. An early Cretaceous episode accounts for the reduction of fission-track age in apatites containing <0.2 wt% Cl and the proportion of short lengths within the overall track length distribution whilst a Cenozoic episode is also required to explain the

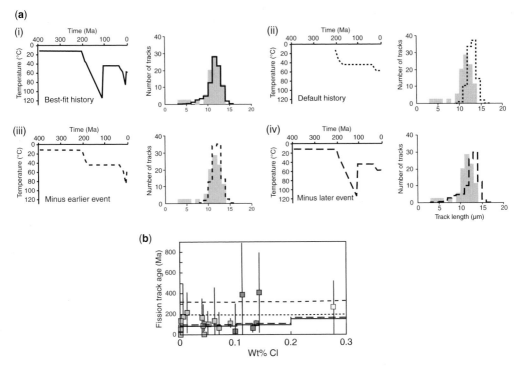

Fig. 4. Process involved with extracting a thermal history solution from AFTA data for Mochras sample GC399-13. Four separate thermal history scenarios are shown (**a**) and for each, the predicted track length distribution is compared with the observed track length distribution. Corresponding predicted trends of fission track age vs. wt% Cl are compared with measured data in (**b**) Four modelled scenarios are shown (i) Maximum palaeotemperature attained prior to early Cretaceous cooling, with additional cooling from a subsequent but lower palaeotemperature peak during the Neogene (best-fit scenario). (ii) Default thermal history, which is constructed using the preserved stratigraphy recorded in the borehole, assuming that all stratigraphic breaks represent hiatuses (i.e. no deposition or erosion). A thermal history is then derived by assuming that the present geothermal gradient has remained constant through time since the deposition of the oldest sediments. (iii) Maximum palaeotemperatures reached prior to Neogene cooling, with no early Cretaceous episode. (iv) Maximum palaeotemperatures reached prior to early Cretaceous cooling, with no Neogene event. The thermal history solution involving an early Cretaceous maximum and a lower Neogene peak clearly provides the best fit to the measured track length distribution and the variation of fission track age vs. wt% Cl. Scenarios involving only one phase of cooling and which omit either the early or late cooling events cannot adequately explain all facets of the fission-track length and age data.

shortening of the main mode in the track length distribution (Fig. 4). If either of these episodes is omitted, the predictions may fail to match one or more facets of the basic AFTA parameters (Fig. 4).

A more detailed temperature–time history for sample GC399-13 is shown in Figure 5. Best estimates of maximum palaeotemperature and time of cooling for each AFTA sample analysed in this study have been obtained using maximum likelihood theory similar to the method described by Gallagher (1995). The systematic variation of both the timing of the onset of cooling and the peak palaeotemperature around the best fit values allows the range of conditions for which the modelled parameters are consistent with the measured data within 95% confidence limits to be defined.

Following deposition around 220 Ma, sample GC399-13 was heated during burial to a maximum palaeotemperature of 105–110 °C. This compares well with palaeotemperatures estimated from VR samples (102–104 °C) at slightly shallower depths (Fig. 6), especially considering a usual precision of 5–10 °C on VR-derived palaeotemperatures (Duddy et al. 1994). Cooling from this palaeotemperature peak began at some time between 150 and 80 Ma. A recent synthesis of all available AFTA data from the Irish Sea basin system and the marginal landmasses has identified a regionally extensive early Cretaceous (120–115 Ma) cooling episode which is interpreted as recording a kilometre-scale exhumation event which is also supported by many geological

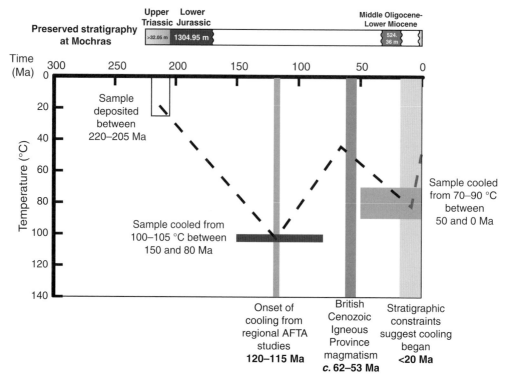

Fig. 5. Schematic illustration of the preferred thermal history interpretation for AFTA sample GC399-13. Rectangular boxes represent estimates of timing and temperatures of palaeothermal episodes within ±95% confidence limits. Estimate of timing of early Cretaceous exhumation episode based on regional AFTA dataset reported in Holford (2006). Timing of magmatic activity related to the British Cenozoic Igneous Province based on Mussett *et al.* (1988). Mochras stratigraphy based on Woodland (1971) and Tappin *et al.* (1994).

observations (Holford 2006). The early cooling episode recorded by AFTA data at Mochras is thus attributed to early Cretaceous exhumation. The later palaeothermal episode recorded by GC399-13 involves cooling from a lower palaeotemperature peak of between 70–90 °C beginning between 50 and 0 Ma. The heating prior to this cooling episode most likely occurred during Cenozoic burial, and the fact that lower Miocene sediments have been identified at Mochras (Herbert-Smith 1979) means that this second cooling episode probably began during the post-early Miocene (e.g. <20 Ma). The timing of magmatic activity associated with the British Palaeogene Igneous Province (*c.* 63–52 Ma; Mussett *et al.* 1988) is indicated in Figure 5 in order to highlight the fact that this sample does not require any early Palaeogene palaeothermal effects in order to explain the measured AFTA parameters. This is a surprising result given the proximity of Mochras to the EISB, which has been highlighted as a focus of both substantial early Palaeogene

exhumation and palaeothermal activity (e.g. Green *et al.* 1997; Rowley & White 1998; Holford *et al.* 2005b).

In Figure 6, all available AFTA and VR palaeotemperature constraints for the Mochras borehole have been plotted against depth and assigned either to the early Cretaceous or Neogene cooling episodes identified and discussed above. Some of the VR data from the Lower Jurassic succession are affected by geochemical suppression (Holford *et al.* 2005a), but palaeotemperatures from the non-suppressed Lower Jurassic VR data are generally consistent with the Cretaceous palaeotemperatures from AFTA (Fig. 6). In combination, the early Cretaceous palaeotemperature constraints from AFTA and VR appear to define a sub-linear profile that is approximately parallel to the present-day geothermal gradient (which has a value of 23.4 °C km^{-1}) (Fig. 6). Fitting a linear profile to the early Cretaceous palaeotemperature provides an estimate of the early Cretaceous palaeogeothermal gradient (Fig. 7a). This has a maximum

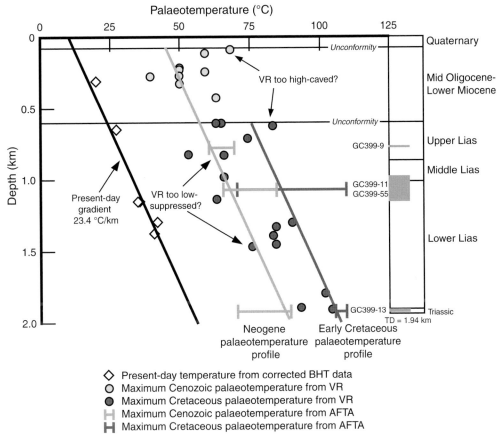

Fig. 6. Palaeotemperature constraints from AFTA and VR data from the Mochras borehole plotted against depth. These are used to infer palaeotemperature profiles prior to Neogene and early Cretaceous cooling episodes, whilst corrected BHT data are used to define the present-day geothermal gradient. A simplified stratigraphic column is also shown. Full details of AFTA and VR data from the Mochras borehole are presented in Holford *et al.* (2005*a*).

likelihood value of $21\,°C\,km^{-1}$ (Fig. 7a). The extrapolation of this palaeotemperature profile to an assumed early Cretaceous palaeosurface temperature of $20\,°C$ (based on palaeoclimatic evidence presented in Yalçin *et al.* 1997) indicates that the Lower Jurassic succession was more deeply buried by 2.55 km prior to early Cretaceous exhumation. Assuming that the early Cretaceous palaeogeothermal gradient was equivalent to the present-day gradient reduces the amount of Middle Jurassic–Lower Cretaceous section required to explain the early Cretaceous palaeotemperatures to between 1.94 and 2.49 km (Fig. 7a). These estimates are in good agreement with the results of Kemp *et al.* (2005), who on the basis of clay mineral assemblages suggested that the

deepest parts of the Lower Jurassic succession at Mochras had been buried to depths of *c*. 3 km. This estimate was based upon an assumed palaeogeothermal gradient of $30\,°C\,km^{-1}$. Since AFTA and VR data indicate that palaeogeothermal gradients at Mochras were equal to or less than the value of the present-day gradient (*c*. $23.4\,°C\,km^{-1}$), the smectite–illite data of Kemp *et al.* (2005) can be reinterpreted as supporting burial depths exceeding 3.5 km.

Palaeotemperatures from Cenozoic VR samples, when combined with constraints on Cenozoic palaeotemperatures from the Jurassic AFTA samples, also define a palaeogeothermal gradient which is sub-parallel with the present-day geothermal gradient. This Cenozoic palaeogeothermal

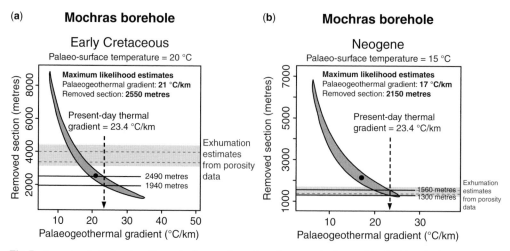

Fig. 7. Amounts of additional section and palaeogeothermal gradients required to explain the (**a**) early Cretaceous and (**b**) Neogene palaeothermal episodes recorded by AFTA and VR data from Mochras. Shaded region defines the allowed range of values for each parameter that are consistent with the measured palaeotemperature constraints within 95% confidence limits. Black dots represent the maximum likelihood estimates. The magnitude of removed section for each episode consistent with a palaeogeothermal gradient with a similar value to the present-day gradient (23.4 $^{\circ}$C km^{-1}) is indicated. Shaded horizontal bars indicate the range of exhumation estimates for each episode as calculated from porosity data (see Fig. 8).

gradient has a maximum likelihood value of 17 $^{\circ}$C km^{-1} (Fig. 7b). Extrapolating these palaeo-temperature profiles to an assumed palaeosurface temperature of 15 $^{\circ}$C indicates that the preserved Oligocene–Miocene section at Mochras was more deeply buried by 2.15 km of additional section prior to the second phase of exhumation recorded by AFTA. If the value of the palaeogeothermal gradient was equivalent to that of the present-day geotherm, this implies that between 1.3–1.56 km of additional post-early Miocene sediments were deposited at Mochras prior to exhumation (Fig. 7b).

In order to corroborate these estimates of deeper burial based on palaeotemperature data, the formation density log acquired at Mochras (Woodland 1971) has been used to evaluate the variation of porosity with depth within the preserved sediments. The calculated porosities from the fine-grained units within Jurassic and Cenozoic successions have then been compared with Sclater & Christie's (1980) compaction trend for Central Graben (North Sea) shales; the vertical (i.e. depth) displacement of the observed porosities from the normal, unexhumed trend gives a measure of apparent exhumation (E_A) (i.e. exhumation which is not subsequently reversed by burial) (Hillis 1995; Corcoran & Doré 2005). The evidence from AFTA and VR data, which indicate that geothermal gradients at Mochras have remained at consistently low values (<23.4 $^{\circ}$C km^{-1}) over time suggests that the effects related to thermochemical

compaction (which generally occurs at temperatures exceeding 80 $^{\circ}$C; Bjørkum *et al.* 2001) are probably unimportant at Mochras, and hence mechanical compaction during burial is likely to exert the principal control on porosity reduction. Further details of the methodology employed in the analysis of compaction data from Mochras are provided by Holford *et al.* (2005*a*).

Densities and calculated porosities for the Mochras borehole are shown in Figure 8. Within the Oligocene–Miocene succession, calculated porosities decrease from *c.* 30–32% at depths of around 100 m to *c.* 20–22% at the base of the Oligocene (*c.* 600 m). Comparing these calculated porosities with the Sclater & Christie (1980) compaction trend for North Sea shales yields apparent exhumation estimates of 1.32–1.48 km for the Oligocene–Miocene succession. In order to determine magnitudes of total exhumation (E_T) it is necessary to add the amount of post-exhumation burial (B_E) to E_A. Thus, accounting for the 77.47 m of Quaternary sediments encountered at Mochras, this indicates that the preserved Oligocene–Miocene succession has been more deeply buried by 1.39–1.56 km prior to exhumation. Compaction data from the Lower Jurassic succession yield estimates of 2.75–3.44 for E_A. Correcting for the 601.83 m of Cenozoic sediments yields E_T estimates of 3.35–4.04 km. The estimates of the amounts by which the Cenozoic and Lower Jurassic successions were more deeply buried prior to exhumation from both compaction and palaeothermal data are compared in Figure 7. For both exhumation episodes the amounts of deeper burial indicated by the compaction data are well within the ranges of values allowed by AFTA and VR. In particular, the estimates of deeper burial prior to the Neogene exhumation episode from the compaction data (1.39–1.56 km) are in excellent agreement with those from AFTA and VR if it is assumed that the palaeogeothermal gradient was equivalent to the present-day gradient (1.3–1.56 km) (Fig. 7).

The quantitative constraints on former burial depths from palaeothermal and compaction data, in combination with the preserved stratigraphy encountered by the borehole, have been used to reconstruct the post-Triassic burial history of Mochras. Two end-member burial history reconstructions are presented in Figure 9. These burial histories are identical in most respects, with the main difference between them being the amount of burial and exhumation during late Cretaceous–early Palaeogene times. Both histories assume a constant geothermal gradient throughout time (23.4 °C km^{-1}) and incorporate 2.5 km of additional post-Lower Jurassic sediments which are completely removed during early Cretaceous (120–115 Ma) exhumation. Model 1 incorporates no burial or exhumation during the late Cretaceous–early Palaeogene; on the basis of regional geological evidence (e.g. widespread deposition of Upper Cretaceous Chalk (Ziegler 1990), AFTA results suggesting early Palaeogene exhumation across northern England (Green 2002)) this scenario is unlikely. Model 2 includes 0.8 km of late Cretaceous burial, with these sediments completely removed by exhumation beginning at 60 Ma. Assuming a constant geothermal gradient of 23.4 °C km^{-1} throughout the modelled history and an early Palaeogene surface temperature of 20 °C, 0.8 km is the maximum amount of late Cretaceous burial allowed by AFTA sample GC399-13 (Fig. 5). Thermal history modelling of this sample indicates that it cooled from a palaeotemperature peak of between 70–90 °C at some point between 50 and 0 Ma (Fig. 5). This suggests that this sample was not exposed to temperatures in excess of 70 °C during early Palaeogene times (i.e. before 50 Ma); under the modelled scenario therefore, 0.8 km is the maximum amount of late Cretaceous burial/early Palaeogene exhumation that could have occurred at Mochras without affecting the measured AFTA parameters. This figure is much lower than previous estimates of the magnitude of early Palaeogene exhumation across NW Wales and the adjacent EISB, which suggested exhumation of up to 2.5 km (e.g. Cope 1994; Rowley & White 1998).

To summarize, the synthesis of palaeothermal and compaction data from the Mochras borehole reveals evidence for two major cycles of burial and exhumation during the Mesozoic–Cenozoic. AFTA, VR and compaction data show that the preserved 1.3 km thick Lower Jurassic succession has been more deeply buried by up to 2.5 km prior to Cretaceous exhumation; comparison with regional AFTA results (Holford et al. 2005b; Holford 2006) suggests that this exhumation began during the early Cretaceous (120–115 Ma). Following this major exhumation episode, AFTA data from Mochras allow a maximum of 0.8 km of late Cretaceous burial/early Palaeogene exhumation. This value is much lower than many other estimates of early Palaeogene exhumation in the Irish Sea basin system (e.g. Cope 1994; Rowley & White 1998), and is suggestive of major heterogeneities in early Palaeogene exhumation patterns across this region. Palaeothermal and compaction data show that the main phase of Cenozoic exhumation in this part of the Irish Sea basin system occurred during the Neogene.

The discovery of a c. 520 m thick Oligocene–Miocene sedimentary succession by the drilling of Mochras in the late 1960s was, at the time, a surprising result (Woodland 1971) because mid–late Cenozoic rocks are rarely preserved in the British Isles (Curry 1992). However, the analysis of the palaeothermal and mechanical properties of the Oligocene–Lower Miocene deposits indicates that they have in fact been more deeply buried by up to 1.5 km of post-lower Miocene sediments, which were eroded prior to the deposition of a thin veneer of Quaternary sediments in the CBB. The recognition of this major late Cenozoic episode has profound implications, not only for the relative importance of Palaeogene and Neogene events in the Cenozoic exhumation of the Irish Sea basin system, but also for the mid–late Cenozoic palaeogeography of the Western UKCS. Assessing the cause of the significant Neogene exhumation episode in the CBB is difficult; its fill has been penetrated by only one borehole (Mochras), and due to the relative lack of hydrocarbon exploration few seismic reflection data are available for this basin. In contrast, the en-echelon SGCB which also contains thick sequences of mid-Cenozoic deposits, has experienced a long history of exploration (e.g. Barr et al. 1981). A number of exploration wells have been drilled in the SGCB, and several parts of the basin benefit from dense 2D seismic reflection coverage. In the next part of this paper, palaeothermal and compaction data are used to constrain the magnitude of Neogene exhumation in the SGCB and seismic reflection data are used to show the

Mochras borehole

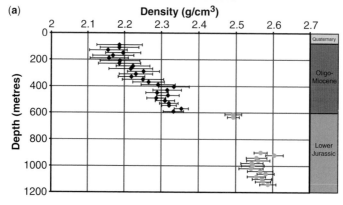

(a)

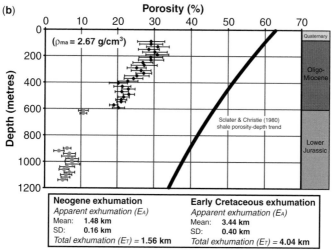

(b)

Neogene exhumation	Early Cretaceous exhumation
Apparent exhumation (E_A)	*Apparent exhumation (E_A)*
Mean: **1.48 km**	Mean: **3.44 km**
SD: 0.16 km	SD: 0.40 km
Total exhumation (E_T) = **1.56 km**	*Total exhumation (E_T) =* **4.04 km**

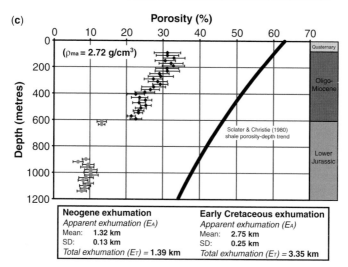

(c)

Neogene exhumation	Early Cretaceous exhumation
Apparent exhumation (E_A)	*Apparent exhumation (E_A)*
Mean: **1.32 km**	Mean: **2.75 km**
SD: 0.13 km	SD: 0.25 km
Total exhumation (E_T) = **1.39 km**	*Total exhumation (E_T) =* **3.35 km**

important role of compressional deformation as a driving mechanism behind this exhumation.

Neogene exhumation in the St George's Channel Basin

The SGCB is a NE–SW trending half-graben which is downfaulted along its SE margin against the Palaeozoic Welsh Massif by the Bala–St George's fault system, a major reactivated Caledonian lineament (Barr *et al.* 1981). The SGCB is one of the deepest basins on the UKCS, with approximately 3 km of undeformed Carboniferous strata overlain by a post-Variscan sedimentary infill which locally exceeds 7 km (Tappin *et al.* 1994). Since no wells or boreholes have penetrated the complete succession, the stratigraphy of the basin fill is poorly constrained (Tappin *et al.* 1994). Individual exploration wells have encountered thick sequences of Triassic, Jurassic and Cenozoic sediments however (Barr *et al.* 1981; Dobson & Whittington 1987; Tappin *et al.* 1994).

Using a combination of seismic reflection, compaction and palaeothermal data Williams *et al.* (2005) identified three important phases of exhumation which affected the SGCB and its margins during the Cretaceous–Cenozoic. Firstly, up to 2.5 km of section was removed from the NW and SE margins of the basin during early Cretaceous times. This episode is recorded by seismic reflection data and AFTA results from the Central Irish Sea Basin (Duncan *et al.* 1998; Green *et al.* 2001*a*) and SW Wales (Williams *et al.* 2005). In contrast to the en-echelon CBB, the main depocentre of the SGCB appears to have been unaffected by this episode. One possible explanation for this is that the deep bathymetry which developed within the SGCB during the Jurassic (Turner 1996) meant that uplift during the early Cretaceous was not accompanied by erosion (Williams *et al.* 2005). Secondly, the SGCB experienced regional exhumation during the late Cretaceous–Palaeogene, responsible for the Jurassic/Palaeogene unconformity recorded on seismic reflection profiles. This event involved a component of NW directed

shortening which was responsible for local contractional fault reactivation along the basin margins (Williams *et al.* 2005). The SGCB experienced a final phase of exhumation during late Cenozoic times, the evidence for which is recorded by the preserved Palaeogene sediments within the basin. Based on comparison with results from Mochras, where the preserved Lower Miocene sediments provide tight constraints on the timing of exhumation, the late Cenozoic exhumation of the SGCB is assigned a Neogene, probably Miocene, timing.

Figure 10 presents a series of structural contour maps for basal and top Triassic, basal Cenozoic and intra-Eocene levels within the basin, based on the interpretation of a *c.* 3000 km^2 grid of well-tied 2D seismic reflection data (Williams *et al.* 2005). There are several lines of evidence for Neogene shortening of the basin from these maps. Structural culminations located along right-stepping jogs on the main NE-trending fault systems of the basin (Fig. 10c, d) record their left-lateral reactivation during Neogene compression (Williams *et al.* 2005). Furthermore, Figure 10c and d shows the presence of a broad, NW-trending anticline located within the main depocentre of basin which is confined to the Palaeogene succession; this kind of evidence (i.e. disharmonic folding, thin-skinned deformation) is typical of that used to recognize the compressional shortening of formerly extensional sedimentary basins (Turner & Williams 2004). In other parts of the basin the Palaeogene and Mesozoic sequences display a significant, consistent structural dip (e.g. Fig. 11) indicating a post-Palaeogene timing of deformation. The core of this Neogene fold is penetrated by two exploration wells, 106/24a-2b and 106/24-1. AFTA and VR data from these wells permit the magnitude of exhumation associated with Neogene compressional deformation to be estimated directly.

106/24a-2b

A palaeotemperature–depth plot for 106/24a-2b is shown in Figure 12a. Corrected BHT data indicate a present-day geothermal gradient of 32 °C km^{-1} in this well. The maximum palaeotemperatures

---

Fig. 8. Density and calculated porosity data for the Mochras borehole. The density log was filtered to remove spurious data and unwanted (i.e. non-shale) lithologies following the procedures reported in Holford *et al.* (2005*a*). For shales, the largest source of error when converting density data to porosities arises from the highly variable nature of shale matrix densities (Rider 1996). For this reason, two sets of porosities have been calculated using end member matrix densities of 2.67 g cm^{-3} and 2.72 g cm^{-3}. Error bars represent ±1 standard deviation. (**a**) Bulk density (g cm^{-3}) data for the Mochras borehole. Note the abrupt increase in density across the Cenozoic/Jurassic unconformity. (**b**) Porosities calculated using equation (2) assuming a matrix density of 2.67 g cm^{-3}. Neogene (calculated using Oligo-Miocene porosity data) and early Cretaceous (calculated using Lower Jurassic porosity data) apparent and total exhumation estimates (cf. Hillis 1995) relative to the Sclater & Christie (1980) shale porosity–depth trend. (**c**) Porosity data and exhumation estimates calculated assuming a matrix density of 2.72 g cm^{-3}.

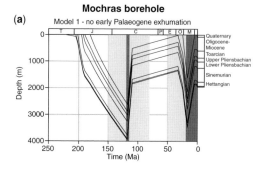

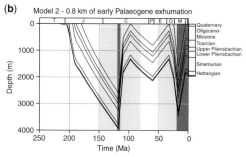

Fig. 9. Two reconstructed burial histories for the Mochras borehole. Both histories incorporate 2.5 km of Middle and Upper Jurassic sediments removed during early Cretaceous exhumation, and 1.5 km of Miocene sediments removed during late Neogene exhumation. Both models assume a constant geothermal gradient through time, with a similar value to the present-day temperature profile (*c*. 23.4 °C km^{-1}). Vertical light grey shaded bars represent estimates of the onset of exhumation-related cooling as indicated by AFTA sample GC399-13, whereas dark grey bars represent the overall estimates of the onset of exhumation based on stratigraphic constraints and regional AFTA results. (**a**) The first history assumes no burial or exhumation during late Cretaceous–early Palaeogene times; (**b**) the second burial history incorporates 0.8 km of Upper Cretaceous section, removed during an early Palaeogene exhumation event. Assuming an invariant geothermal gradient of 23.4 °C km^{-1}, 0.8 km is the maximum amount of early Palaeogene exhumation that could have occurred without affecting the measured AFTA parameters (cf. Fig. 5).

experienced by the Oligocene and Jurassic units have been estimated using 22 VR and two AFTA samples. All of these samples have been hotter in the past, and the VR-derived palaeotemperatures are mostly *c*. 30 °C higher than the present-day temperatures in the well. The palaeotemperatures from AFTA and VR are in good agreement with each other, and collectively define an approximately linear palaeotemperature profile. The fact that VR-derived palaeotemperatures from both the Oligocene and Jurassic successions shown no

significant offset across the top-Jurassic unconformity (Fig. 12a) indicates that maximum palaeotemperatures, and hence maximum burial depths within this well, were attained following the deposition of the preserved Cenozoic succession. Assuming that the palaeogeothermal gradient prior to exhumation had a similar value to the present-day gradient (32 °C km^{-1}) indicates that the preserved section was more deeply buried by between 0.8–1 km prior to Neogene exhumation (Fig. 12b). This is in excellent agreement with the amount of deeper burial at this location estimated from compaction data; based on the analysis of anomalously high sonic velocities within the Upper Triassic Mercia Mudstone Group succession encountered by this well, Williams *et al*. (2005) estimated that the pre-Jurassic units had been more deeply buried by *c*. 1 km. Although palaeothermal and compaction data provide no direct evidence for any significant late Cretaceous–early Palaeogene exhumation, appreciable exhumation would be allowed at this time provided that the thickness of eroded section did not exceed that accumulated during subsequent burial (Fig. 12c).

106/24-1

Similar results regarding Neogene exhumation magnitudes are provided by palaeothermal data from 106/24-1, which also penetrated the crest of the Neogene inversion anticline (Fig. 10). Three bottom-hole temperature measurements for this well define a linear present-day geothermal gradient with a value of 29.4 °C km^{-1} for this well, which encountered *c*. 0.6 km of Eocene–Oligocene sediments similar to those recovered from Mochras which rest unconformably upon almost 2 km of Upper–Middle Jurassic mudstones (Tappin *et al*. 1994). VR data from this well define a dog-leg profile, with VR-derived palaeotemperatures within the Palaeogene and uppermost Jurassic successions around 20 °C higher than present-day temperatures (Fig. 13a). However, below depths of *c*. 1.5 km the palaeotemperature estimates from VR converge with the present-day temperature profile. The lower VR values within the overall trend have been interpreted to have been affected by geochemical suppression, resulting in anomalously low reflectances (Carr 2000). Suppression commonly affects hydrogen-rich marine facies such as the Lower Jurassic mudstones which are widely distributed across the British Isles (Scotchman 2001), including some of the Lower Jurassic VR samples from Mochras (Holford *et al*. 2005*a*).

Thermal history analysis of a single Bathonian-aged AFTA sample obtained from this well from a depth of 2408 m indicated that this

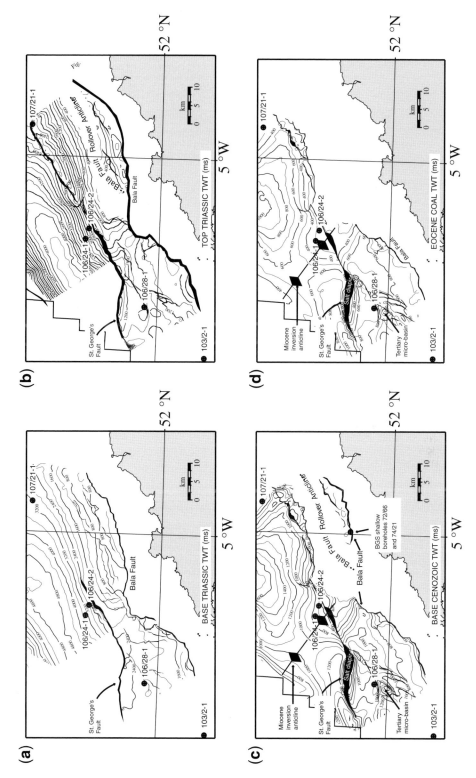

Fig. 10. (a–d) Structural contours at basal Triassic (a), top Triassic (b), basal Cenozoic (c) and intra-Eocene levels (d) based on seismic mapping in the SGCB. Contours are in two-way travel time and fault traces are shaded black. Note the presence of a broad NW–SE trending anticline which is confined to the Cenozoic succession (c–d) and the core of which is penetrated by exploration wells 106/24a-2b and 106/24-1. Note also the coincidence of structural culminations with right-stepping bends on the main NE-trending fault systems. This is interpreted as a consequence of their reactivation in left-lateral shear during Neogene transpressional shortening of the basin. After Williams *et al.* (2005).

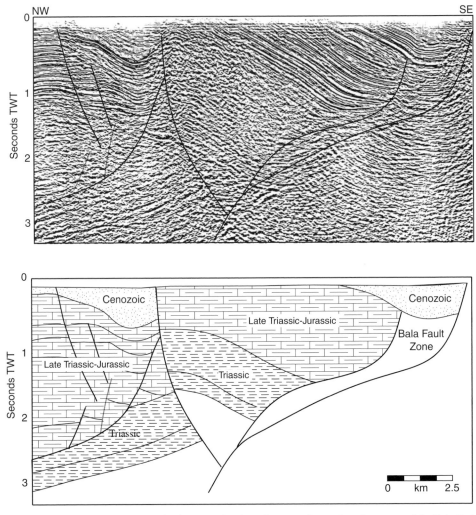

Fig. 11. Seismic profile and accompanying interpretation through a severely reactivated segment of the Bala Fault, along the SE margin of the St George's Channel Basin. Neogene shortening has been accommodated by reverse displacement along the low-angle Bala Fault. The Bala Fault has a ramp-flat geometry, and the buttressing effect of the ramp arrested reverse displacement with further shortening accommodated by the formation of a NW-trending thrust fault splaying from the Bala Fault. Note the significant structural dip of the Cenozoic (Eocene–Oligocene) sequence, which is almost parallel with that of the Mesozoic succession. Modified after Williams *et al.* (2005).

sample had cooled from a maximum palaeotemperature of between 75–90 °C at some time between its deposition and the present-day. Assuming that the palaeotemperatures from the vitrinite samples at depths >1.5 km are erroneous due to suppression, combining the shallower VR data with the palaeotemperature constraints from AFTA enables the determination of a palaeogeothermal gradient related to Palaeogene/post-Palaeogene burial-related heating. As in the case of 106/24a-2b, palaeotemperatures from VR show

no significant offset across the Palaeogene/Jurassic unconformity, suggesting that maximum burial at this location was also occurred during the Cenozoic (Fig. 13a, c). Assuming the value of the palaeogeothermal gradient to be equivalent to the present-day gradient reduces the amount of additional Palaeogene–Neogene section required to explain the palaeotemperature constraints to between 0.65–0.9 km. This estimate is similar to that obtained for the nearby 106/24a-2b well (0.8–1.0 km), and considered together these results

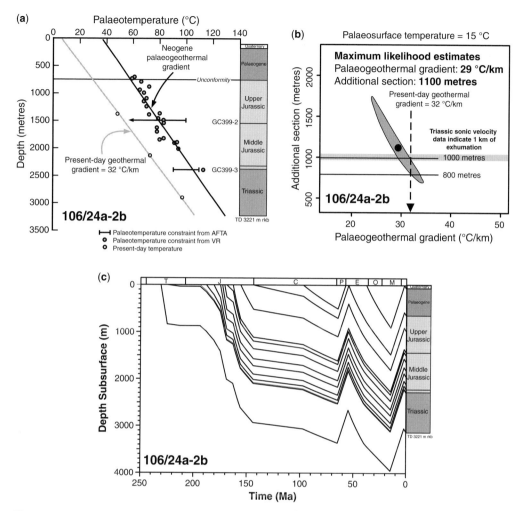

Fig. 12. (**a**) Palaeotemperature–depth plot for SGCB exploration well 106/24a-2b. (**b**) Amounts of additional section and palaeogeothermal gradients required to explain the palaeotemperatures prior to Neogene exhumation at this location. The shaded region defines the allowed range of values for each parameter that are consistent with the measured palaeotemperature constraints within 95% confidence limits. Black dots represent the maximum likelihood estimates. (**c**) Burial history plot for well 106/24a-2b, reconstructed using (i) the preserved stratigraphy penetrated by the well and (ii) constraints on deeper burial and thermal history provided by palaeothermal and compaction data. This shows that maximum burial depths at 106/24a-2b were reached prior to Neogene exhumation. This scenario incorporates *c.* 1 km of exhumation during the early Palaeogene, although it is emphasized that palaeothermal data place no constraints on the amount of exhumation at this time.

provide tight, direct constraints on the magnitude of Neogene exhumation caused by compressional deformation in the SGCB.

106/28-1

Elsewhere in the basin, palaeothermal data record similar magnitudes of Neogene exhumation. Exploration well 106/28-1 drilled the footwall of the inverted St George's Fault, on the SE margin

of the basin. It penetrated a thick Triassic succession overlain by a thin Lower Jurassic sequence and *c.* 0.7 km of Eocene–Oligocene sediments (Tappin *et al.* 1994). Seventeen VR samples encompass the Palaeogene and Lower Jurassic sequences, whereas a single AFTA sample from the Triassic succession provides useful constraints on palaeotemperatures in the deeper parts of the section, where VR data are unavailable due to the terrestrial origin of the Triassic succession (Fig. 14a).

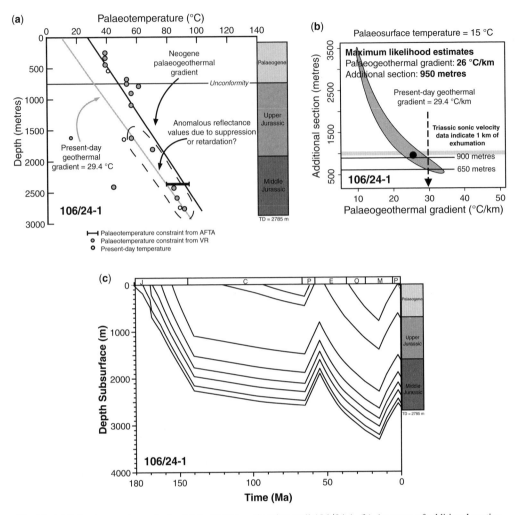

Fig. 13. (a) Palaeotemperature–depth plot for SGCB exploration well 106/24-1. (b) Amounts of additional section and palaeogeothermal gradients required to explain the palaeotemperatures prior to Neogene exhumation at this location. The shaded region defines the allowed range of values for each parameter that are consistent with the measured palaeotemperature constraints within 95% confidence limits. Black dots represent the maximum likelihood estimates. (c) Burial history plot for well 106/24-1, showing that maximum burial depths were reached prior to Neogene exhumation. As with 106/24a-2b, this scenario also incorporates *c.* 1 km of exhumation during the early Palaeogene.

VR-derived palaeotemperatures define an approximately linear palaeogeothermal gradient which is similar in profile and value of the present-day geothermal gradient (34.7 °C km^{-1}) (Fig. 14a). As with other examples discussed in this paper, the consistency of palaeotemperature data either side of the Palaeogene/Lower Jurassic unconformity attests to maximum burial of the preserved Mesozoic and Cenozoic units in the SGCB occurring prior to Neogene exhumation. Thermal history modelling of AFTA parameters from the Triassic sample reveals evidence for one palaeothermal episode, involving cooling from a palaeotemperature of 90–110 °C at some point following deposition. The range of palaeotemperatures indicated by AFTA are in good agreement with a palaeotemperature profile fitted to the palaeothermal constraints from VR (Fig. 14a), which strongly suggests that the AFTA and VR data record the same burial episode. Assuming a palaeogeothermal gradient with a value equivalent to that of the present-day geotherm for this well indicates that the preserved section in this well was more deeply buried by an additional 0.65–0.9 km of

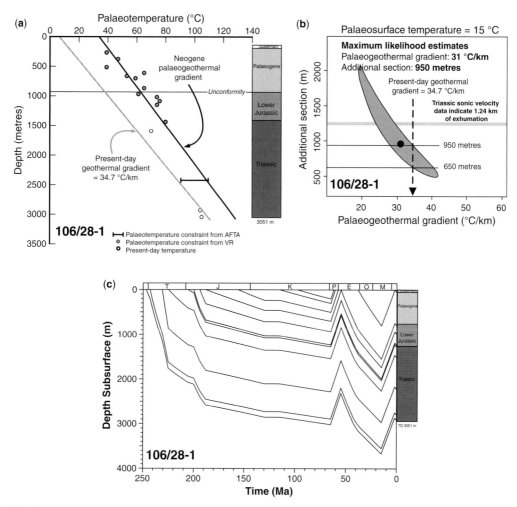

Fig. 14. (**a**) Palaeotemperature–depth plot for SGCB exploration well 106/28-1. (**b**) Amounts of additional section and palaeogeothermal gradients required to explain the palaeotemperatures prior to Neogene exhumation at this location. The shaded region defines the allowed range of values for each parameter that are consistent with the measured palaeotemperature constraints within 95% confidence limits. Black dots represent the maximum likelihood estimates. (**c**) Burial history plot for well 106/28-1, showing that maximum burial depths were reached prior to Neogene exhumation. As with previous examples, this scenario also incorporates *c.* 1 km of exhumation during the early Palaeogene.

Palaeogene–Neogene section which was subsequently eroded (Fig. 14b). This estimate is in broad agreement with the amount of deeper burial of the Triassic succession inferred from Mercia Mudstone Group sonic velocity data (*c.* 1.24 km; Williams *et al.* 2005) (which in itself, falls well within the range of values for deeper burial allowed by palaeothermal data (Fig. 14b)).

Estimates of the amount of deeper burial prior to Neogene exhumation for all wells and boreholes from the southern Irish Sea which have been analysed for this study are shown in Figure 15. A

striking feature revealed in this diagram is the consistency of the exhumation estimates which have been obtained for individual wells using separate techniques—palaeothermal data, compaction data (using density and sonic velocity logs) and also erosion estimates based on seismic reflection data (Fig. 15). This overall consistency serves to confirm the magnitude of Neogene exhumation in this region and also validates the reliability of the separate approaches which have been employed to calculate exhumation. Since most of the wells in the SGCB are drilled on inversion structures

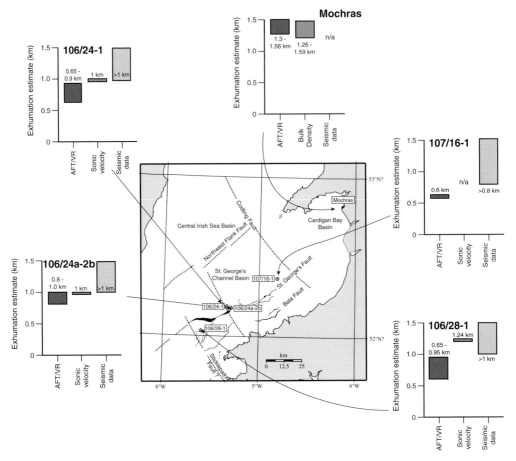

Fig. 15. Comparison between estimates of the magnitude of Neogene exhumation at various well locations in the St George's Channel and Cardigan Bay basins obtained from three different methods: thermal history analysis (AFTA and VR data), sonic velocity analysis and reconstructions of the thickness of eroded section from interpretations of reflection seismic data. The quoted values from thermal history data are estimates which assume that palaeogeothermal gradients were equivalent to the values of the present-day gradient. The estimates for each well are generally in good agreement, indicating a maximum of 1.5 km of Neogene erosion across the southern Irish Sea.

(e.g. 107/16-1; Fig. 16) where exhumation magnitudes are likely to be highest, these estimates should be regarded as upper limits on the total amount of Neogene exhumation in this basin. In detail, the actual patterns of exhumation within the basin are likely to be more heterogeneous than the results presented here suggest. Compressional shortening in sedimentary basins is characteristically non-uniform (Turner & Williams 2004). This non-uniformity is expressed on a variety of scales, from the contractional reactivation of a single extensional fault (e.g. Williams *et al.* 1989) and the selective reactivation of faults within a synthetic fault array (e.g. Sibson 1995) to the differential shortening of the crust and lithosphere (e.g. Nielsen & Hansen 2000). A major consequence of

non-uniform shortening is that exhumation patterns are typically heterogeneous (cf. Argent *et al.* 2002). Following on from this point, Williams *et al.* (2005) have suggested that Neogene exhumation in the SGCB is likely to have been highly variable due to the noncoaxial strain history during the inversion episode.

Discussion: implications for the timing and causes of Cenozoic exhumation in the Irish Sea

AFTA, VR and compaction data from boreholes and wells in the southern Irish Sea show that the preserved Cenozoic sediments in these basins

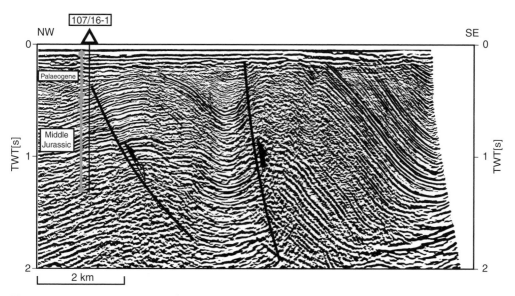

Fig. 16. Seismic line through well 107/16-1 located in the NE SGCB. The section is displayed with a significant component of vertical exaggeration to highlight the reactivated fault plane that cuts well 107/16-1.

were more deeply buried by up to 1.5 km prior to Neogene exhumation. Moreover, seismic reflection data provide abundant evidence for the compressional shortening of the preserved Cenozoic strata, indicating that this was the principal cause of this exhumation episode. The amount of bulk Cenozoic shortening in the southern Irish Sea has been estimated following the line-length restoration of the uppermost Lower Jurassic marker horizon on a cross-section which extends from the SGCB, through the St Tudwal's Arch to the Central Irish Sea Basin (Fig. 17). The Lower Jurassic succession in this cross-section exhibits pronounced thickening

towards the uplifted structural culmination of St Tudwal's Arch (offshore Llŷn Peninsula), with bulk shortening estimated at c. 15% (Ware & Turner 2002). The uniform shortening of a hypothetical column of continental lithosphere 125 km in thickness (crust = 30 km, crustal density = $2.8 \, \text{g cm}^{-3}$, mantle density = 3.3 g cm^{-3}) by 15% should result in a maximum value of 1.5 km of exhumation (following the isostatic calculations of Brodie & White 1995), similar to the upper limit of Neogene exhumation indicated by palaeothermal and compaction data from the southern Irish Sea.

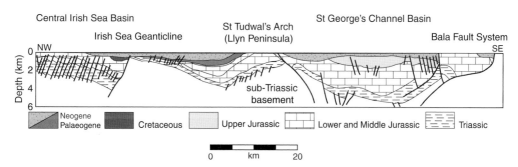

Fig. 17. Cross-section through the southern Irish Sea, from the St George's Channel Basin to the Central Irish Sea Basin, through the St Tudwal's Arch (offshore Llŷn Peninsula). This cross-section exemplifies the inversion of structural relief which often occurs during the compressional shortening of sedimentary basins; note how the syntectonic Lower–Middle Jurassic depocentre exhibits pronounced thickening towards the uplifted structural culmination of St Tudwal's Arch. Note also, to the immediate SE of St Tudwal's Arch, an anticline within the Jurassic succession, the crest of which has been truncated by the base Palaeogene succession, indicating a pre-Neogene (early Palaeogene?) phase of compressional deformation within the southern Irish Sea.

To the NW of this cross-section, the general absence of typical tectonic inversion structures (e.g. contractionally reactivated normal faults) in the East Irish Sea has led some workers to rule out compressional shortening as a driving mechanism of exhumation in this basin (Brodie & White 1995). However, as argued by Ware & Turner (2002) and Williams *et al.* (2005), given that inversion geometries are most pronounced in the shallow parts of compressionally shortened basins where reverse fault displacements are greatest, the evidence for inversion may be largely obliterated in deeply exhumed basins such as the East Irish Sea. Moreover, AFTA data from the East Irish Sea provides evidence for up to 1 km of exhumation which began between 30 and 10 Ma (Holford 2006), consistent with the timing of compressional shortening and exhumation in the southern Irish Sea. It is probable that a substantial proportion of exhumation in the East Irish Sea which has previously been attributed to early Palaeogene events actually occurred during the Neogene.

In the southern Irish Sea it has not been possible to constrain the magnitude of early Palaeogene exhumation directly. In the SGCB maximum burial depths of the preserved sedimentary succession were attained during the mid–late Cenozoic, whereas AFTA data from Mochras reveal no evidence for elevated palaeotemperatures during the early Palaeogene, and hence do not require significant exhumation at this time. The fact that AFTA data from several other parts of the Irish Sea basins and their margins indicate substantial early Palaeogene exhumation e.g. up to 2 km in the Central Irish Sea Basin (Green *et al.* 2001*a*) and up to 1.5 km in northern England (Green 2002) suggests that early Palaeogene exhumation patterns were markedly heterogeneous.

Early Palaeogene exhumation in the British Isles is commonly attributed to processes associated with mantle plume activity (e.g. underplating, thermal uplift) (Brodie & White 1994; White & Lovell 1997; Jones *et al.* 2002). Theoretical modelling of such processes predicts the occurrences of broad, epeirogenic regional uplift over horizontal distances of hundreds to thousands of kilometres (e.g. White & McKenzie 1989). Epeirogenic uplift processes should result in smooth, progressive variations in exhumation patterns (Argent *et al.* 2002). The observed early Palaeogene exhumation patterns in the Irish Sea would appear to be inconsistent with a sole, epeirogenic driving mechanism, although they could be explained in terms of compressional shortening superimposed upon epeirogenic uplift (Williams *et al.* 2005). Given that the Irish Sea is thought to be a locus of Iceland Plume-related magmatic underplating during the early Palaeogene, the observation of no substantial coeval exhumation

recorded by AFTA data from Mochras, where the preserved Cenozoic sedimentary succession is overcompacted, suggests that the role of underplating as a driving mechanism of Cenozoic exhumation in the Irish Sea region has been overstated. It is difficult to prove the existence of underplating because the lower crust cannot be sampled directly, thus its composition and age cannot be determined. There is good evidence from wide-angle seismic data for thick (up to 10 km) bodies of underplated material along parts of the Atlantic margin (e.g. Hatton Bank), where there is also excellent evidence for extensive surface magmatism in the form of widespread packages of seaward-dipping reflectors (White & McKenzie 1989; Vogt *et al.* 1998), but there is no such evidence for similar underplated bodies beneath the Irish Sea basins (e.g. Shaw Champion *et al.* 2006). Furthermore, early Palaeogene underplating should have resulted in permanent uplift across the Irish Sea basin system (Brodie & White 1995), but the St George's Channel and Cardigan Bay basins contain significant thicknesses of Palaeogene–Neogene sediments, whilst most parts of this region are below sea-level at present. All of the available observational data point to compressional shortening, rather than magmatic underplating, being the principal driving mechanism of Cenozoic exhumation in the Irish Sea region.

The synthesis of an extensive AFTA dataset incorporating samples from the all parts of the Irish Sea basin system reported in Holford (2006) reveals evidence for a regional exhumation-related late Cenozoic cooling episode which began between 25 and 15 Ma (Fig. 18). The additional stratigraphic constraints from Mochras, where sediments of early Miocene age are preserved (Herbert-Smith 1979) help refine the timing of this event to beginning between ?20 and 15 Ma (Fig. 18). This dataset includes samples from the onshore landmasses which surround the mostly submerged Irish Sea basins (e.g. northern England, Ireland and Wales). The Neogene exhumation episode observed within the offshore sedimentary basins is also recorded by AFTA data from the apparently stable basin margins. For example, AFTA data from across onshore Ireland reveal evidence for regional cooling which began between 25 and 15 Ma and is also interpreted in terms of kilometre-scale exhumation (Green *et al.* 2000). The general absence of Mesozoic–Cenozoic sediments and lack of seismic reflection data from these non-basinal regions makes it difficult to detect the possible contribution of compressional deformation to this exhumation, although it is noted that both Bevins *et al.* (1996) and Cunningham *et al.* (2004) have reported evidence for Cenozoic tectonic deformation (i.e. fault

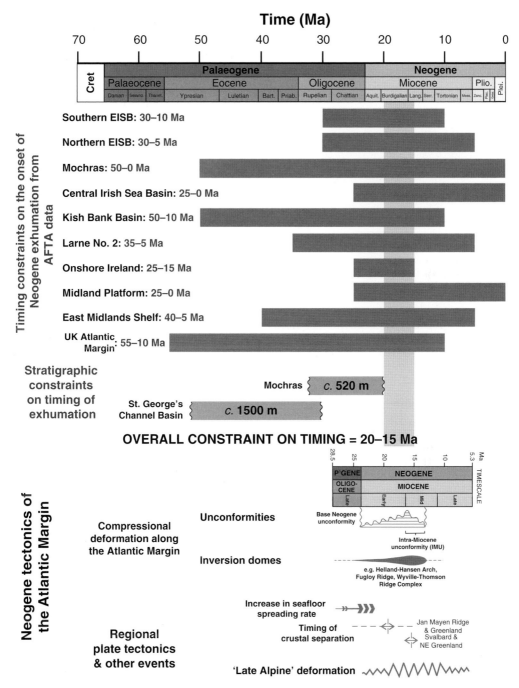

Fig. 18. Cenozoic event stratigraphy diagram for the British Isles and Atlantic margin. Constraints on the onset of exhumation-related cooling provided by AFTA data from both within and outwith the Irish Sea basin system are compared with stratigraphic constraints on the timing of exhumation in an attempt to identify the timing of regional Neogene exhumation. This analysis suggests a regional onset of exhumation beginning between 20 and 15 Ma. The timing of important regional tectonic events, derived from Lundin & Doré (2002) and Stoker *et al.* (2005) are highlighted for comparative purposes. Timescale modified after Gradstein *et al.* (2004).

movement) in North Wales and SE Ireland respectively, the kinematics of which are similar to those of Neogene compressional and transpressional shortening in the SGCB (Turner 1997; Williams *et al.* 2005) and Central Irish Sea Basin (Izatt *et al.* 2001). One possible model which can account for the Neogene exhumation of both the Irish Sea basins and their margins solely in terms of compressional shortening is that of Hillis (1992). Hillis (1992) attempted to reconcile the observation of localized compressional deformation superimposed upon more regional Cenozoic exhumation across the British Isles by invoking a two-layer (i.e. depth-dependent) model of lithospheric compression, analogous to more familiar two-layer models of lithospheric extension (e.g. Kusznir & Ziegler 1992; Davis & Kusznir 2004). Under this scenario, compressional shortening and thickening in the lower crust and lithospheric mantle may be laterally displaced from, or occur across a broader wavelength than the compressional shortening in the brittle upper crust, and thereby explains the regional component of exhumation which extends beyond the inverted sedimentary basins (Hillis 1992). Additionally or alternatively, the Neogene compressional shortening observed in the southern Irish Sea basins may be superimposed on the enigmatic regional Neogene uplift event which has been reported from many parts of the Atlantic margins (e.g. Doré *et al.* 1999; Thomson *et al.* 1999; Japsen & Chalmers 2000; Japsen *et al.* 2005; Bonow *et al.* 2006).

Outwith the Irish Sea, Neogene compressional shortening has been identified within many sedimentary basins around the British Isles, including the southern North Sea (Badley *et al.* 1989), the Wessex Basin (Chadwick & Evans 2005) and in Mesozoic–Cenozoic basins along the UK Atlantic margin (Stoker *et al.* 2005). The timing of these episodes of compressional deformation is very similar to that identified by this study. Along the UK Atlantic margin for example, compressional deformation at *c.* 16 Ma contributed to the development of a widespread intra-Miocene unconformity (Stoker *et al.* 2005).

There is strong evidence for substantial coeval exhumation across parts of the Atlantic margin from AFTA data. For example, AFTA and VR data from the 204/19-1 well located on the Westray Ridge in the Faroe–Shetland Basin indicate that between 0.63 and 0.9 km of Eocene–Oligocene strata were eroded prior to late Miocene sedimentation (Parnell *et al.* 2005). The correlation between the timing of the compressional deformation and exhumation of the UK Atlantic margin and the Irish Sea basin system (e.g. Fig. 18) is an important observation, which implies that the forces which caused the

deformation along the margin may also have been responsible for the compressional deformation and kilometre-scale exhumation of an intraplate sedimentary basin located at least 1000 km from the most proximal plate boundary or margin.

The source of the compressional stress responsible for the deformation observed in sedimentary basins around the British Isles during the Neogene has mostly been attributed to either late Alpine lithospheric shortening (e.g. Ziegler *et al.* 1995, 1998; Blundell 2002) or Atlantic seafloor spreading and associated ridge-push forces (e.g. Boldreel & Andersen 1993, 1998; Lundin & Doré 2002; Stoker *et al.* 2005). Studies of the origins of the present-day regional stress fields in the interiors of both the European (Gölke & Coblentz 1996) and Indo-Australasian plates (Reynolds *et al.* 2002) using finite element analyses have shown that the state of stress at any point within the plate is a function of the net torques of all the plate boundary forces (Reynolds *et al.* 2002). This suggests that the Neogene compressional deformation in the Irish Sea is a function of both Atlantic ridge-push forces and Alpine lithospheric shortening. In this respect, it is worth drawing attention to Figure 18 which shows that the Neogene compression-driven exhumation of the Irish Sea basins was coeval with both the separation of the Jan Mayen microcontinent from Greenland and the late Alpine phase of collisional shortening in central and western Europe (cf. Stoker *et al.* 2005). These observations show that plate boundary deformation events play an important role in the generation of vertical tectonic motions across continental interiors, and are capable of causing the kilometre-scale exhumation of intraplate regions.

Conclusions

- The presence of up to 1.5 km of preserved Cenozoic sediments within the southern Irish Sea has enabled the effects of late Cenozoic exhumation within the Irish Sea basin system to be separated from those of earlier events. Palaeothermal (AFTA and VR) and compaction data have been used to calculate Neogene exhumation magnitudes whilst seismic reflection data have been used to constrain the origins of the exhumation.
- AFTA, VR and compaction (density-log derived porosity) data have been used to determine the thermal and exhumation histories of the Mochras borehole which penetrated the sedimentary fill of the Cardigan Bay Basin. Palaeothermal and compaction data reveal that the preserved Lower Jurassic succession within this basin was more deeply buried by

c. 2.5 km of additional section prior to early Cretaceous exhumation, whilst the preserved late Oligocene–early Miocene succession was more deeply buried by an additional *c*. 1.5 km of Miocene sediments prior to Neogene exhumation. AFTA data from this borehole provide no evidence for early Palaeogene cooling, and hence exhumation at this location. This is a surprising result, since many previous studies have described the Irish Sea basin system as the locus of early Palaeogene exhumation across the British Isles.

• Palaeothermal and compaction data from exploration wells in the St George's Channel Basin show that the preserved Eocene–Oligocene rocks in this basin were more deeply buried by up to 1 km of additional section prior to Neogene exhumation. Maximum burial depths of the Mesozoic succession in this basin were also attained prior to Neogene exhumation, and hence it is not possible to constrain magnitudes of early Cretaceous and early Palaeogene exhumation directly.

• These results raise important questions regarding the driving mechanisms of early Palaeogene exhumation, which is commonly attributed to epeirogenic, plume-related processes such as magmatic underplating. We believe that the role of underplating as a driving mechanism behind Cenozoic exhumation in the Irish Sea region has been overstated.

• Seismic reflection data show that compressional deformation was the principal mechanism driving Neogene exhumation in the St George's Channel Basin.

• The synthesis of a regional AFTA dataset constrains the onset of late Cenozoic exhumation in the Irish Sea basin system to beginning between 25 and 15 Ma. The preserved lower Miocene sediments at Mochras permit the constraints on the timing of this episode to be refined further to beginning between ?20 and 15 Ma.

• The timing of compressionally-driven exhumation in the southern Irish Sea is coeval with intra-Miocene compression and exhumation observed along the UK Atlantic margin. This suggests that the forces responsible for the deformation of the margin were also responsible for the shortening and exhumation of an intraplate sedimentary basin system located >1000 km from the most proximal plate boundary.

• Finite-element modelling of the origins of stress fields in continental interiors suggests that the state of stress at any point within the plate is a function of the net torques of all the plate boundary forces. The Neogene compression in the Irish Sea is thus probably a function of both Atlantic ridge-push forces and late Alpine lithospheric shortening.

• The results presented in this paper demonstrate that compressional deformation has played an important contributing role to the Neogene exhumation of the NW European continental shelf.

This paper has benefited from discussions with P. Japsen and J. Underhill. Reviewers A. Doré and K. Smith are thanked for their comments on the original manuscript. Some of the results reported here formed part of SPH's PhD research at the University of Birmingham, supported by a NERC-CASE studentship with the British Geological Survey (NER/S/A/2001/05890). Burlington Resources Inc, ChevronTexaco, Exxon Mobil, Shell/Enterprise and Veba Oil & Gas UK are acknowledged for provision of data, and Seismic Micro-Technology are thanked for free provision of their Kingdom Suite seismic interpretation software. GAW and DRT publish with the permission of the Executive Director, British Geological Survey (NERC). The British Geological Survey is also thanked for providing access and permission to sample the Mochras core and to publish Figure 1.

References

AL-KINDI, S., WHITE, N., SINHA, M., ENGLAND, R. & TILEY, R. 2003. Crustal trace of a hot convective sheet. *Geology*, **31**, 207–210.

ARGENT, J. D., STEWART, S. A., GREEN, P. F. & UNDERHILL, J. R. 2002. Heterogeneous exhumation in the Inner Moray Firth, UK North Sea: constraints from new AFTA® and seismic data. *Journal of the Geological Society, London*, **159**, 715–729.

BADLEY, M. E., PRICE, J. D. & BACKSHALL, L. C. 1989. Inversion, reactivated faults and related structures: seismic examples from the southern North Sea. *In*: COOPER, M. A. & WILLIAMS, G. D. (eds) *Inversion Tectonics*. Geological Society, London, Special Publications, **44**, 201–219.

BARR, K. W., COLTER, V. S. & YOUNG, R. 1981. The Geology of the Cardigan Bay–St Georges's Channel Basin. *In*: ILLING, L. V. & HOBSON, G. D. (eds) *Petroleum Geology of the Continental Shelf of North-West Europe*. Heyden, London, 432–444.

BEVINS, R. E., HORAK, J. M., EVANS, A. D. & MORGAN, R. 1996. Palaeogene dyke swarm, NW Wales: evidence for sinistral fault movement. *Journal of the Geological Society, London*, **153**, 177–181.

BJØRKUM, P. A., WALDERHAUG, O. & NADEAU, P. H. 2001. Thermally driven porosity reduction: impact on basin subsidence. *In*: SHANNON, P. M., HAUGHTON, P. D. W. & CORCORAN, D. V. (eds) *The Petroleum Exploration of Ireland's Offshore Basins*. Geological Society, London, Special Publications, **188**, 385–392.

BLUNDELL, D. J. 2002. Cenozoic inversion and uplift of southern Britain. *In*: DORÉ, A. G., CARTWRIGHT, J. A., STOKER, M. S., TURNER, J. P. & WHITE, N. (eds) *Exhumation of the North Atlantic Margin:*

Timing, Mechanisms and Implications for Petroleum Exploration. Geological Society, London, Special Publications, **196**, 85–101.

BOLDREEL, L. O. & ANDERSEN, M. S. 1993. Late Palaeocene to Miocene compression in the Faeroe-Rockall area. *In*: PARKER, J. R. (ed.) *Petroleum Geology of Northwest Europe: Proceedings of the 4th Conference.* Geological Society, London, 1025–1034.

BOLDREEL, L. O. & ANDERSEN, M. S. 1998. Tertiary compressional structures on the Faeroe-Rockall Plateau in relation to northeast Atlantic ridge-push and Alpine foreland stresses. *Tectonophysics*, **300**, 13–28.

BONOW, J. M., LIDMAR-BERGSTRÖM, K. & JAPSEN, P. 2006. Palaeosurfaces in central West Greenland as reference for identification of tectonic movements and estimation of erosion. *Global and Planetary Change*, **50**, 161–183.

BOTT, M. H. P. & BOTT, J. D. J. 2004. The Cenozoic uplift and earthquake belt of mainland Britain as a response to an underlying hot, low-density upper mantle. *Journal of the Geological Society, London*, **161**, 19–29.

BRAY, R., GREEN, P. F. & DUDDY, I. R. 1992. Thermal history reconstruction in sedimentary basins using apatite fission track analysis and vitrinite reflectance data: a case study from the east Midlands of England and the Southern North Sea. *In*: HARDMAN, R. F. P. (ed.) *Exploration Britain: Into the Next Decade.* Geological Society, London, Special Publications, **67**, 3–25.

BRODIE, J. & WHITE, N. 1994. Sedimentary basin inversion caused by igneous underplating. *Geology*, **22**, 147–150.

BRODIE, J. & WHITE, N. 1995. The link between sedimentary basin inversion and igneous underplating. *In*: BUCHANAN, J. G. & BUCHANAN, P. G. (eds) *Basin Inversion.* Geological Society, London, Special Publication, **88**, 21–38.

CARR, A. D. 2000. Suppression and retardation of vitrinite reflectance, part 1. Formation and significance for hydrocarbon generation. *Journal of Petroleum Geology*, **23**, 313–343.

CHADWICK, R. A. & EVANS, D. J. 2005. *A Seismic Atlas of Southern Britain – Images of Subsurface Structure.* British Geological Survey, Occasional Publication No. 7.

CHADWICK, R. A., KIRBY, G. A. & BAILY, H. E. 1994. The post-Triassic structural evolution of north-west England and adjacent parts of the East Irish Sea. *Proceedings of the Yorkshire Geological Society*, **50**, 91–102.

CLOETINGH, S., GRADSTEIN, F. M., KOOI, H., GRANT, A. C. & KAMINSKI, M. 1990. Plate reorganization – a cause of rapid late Neogene subsidence and sedimentation around the North Atlantic? *Journal of the Geological Society, London*, **147**, 495–506.

COPE, J. C. W. 1994. A latest Cretaceous hotspot and the southeasterly tilt of Britain. *Journal of Geological Society, London*, **151**, 905–908.

CORCORAN, D. V. & DORÉ, A. G. 2005. A review of techniques for the estimation of magnitude and timing of exhumation in offshore basins. *Earth-Science Reviews*, **72**, 129–168.

COWARD, M. P. 1995. Structural and tectonic setting of the Permo-Triassic basins of northwest Europe. *In*: BOLDY, S. A. R. (ed.) *Permian and Triassic Rifting in Northwest Europe.* Geological Society, London, Special Publications, **91**, 7–39.

CUNNINGHAM, M. J. M., PHILLIPS, W. E. A. & DENSMORE, A. L. 2004. Evidence for Cenozoic tectonic deformation in SE Ireland and near offshore. *Tectonics*, **23**, 6002, doi:10.1029/2003TC001597.

CURRY, D. 1992. Tertiary. *In*: DUFF, P. McL. D. & SMITH, A. J. (eds) *Geology of England and Wales.* Geological Society, London, 389–411.

DAVIS, M. & KUSZNIR, N. J. 2004. Depth-dependent lithospheric stretching at rifted continental margins. *In*: KARNER, G. D. (ed.) *Proceedings of NSF Rifted Margins Theoretical Institute.* Columbia University Press, New York, 92–136.

DOBSON, M. R. & WHITTINGTON, R. J. 1987. The geology of Cardigan Bay. *Proceedings of the Geologists' Association*, **98**, 331–353.

DORÉ, A. G., LUNDIN, E. R., JENSEN, L. N., BIRKELAND, Ø., ELIASSEN, P. E. & FILCHER, C. 1999. Principal tectonic events in the evolution of the northwest European Atlantic margin. *In*: FLEET, A. J. & BOLDY, S. A. R. (eds) *Petroleum Geology of Northwest Europe: Proceedings of the 5th Conference.* The Geological Society, London, 41–61.

DORÉ, A. G., CARTWRIGHT, J. A., STOKER, M. S., TURNER, J. P. & WHITE, N. 2002a. Exhumation of the North Atlantic margin: introduction and background. *In*: DORÉ, A. G., CARTWRIGHT, J. A., STOKER, M. S., TURNER, J. P. & WHITE, N. (eds) *Exhumation of the North Atlantic Margin: Timing, Mechanisms and Implications for Petroleum Exploration.* Geological Society, London, Special Publications, **196**, 1–12.

DORÉ, A. G., CORCORAN, D. V. & SCOTCHMAN, I. C. 2002b. Prediction of the hydrocarbon system in exhumed basins, and application to the NW European margin. *In*: DORÉ, A. G., CARTWRIGHT, J. A., STOKER, M. S., TURNER, J. P. & WHITE, N. (eds) *Exhumation of the North Atlantic Margin: Timing, Mechanisms and Implications for Petroleum Exploration.* Geological Society, London, Special Publications, **196**, 401–429.

DUDDY, I. R., GREEN, P. F., BRAY, R. J. & HEGARTY, K. A. 1994. Recognition of the thermal effects of fluid flow in sedimentary basins. *In*: PARNELL, J. (ed.) *Geofluids: Origin, Migration and Evolution of Fluids in Sedimentary Basins.* Geological Society, London, Special Publications, **78**, 325–345.

DUNCAN, W. I., GREEN, P. F. & DUDDY, I. R. 1998. Source rock burial history and seal effectiveness: key facets to understanding hydrocarbon exploration potential in the East and Central Irish Sea Basins. *AAPG Bulletin*, **82**, 1401–1415.

GALBRAITH, R. F. & LASLETT, G. M. 1993. Statistical methods for mixed fission track ages. *Nuclear Tracks*, **21**, 459–470.

GALLAGHER, K. 1995. Evolving temperature histories from apatite fission-track data. *Earth and Planetary Science Letters*, **136**, 421–435.

GILES, M. R., INDRELID, S. L. & JAMES, D. M. D. 1998. Compaction – the great unknown in basin modelling. *In*: DÜPPENBECKER, S. J. & ILIFFE, J. E. (eds) *Basin Modelling: Practice and Progress*. Geological Society, London, Special Publications, **141**, 15–43.

GÖLKE, M. & COBLENTZ, D. 1996. Origins of the European regional stress field. *Tectonophysics*, **266**, 11–24.

GRADSTEIN, F. M., OGG, J. G. & SMITH, A. G. 2004. *A Geologic Time Scale 2004*. Cambridge University Press, Cambridge.

GREEN, P. F. 2002. Early Tertiary palaeo-thermal effects in Northern England: reconciling results from apatite fission track analysis with geological evidence. *Tectonophysics*, **349**, 131–144.

GREEN, P. F. 2005. Burial and exhumation histories of Carboniferous rocks of the Southern North Sea and onshore UK, with particular emphasis on post-Carboniferous events. *In*: COLLINSON, J. D., EVANS, D. J., HOLLIDAY, D. W. & JONES, N. S. (eds) *Carboniferous Hydrocarbon Resources: The Southern North Sea and Surrounding Areas*. Yorkshire Geological Society Occasional Publication Series, **7**, 25–34.

GREEN, P. F., DUDDY, I. R., GLEADOW, A. J. R., TINGATE, P. R. & LASLETT, G. M. 1986. Thermal annealing of fission tracks in apatite 1. A qualitative description. *Chemical Geology*, **59**, 237–253.

GREEN, P. F., DUDDY, I. R. & BRAY, R. J. 1997. Variation in thermal history styles around the Irish Sea and adjacent areas: implications for hydrocarbon occurrence and tectonic evolution. *In*: MEADOWS, N. S., TRUEBLOOD, S. P., HARDMAN, M. & COWAN, G. (eds) *Petroleum Geology of the Irish Sea and Adjacent Areas*. Geological Society, London, Special Publications, **124**, 73–93.

GREEN, P. F., DUDDY, I. R., HEGARTY, K. A., BRAY, R. J., SEVASTOPULO, G. D., CLAYTON, G. & JOHNSTON, D. 2000. The post-Carboniferous evolution of Ireland: evidence from thermal history reconstruction. *Proceedings of the Geologists' Association*, **111**, 307–320.

GREEN, P. F., DUDDY, I. R., BRAY, R. J., DUNCAN, W. I. & CORCORAN, D. V. 2001a. The influence of thermal history on hydrocarbon prospectivity in the Central Irish Sea Basin. *In*: SHANNON, P. M., HAUGHTON, P. D. W. & CORCORAN, D. V. (eds) *The Petroleum Exploration of Ireland's Offshore Basins*. Geological Society, London, Special Publications, **188**, 171–188.

GREEN, P. F., THOMSON, K. & HUDSON, J. D. 2001b. Recognising tectonic events in undeformed regions: contrasting results from the Midland Platform and East Midlands Shelf, Central England. *Journal of the Geological Society, London*, **158**, 59–73.

GREEN, P. F., DUDDY, I. R. & HEGARTY, K. A. 2002. Quantifying exhumation in sedimentary basins of the UK from apatite fission track analysis and vitrinite reflectance data: precision, accuracy and latest results. *In*: DORÉ, A. G., CARTWRIGHT, J. A., STOKER, M. S., TURNER, J. P. & WHITE, N. (eds) *Exhumation of the North Atlantic Margin: Timing, Mechanisms and Implications for Petroleum Exploration*. Geological Society, London, Special Publications, **196**, 331–354.

GREEN, P. F., DUDDY, I. R. & HEGARTY, K. A. 2005. Comment on compositional and structural control on fission track annealing in apatite. *Chemical Geology*, **214**, 351–358.

HALLAM, A. 1992. Jurassic. *In*: DUFF, P. McL. D. & SMITH, A. J. (eds) *Geology of England and Wales*. Geological Society, London, 325–354.

HERBERT-SMITH, M. 1979. The age of the Tertiary deposits of the Llanbedr (Mochras Farm) borehole as determined from palynological studies. *Report of the Institute of Geological Sciences*, London, No. 78/24, 15–29.

HILLIS, R. R. 1991. Chalk porosity and Tertiary uplift, Western Approaches Trough, SW UK and NW French continental shelves. *Journal of the Geological Society, London*, **148**, 669–679.

HILLIS, R. R. 1992. A two-layer lithospheric compressional model for the Tertiary uplift of the southern United Kingdom. *Geophysical Research Letters*, **19**, 573–576.

HILLIS, R. R. 1995. Regional Tertiary exhumation in and around the United Kingdom. *In*: BUCHANAN, J. G. & BUCHANAN, P. G. (eds) *Basin Inversion*. Geological Society, London, Special Publications, **88**, 167–190.

HOLFORD, S. P. 2006. *The Mesozoic-Cenozoic Exhumation History of the Irish Sea Basin System, Western UK*. Ph.D. Thesis, University of Birmingham, UK.

HOLFORD, S. P., GREEN, P. F. & TURNER, J. P. 2005a. Palaeothermal and compaction studies in the Mochras borehole (NW Wales) reveal early Cretaceous and Neogene exhumation and argue against regional Palaeogene uplift in the southern Irish Sea. *Journal of the Geological Society, London*, **162**, 829–840.

HOLFORD, S. P., TURNER, J. P. & GREEN, P. F. 2005b. Reconstructing the Mesozoic–Cenozoic exhumation history of the Irish Sea basin system using apatite fission-track analysis and vitrinite reflectance data. *In*: DORÉ, A. G. & VINING, B. (eds) *North West Europe and Global Perspectives: Proceedings of the 6th Petroleum Geology Conference*. Geological Society, London, 1095–1108.

IZATT, C., MAIRNGARM, S. & RACEY, A. 2001. Fault distribution and timing in the Central Irish Sea Basin. *In*: SHANNON, P. M., HAUGHTON, P. D. W. & CORCORAN, D. V. (eds) *The Petroleum Exploration of Ireland's Offshore Basins*. Geological Society, London, Special Publications, **188**, 155–169.

JACKSON, D. I. & MULHOLLAND, P. 1993. Tectonic and stratigraphic aspects of the East Irish Sea Basin and adjacent areas: contrasts in their post-Carboniferous structural styles. *In*: PARKER, J. R. (ed.) *Petroleum Geology of Northwest Europe: Proceedings of the 4th Conference*. Geological Society, London, 791–808.

JACKSON, D. I., JACKSON, A. A., EVANS, D., WINGFIELD, R. T. R., BARNES, R. P. & ARTHUR, M. J. 1995. *United Kingdom Offshore Regional Report: The Geology of the Irish Sea*. London. HMSO for the British Geological Survey.

JAPSEN, P. 1997. Regional Neogene exhumation of Britain and the Western North Sea. *Journal of the Geological Society, London*, **154**, 239–247.

JAPSEN, P. 2000. Investigation of multi-phase erosion using reconstructed shale trends based on sonic data,

Sole Pit axis, North Sea. *Global and Planetary Change*, **24**, 189–210.

JAPSEN, P. & CHALMERS, J. A. 2000. Neogene uplift and tectonics around the North Atlantic: overview. *Global and Planetary Change*, **24**, 189–210.

JAPSEN, P., BIDSTRUP, T. & LIDMAR-BERGSTROM, K. 2002. Neogene uplift and erosion of southern Scandinavia induced by the rise of the South Swedish Dome. *In*: DORÉ, A. G., CARTWRIGHT, J. A., STOKER, M. S., TURNER, J. P. & WHITE, N. (eds) *Exhumation of the North Atlantic Margin: Timing, Mechanisms and Implications for Petroleum Exploration*. Geological Society, London, Special Publications, **196**, 183–207.

JAPSEN, P., GREEN, P. F. & CHALMERS, J. A. 2005. Separation of Palaeogene and Neogene uplift on Nuussuaq, West Greenland. *Journal of the Geological Society, London*, **162**, 299–314.

JAPSEN, P., BONOW, J. M., GREEN, P. F., CHALMERS, J. A. & LIDMAR-BERGSTROM, K. 2006. Elevated, passive continental margins: Long-term highs or Neogene uplifts? New evidence from West Greenland. *Earth and Planetary Science Letters*, **248**, 330–339.

JONES, S. M., WHITE, N., CLARKE, B. J., ROWLEY, E. & GALLAGHER, K. 2002. Present and past influence of the Iceland Plume on sedimentation. *In*: DORÉ, A. G., CARTWRIGHT, J. A., STOKER, M. S., TURNER, J. P. & WHITE, N. (eds) *Exhumation of the North Atlantic Margin: Timing, Mechanisms and Implications for Petroleum Exploration*. Geological Society, London, Special Publications, **196**, 13–25.

KEMP, S. J., MERRIMAN, R. J. & BOUCH, J. E. 2005. Clay mineral reaction progress – the maturity and burial history of the Lias Group of England and Wales. *Clay Minerals*, **40**, 43–61.

KUSZNIR, N. J. & ZIEGLER, P. A. 1992. The mechanics of continental extension and sedimentary basin formation: a simple-shear/pure-shear flexural cantilever model. *Tectonophysics*, **215**, 117–131.

LEWIS, C. L. E., GREEN, P. F., CARTER, A. & HURFORD, A. J. 1992. Elevated K/T palaeotemperatures throughout Northwest England: three kilometres of Tertiary erosion? *Earth and Planetary Science Letters*, **112**, 131–145.

LUNDIN, E. R. & DORÉ, A. G. 2002. Mid-Cenozoic postbreakup deformation in the 'passive' margins bordering the Norwegian-Greenland Sea. *Marine and Petroleum Geology*, **19**, 79–93.

MACKAY, L. M., TURNER, J., JONES, S. M. & WHITE, N. J. 2005. Cenozoic vertical motions in the Moray Firth Basin associated with initiation of the Iceland Plume. *Tectonics*, **24**, doi:10.1029/2004TC001683.

MUSSETT, A. E., DAGLEY, P. & SKELHORN, R. R. 1988. Time and duration of activity in the British Tertiary Igneous Province. *In*: MORTON, A. C. & PARSON, L. M. (eds) *Early Tertiary Volcanism and the Opening of the NE Atlantic*. Geological Society, London, Special Publications, **39**, 337–348.

NIELSEN, S. B. & HANSEN, D. L. 2000. Physical explanation of the formation and evolution of inversion zones and marginal troughs. *Geology*, **28**, 875–878.

O'SULLIVAN, K. N. 1979. The sedimentology, geochemistry, and conditions of deposition of the Tertiary rocks of the Llanbedr (Mochras Farm) borehole. *Report of the Institute of Geological Sciences*, London, No. 78/24, 1–13.

PARNELL, J., GREEN, P. F., WATT, G. & MIDDLETON, D. 2005. Thermal history and oil charge on the UK Atlantic margin. *Petroleum Geoscience*, **11**, 99–112.

PRAEG, D., STOKER, M. S., SHANNON, P. M., CERAMICOLA, S., HJELSTUN, B., LABERG, J. S. & MATHIESEN, A. 2005. Episodic Cenozoic tectonism and the development of the NW European 'passive' continental margin. *Marine and Petroleum Geology*, **22**, 1007–1030.

REDFIELD, T. R., OSMUNDSEN, P. T. & HENDRICKS, B. W. H. 2005. The role of fault reactivation and growth in the uplift of western Fennoscandia. *Journal of the Geological Society, London*, **162**, 1013–1030.

REYNOLDS, S. D., COBLENTZ, D. D. & HILLIS, R. R. 2002. Tectonic forces controlling the regional intraplate stress field in continental Australia: Results from new finite element modelling. *Journal of Geophysical Research*, **107B**, doi:10.1029/2001JB000408.

RIDER, M. H. 1996. *The Geological Interpretation of Well Logs* (2nd edn). Whittles Publishing, Caithness.

ROHRMAN, M. & VAN DER BEEK, P. 1996. Cenozoic postrift domal uplift of North Atlantic margins: An asthenospheric diapirism model. *Geology*, **24**, 901–904.

ROWLEY, E. & WHITE, N. 1998. Inverse modelling of extension and denudation in the East Irish Sea and surrounding areas. *Earth and Planetary Science Letters*, **161**, 57–71.

SCLATER, J. G. & CHRISTIE, P. A. F. 1980. Continental stretching: an explanation of the post-mid-Cretaceous subsidence of the Central North Sea Basin. *Journal of Geophysical Research*, **85**, 3711–3739.

SCOTCHMAN, I. C. 2001. Petroleum geochemistry of the Lower and Middle Jurassic in Atlantic margin basins of Ireland and the UK. *In*: SHANNON, P. M., HAUGHTON, P. D. W. & CORCORAN, D. V. (eds) *The Petroleum Exploration of Ireland's Offshore Basins*. Geological Society, London, Special Publications, **188**, 31–60.

SHAW CHAMPION, M. E., WHITE, N. J., JONES, S. M. & PRIESTLEY, K. F. 2006. Crustal velocity structure of the British Isles; a comparison of receiver functions and wide-angle seismic data. *Geophysical Journal International*, **166**, 795–813.

SIBSON, R. H. 1995. Selective fault reactivation during basin inversion: potential for fluid redistribution through fault-valve action. *In*: BUCHANAN, J. G. & BUCHANAN, P. G. (eds) *Basin Inversion*. Geological Society, London, Special Publications, **88**, 3–21.

STOKER, M. S., HOULT, R. J., NIELSEN, T. *ET AL.* 2005. Sedimentary and oceanographic responses to early Neogene compression on the NW European margin. *Marine and Petroleum Geology*, **22**, 1031–1044.

STUEVOLD, L. M. & ELDHOLM, O. 1996. Cenozoic uplift of Fennoscandia inferred from a study of the mid-Norwegian margin. *Global and Planetary Change*, **12**, 359–386.

TAPPIN, D. R., CHADWICK, R. A., JACKSON, A. A., WINGFIELD, R. T. R. & SMITH, N. J. P. 1994. *The*

Geology of the Cardigan Bay and the Bristol Channel. London: HMSO for the British Geological Survey.

TILEY, R., WHITE, N. & AL-KINDI, S. 2004. Linking Palaeogene denudation and magmatic underplating beneath the British Isles. *Geological Magazine*, **141**, 345–351.

THOMSON, K., GREEN, P. F., WHITHAM, A. G., PRICE, S. P. & UNDERHILL, J. R. 1999. New constraints on the thermal history of North-East Greenland from apatite fission-track analysis. *Geological Society of America Bulletin*, **111**, 1054–1068.

TURNER, J. P. 1996. Gravity-driven nappes and their relation to palaeobathymetry: examples from West Africa and Cardigan Bay, UK. *In*: BUCHANAN, P. G. & NIEUWLAND, D. A. (eds) *Modern Developments in Structural Interpretation, Validation and Modelling.* Geological Society, London, Special Publications, **99**, 345–362.

TURNER, J. P. 1997. Strike-slip fault reactivation in the Cardigan Bay basin. *Journal of the Geological Society, London*, **154**, 5–8.

TURNER, J. P. & WILLIAMS, G. A. 2004. Sedimentary basin inversion and intra-plate shortening. *Earth-Science Reviews*, **65**, 277–304.

VOGT, U., MAKRIS, J., O'REILLY, B. M., HAUSER, F., READMAN, P. W. & BRIAN JACOB, A. W. 1998. The Hatton Basin and continental margin: Crustal structure from wide-angle seismic and gravity data. *Journal of Geophysical Research*, **103B**, 12545–12566.

WARE, P. D. & TURNER, J. P. 2002. Sonic velocity analysis of the Tertiary denudation of the Irish Sea basin. *In*: DORÉ, A. G., CARTWRIGHT, J., STOKER, M. S., TURNER, J. P. & WHITE, N. (eds) *Exhumation of the North Atlantic Margin: Timing, Mechanisms and Implications for Petroleum Exploration.* Geological Society, London, Special Publications, **196**, 355–370.

WELCH, M. J. & TURNER, J. P. 2000. Triassic-Jurassic development of the St. George's Channel basin, offshore Wales, UK. *Marine and Petroleum Geology*, **17**, 723–750.

WHITE, N. & LOVELL, B. 1997. Measuring the pulse of a plume with the sedimentary record. *Nature*, **387**, 888–891.

WHITE, R. S. & MCKENZIE, D. P. 1989. Magmatism at Rift Zones: The Generation of Volcanic Continental Margins and Flood Basalts. *Journal of Geophysical Research*, **94B**, 7685–7729.

WILLIAMS, G. A., TURNER, J. P. & HOLFORD, S. P. 2005. Inversion and exhumation of the St George's Channel Basin, offshore Wales, UK. *Journal of the Geological Society, London*, **162**, 97–110.

WILLIAMS, G. D., POWELL, C. M. & COOPER, M. A. 1989. Geometry and kinematics of inversion tectonics. *In*: COOPER, M. A. & WILLIAMS, G. D. (eds) *Inversion Tectonics.* Geological Society, London, Special Publications, **44**, 3–15.

WOODLAND, A. W. (ed.) 1971. *The Llanbedr (Mochras Farm) borehole.* Report of the Institute of Geological Sciences, London, No. 71/18.

YALÇIN, M. N., LITTKE, R. & SACHSENHOFER, R. F. 1997. Thermal history of sedimentary basins. *In*: WELTE, D. H., HORSFIELD, B. & BAKER, D. R. (eds) *Petroleum and Basin Evolution*, Springer, Berlin, 71–167.

ZIEGLER, P. A. 1990. *Geological Atlas of Western and Central Europe.* Shell International Petroleum Maatschappij B.V., The Hague.

ZIEGLER, P. A. 2004. Europe: Permian to Recent Evolution. *In*: SELLEY, R. C., COCKS, L. R. & PLIMER, I. R. (eds) *The Encyclopedia of Geology.* Elsevier, Amsterdam, 102–125.

ZIEGLER, P. A., CLOETINGH, S. & VAN WEES, J-D. 1995. Dynamics of intra-plate compressional deformation: the Alpine foreland and other examples. *Tectonophysics*, **252**, 7–59.

ZIEGLER, P. A., VAN WEES, J-D. & CLOETINGH, S. 1998. Mechanical controls on collision-related compressional intraplate deformation. *Tectonophysics*, **300**, 103–129.

The effects of Cenozoic compression within the Faroe–Shetland Basin and adjacent areas

J. DEREK RITCHIE, HOWARD JOHNSON, MARTYN F. QUINN & ROBERT W. GATLIFF

British Geological Survey, Murchison House, West Mains Road, Edinburgh EH9 3LA, UK
(e-mail:d.ritchie@bgs.ac.uk)

Abstract: The effects of Cenozoic compression within the Faroe–Shetland Basin and surrounding areas are mainly manifested in the form of growth folds. The scale and orientation of the folds varies significantly, with axial trace lengths ranging between less than 10 to over 250 km and trends including east, NE-, NNE-, ENW-, NNW- and WNW. The NE-trending features are the most numerous, though they are mainly restricted to the NE Faroe–Shetland Basin where an inherited Caledonian structural grain is most prevalent. Limited evidence exists for late Paleocene and early Eocene activity along the Wyville Thomson Ridge, whereas mid–late Eocene and Oligocene fold growth is more common in the SW Faroe–Shetland Basin. Although the effects of well-defined early–mid Miocene deformation appear to be mainly constrained to the NE Faroe–Shetland Basin, this phase of activity is also inferred to have been responsible for major growth of the Wyville Thomson Ridge. Early Pliocene fold growth is observed within the Faroe–Shetland Basin and adjacent areas, with raised seabed profiles over some of the anticlinal features suggesting that the effects of compressional stress continue at the present day. Despite the variation in trend and size of growth folds, there is, we believe, similarity in their local mechanism of emplacement, with buttressing of sedimentary successions against pre-existing basement architecture and igneous intrusions being of particular significance. However, the lack of obvious spatial or temporal pattern to fold growth development within the NE Atlantic margin as a whole mitigates against a single regional driving mechanism being able to explain the current distribution, orientation and timing of the folds.

There have been numerous studies of the causes, nature, timing and effects of Cenozoic compression within the NE Atlantic margin, particularly in the Vøring Basin offshore Norway (e.g. Blystad *et al.* 1995; Doré & Lundin 1996; Vågnes *et al.* 1998; Lundin & Doré 2002; Mosar *et al.* 2002; Løseth & Henriksen 2005), but also further to the SW within the Faroe–Shetland Basin, Wyville Thomson Ridge, Hatton Bank and Hatton Basin areas (e.g. Boldreel & Andersen 1993, 1994, 1998; Lamers & Carmichael 1999; Tate *et al.* 1999; Andersen *et al.* 2002; Ritchie *et al.* 2003; Sørensen 2003; Davis *et al.* 2004; Smallwood 2004; Johnson *et al.* 2005; Stoker *et al.* 2005a, b). The main objective of this study is to produce, for the first time, an evaluation of the Faroe–Shetland Basin as a whole regarding the distribution, nature and timing of compression, set within a much wider geographical context. This includes a new light on the evolution of fold growth structures within the SW Faroe–Shetland Basin. Potentially, the topic of Cenozoic fold growth is particularly important in economic terms, as hydrocarbon discoveries such as 'Marjun' (well 6004/16-1Z) (e.g. Smallwood & Kirk 2005) and 'Tobermory' (well 214/04-1) have been made within Cenozoic growth anticlines.

The Faroe–Shetland Basin (Fig. 1) is approximately 400 km long and 175 km wide and comprises a generally NE-trending complex of sub-basins and intra-basinal highs. The basin has a long history of development dating back to Late Palaeozoic times (e.g. Duindam & van Hoorn 1987; Hitchen & Ritchie 1987; Rumph *et al.* 1993; Stoker *et al.* 1993; Dean *et al.* 1999; Doré *et al.* 1999; Lamers & Carmichael 1999; Roberts *et al.* 1999; Smallwood & Kirk 2005). Basin formation was probably initiated during Devonian times, with additional relatively minor rift phases during the Permo-Triassic and Jurassic. However, the main episode of basin formation occurred during Cretaceous times (e.g. Duindam & van Hoorn 1987; Dean *et al.* 1999; Doré *et al.* 1999; Lamers & Carmichael 1999; Roberts *et al.* 1999). This was followed by post-rift subsidence during the Cenozoic (e.g. Turner & Scrutton 1993), though there is evidence for continuing extension in places until the early to mid Paleocene (e.g. Smallwood & Gill 2002). Regional dynamic uplift attributable to the initiation of the Iceland Plume is postulated during the mid to late Paleocene (e.g. White & Mackenzie 1989; Nadin *et al.* 1997) and was succeeded in earliest Eocene times by the onset of seafloor spreading within the Iceland and

From: JOHNSON, H., DORÉ, A. G., GATLIFF, R. W., HOLDSWORTH, R., LUNDIN, E. R. & RITCHIE, J. D. (eds)
The Nature and Origin of Compression in Passive Margins. Geological Society, London, Special Publications,
306, 121–136. DOI: 10.1144/SP306.5   0305-8719/08/$15.00 © The Geological Society of London 2008.

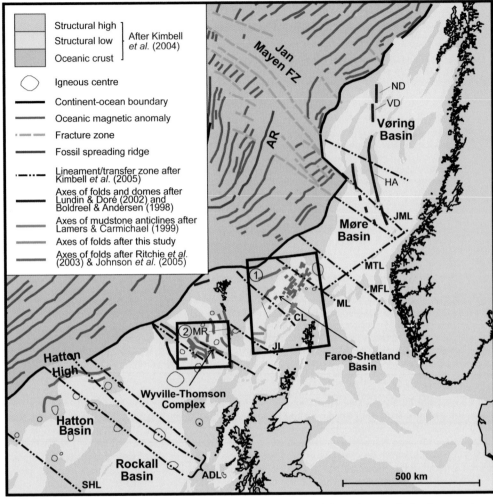

Fig. 1. Summary distribution map of the main compressional Cenozoic anticlines, domes and related structural features within the NE Atlantic margin (modified from Ritchie *et al.* 2003; Kimbell *et al.* 2004 and Johnson *et al.* 2005). Inset 1 = Faroe–Shetland area (see Fig. 2); Inset 2 = Wyville Thomson area (see Fig. 7). Abbreviations: ADL, Anton Dohrn Lineament; AR, Aegir Ridge; HA, Helland-Hansen Arch; JL, Judd Lineament; JML, Jan Mayen Lineament; ML, Magnus Lineament; MR, Munkagrunnur Ridge; ND, Naglfar Dome; SHL, South Hatton Lineament; VD, Vema Dome.

Norwegian basins. Renewed Eocene post-rift subsidence within the Faroe–Shetland Basin was interrupted at various stages by pulses of Palaeogene and Neogene compression (e.g. Ritchie *et al.* 2003; Davis *et al.* 2004; Smallwood 2004; Johnson *et al.* 2005; Stoker *et al.* 2005*a, b*) and by regional uplift/tilting of the basin margin (e.g. Andersen 2000; Stoker *et al.* 2002; Davis *et al.* 2004; Stoker *et al.* 2005*a, b*). In the following sections, the nature, timing and distribution of the Cenozoic growth folds in the Faroe–Shetland Basin and adjacent areas are summarized using interpreted

commercial seismic data and wells. An assessment of the age of fold growth development is derived from the dating of key unconformities in wells (e.g. Stoker *et al.* 2001; STRATAGEM, partners 2002; Davies & Cartwright 2002) and analysis of stratal pattern development.

NE Faroe–Shetland basin

Within the NE part of Faroe–Shetland Basin, numerous growth folds, mud anticlines and a rare

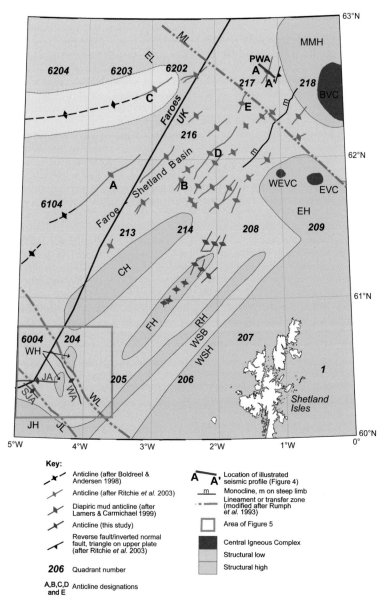

Key:

Anticline (after Boldreel & Andersen 1998)

Anticline (after Ritchie *et al.* 2003)

Diapiric mud anticline (after Lamers & Carmichael 1999)

Anticline (this study)

Reverse fault/inverted normal fault, triangle on upper plate (after Ritchie *et al.* 2003)

206 Quadrant number

A,B,C,D and E — Anticline designations

A — A' Location of illustrated seismic profile (Figure 4)

m — Monocline, m on steep limb

Lineament or transfer zone (modified after Rumph *et al.* 1993)

Area of Figure 5

Central Igneous Complex

Structural low

Structural high

Fig. 2. Summary map of the main compressional features within the Faroe–Shetland Basin area (modified from Ritchie *et al.* 2003 and Johnson *et al.* 2005). Abbreviations as for Figure 1 except: BVC, Brendan Volcanic Centre; CH, Corona High; EH, Erlend High; EVC, Erlend Volcanic Centre; FH, Flett High; JA, Judd Anticline; JH, Judd High; JL, Judd Lineament; ML, Magnus Lineament; MMH, Møre Marginal High; PWA, Pilot Whale Anticline; RH, Rona High; SJA, South Judd Anticline; WA, Westray Anticline; WEVC, West Erlend Volcanic Centre; WH, Westray High; WL, Westray Lineament; WSB, West Shetland Basin; WSH, West Shetland High.

reverse fault have been mapped using 2D commercial seismic reflection data (Fig. 2) (e.g. Boldreel & Andersen 1998; Lamers & Carmichael 1999; Ritchie *et al.* 2003; Davis *et al.* 2004; Johnson *et al.* 2005). These growth fold structures can be categorized into three distinct groups on the basis of their trend/genesis, namely: (1) NE-trending growth folds; (2) NNE-trending growth folds; and (3) NE-trending mud anticlines and diapirs (Fig. 2).

NE-trending growth folds

The vast majority of growth folds within the NE Faroe–Shetland Basin display a NE trend (Fig. 2). The axial traces of these anticlines and monoclines vary in length significantly, with the largest extending over 70 km. The fold amplitudes range up to 3000 m, and both symmetrical and asymmetrical forms are present. The ages of the seismic horizons used in evaluating the timing of formation of the structures largely follows the stratigraphic schemes of STRATAGEM partners (2002) and Davies & Cartwright (2002), Ritchie *et al.* (2003) and Johnson *et al.* (2005). The growth folds are generally only clearly observed at top Palaeogene lavas and younger stratigraphic levels, as the presence of these lavas and also contemporaneous igneous intrusive complexes, effectively mask the deeper structure of the basin (e.g. Ritchie *et al.* 2003, figs 5, 7, 8 & 9). Though the structure and nature of the pre-Cenozoic succession is largely obscured in this area, the main trend of the growth anticlines is parallel with the pervasive NE Caledonian/pre-Caledonian structural grain that dominates this part of the margin (e.g. Duindam & van Hoorn 1987; Hitchen & Ritchie 1987; Stoker *et al.* 1993; Dean *et al.* 1999; Roberts *et al.* 1999; Coward *et al.* 2003), perhaps suggesting a link between pre-existing structural architecture, i.e. the presence of deeply buried NE-trending tilted fault blocks, and subsequent growth fold development. NE-trending anticlines, comprising folds A–D and the Pilot Whale Anticline (Fig. 2) have previously been described by Ritchie *et al.* (2003) and are considered representative of growth folds within this part of the basin. These were mainly developed in early to mid Miocene times, though some also show early Pliocene growth (Fig. 3). There is some biostratigraphical evidence from well 214/04-1 of a late Eocene unconformity (separating upper Eocene from lower Oligocene/upper Eocene strata) as documented by Davies & Cartwright (2002). There is also limited supporting seismic evidence for growth fold development at the time (Davies & Cartwright 2002, fig. 5). However, the widespread effects of any compression on the Eocene and Oligocene succession remain difficult to assess due to seismic masking by pervasive polygonal faulting. However, there are signs of limited fold growth during this time associated with the development of Anticline C (Fugloy Ridge) (e.g. Boldreel & Andersen 1998; Ritchie *et al.* 2003; Johnson *et al.* 2005).

NNE-trending growth folds

The NNE-trending Pilot Whale Anticline is one of only two significant growth folds with this orientation in NE Faroe–Shetland Basin (Fig. 4). The axial trace of this slightly asymmetrical anticline extends for about 20 km and lies close to the extreme NE margin of the Faroe–Shetland Basin (Fig. 2). The fold is clearly imaged at top Palaeogene lavas level, with an amplitude of approximately 1400 m (Fig. 4). The anticline is defined by the top Palaeogene lavas and the diagenetic Opal A–Opal C/T transformation horizon (Ritchie *et al.* 2003; Johnson *et al.* 2005). This diagenetic horizon has a late Miocene age ascribed to its formation by Davis & Cartwright (2002) (Fig. 3). The relatively undeformed mid Pliocene to Recent succession becomes thinner over the crest of the anticline possibly suggesting relative sea level rise and passive burial of the structure.

The growth of the Pilot Whale Anticline is, we believe, closely associated with the development of the Pilot Whale Diapirs (Haflidason *et al.* 1996) and the associated seabed mud mounds and subsurface injection features that can be observed from seismic data (Fig. 4). This association of diapirs, seabed mounds and injection features is similar to phenomena described from the Norwegian margin around the Vema and Naglfar domes and the Helland Hansen and Modgunn arches, and in the North Viking Graben area (e.g. Hjelstuen *et al.* 1997; Hovland *et al.* 1998). The morphological expression of the Pilot Whale mud mounds ranges from almost circular features, to complex groups with irregular perimeters. They rise to at least 120 m above the sea bed and have been described as comprising sediments that range in age from Pliocene to Oligocene. The development of the mud mounds, diapirs and intrusive features is considered here to have been triggered initially by the growth of the Pilot Whale Anticline from early Pliocene times onwards. Before mobilization and injection, the Eocene and Oligocene succession within the NE Faroe–Shetland Basin is inferred to have comprised mainly smectite-rich, under-compacted, low-density mudstones that were subsequently mantled by a seismically well-layered, mainly fine-grained Pliocene and younger succession. It is suggested that the growth of the Pilot Whale Anticline may have facilitated fracturing and breaching of the Eocene and younger successions, and that the developing anticline may have acted as a focus for the migration of fluids and the mobilization of this under-compacted, overpressured, low-density succession. The interpreted presence of *v*-brights which are considered to indicate gas or water charged sandstone ring dykes (Huuse & Mikelson 2004) within the Eocene interval suggests that the natural buoyancy of this succession may have been significantly assisted by gas, fluid and sediment injection.

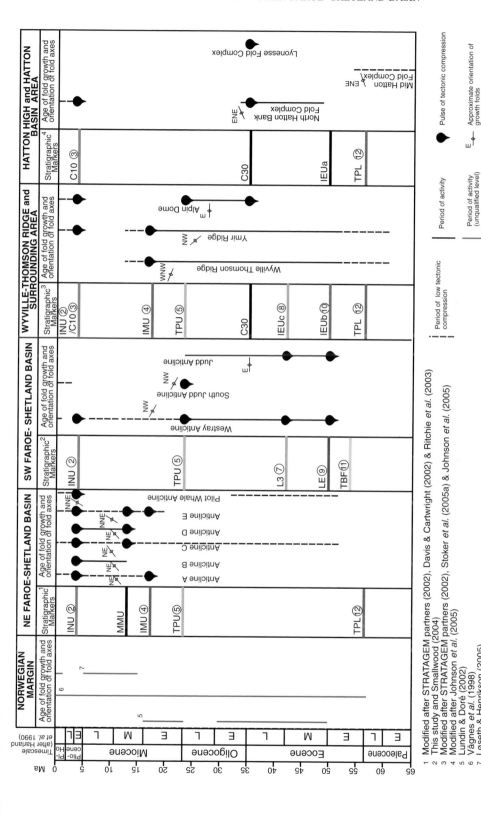

Fig. 3. Summary chart of the timing/duration of Cenozoic fold growth development within the Faroe–Shetland Basin and adjacent areas within the NE Atlantic margin (modified from Ritchie *et al.* 2003 and Johnson *et al.* 2005). Abbreviations: ③C10, Early Pliocene Unconformity; C30, Late Eocene Unconformity; IEUa, Intra-Eocene unconformities; ④IMU, Intra-Miocene Unconformity; ②INU, Intra-Neogene (Early Pliocene) Unconformity; ⑦L3, Mid Eocene (late Lutetian); ⑨LE, Early Eocene (latest Ypresian) Unconformity; MMU, Mid Miocene Unconformity; ⑤TPU, Top Palaeogene lavas; ⑫TPL, Top Palaeogene Unconformity; ⑪TBF, Top Balder Formation; ⑫TPL, Top Palaeogene Unconformity.

1 Modified after STRATAGEM partners (2002), Davis & Cartwright (2002) & Ritchie *et al.* (2003)
2 This study and Smallwood (2004)
3 Modified after STRATAGEM partners (2002), Stoker *et al.* (2005a) & Johnson *et al.* (2005)
4 Modified after Johnson *et al.* (2005)
5 Lundin & Doré (2002)
6 Vågnes *et al.* (1998)
7 Løseth & Henriksen (2005)

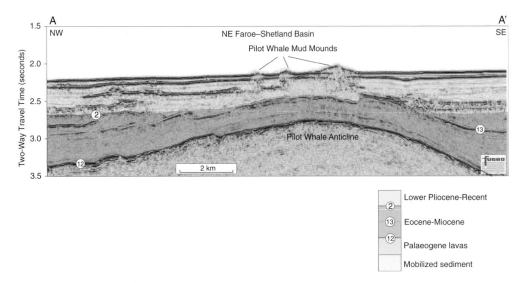

Fig. 4. Seismic profile A–A' across the Pilot Whale Anticline within the NE Faroe–Shetland Basin. See Figure 2 for location of profile. Abbreviations: ②INU, Intra-Neogene (Early Pliocene) Unconformity and ⑫TPL, Top Palaeogene lavas. Note that ⑬Opal A–Opal C/T transformation horizon is a diagenetic reflector of late Miocene age (Davies & Cartwright 2002).

Ritchie *et al.* (2003) speculated, from strain ellipse analysis, that the generation of the NNE-trending Pilot Whale Anticline may have been caused by sinistral strike-slip fault movement along the Magnus Lineament or Transfer Zone (Fig. 2). This hypothesis is similar to that promulgated by Doré & Lundin (1996) for the NNE- to north-trending Cenozoic anticlines and domes observed within the Norwegian margin. However, it is now considered more likely that the Pilot Whale Anticline formed as a result of buttressing of basin fill against Palaeozoic and older basement of the Møre Marginal High which includes the basic igneous plutonic mass that forms the core of the Brendan Volcanic Centre (Fig. 2). Regionally, the NNE-trending Pilot Whale Anticline represents the most southerly of a series of NNE- to north-trending domes and anticlines that are extensively developed along the Norwegian margin (Fig. 1), though it is separated from them by a considerable expanse in the Møre Basin where no anticlines have been reported. To the SW of the Pilot Whale Anticline, the compressional folds follow mainly NE trends within the Faroe–Shetland Basin.

NE- to NNE-trending mud anticlines and diapirs

Linear NE- to NNE-trending mud anticlines with axial traces varying between 5 and 20 km in length have been described by Lamers &

Carmichael (1999, fig. 13) around the southern half of Quadrant 214 (Fig. 2). Those authors believe that Upper Cretaceous and lowermost Paleocene (T10 stratigraphic interval of Ebdon *et al.* 1995) argillaceous rocks within the Faroe–Shetland Basin were mobilized during a period of 'instability' in early Paleocene (T20 to T30 intervals) times, to form the basement-detached, linear mudstone-cored anticlines. Speculatively, it is conceivable that a distinct phase of compression in early Paleocene times was the direct trigger for the formation of these structures, initiating their mobilization and development into discrete linear mudstone walls or anticlines. Such compression may have been associated with inversion of postulated underlying mainly NE-trending extensional Mesozoic faults. The effects of compression are described elsewhere within the Faroe–Shetland area during Paleocene times, with for example, broad inversion of the Judd sub-basin (Roberts *et al.* 1999) and also fold growth associated with the initiation of the Wyville Thomson Ridge (Fig. 3) (e.g. Boldreel & Andersen 1993; Johnson *et al.* 2005).

SW Faroe–Shetland basin

A group of three closely related anticlinal structures here named the Judd, Westray and South Judd anticlines have been identified using BP proprietary seismic data within the Judd sub-basin and

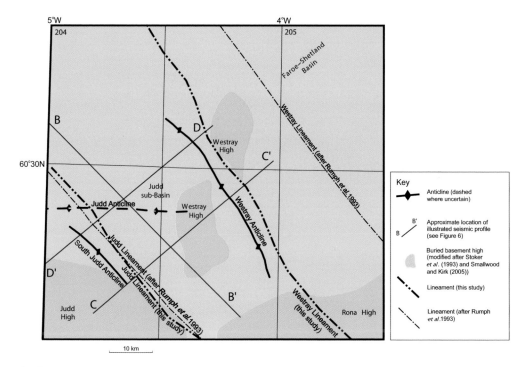

Fig. 5. Distribution of growth folds from BP proprietary seismic data in the SW Faroe–Shetland Basin.

immediately adjacent area (Figs 2 & 5). The age of the seismic horizons used in the evaluation of the timing of formation of these anticlines follows the seismic stratigraphic scheme of Smallwood (2004) and Smallwood & Kirk (2005).

Judd Anticline

The Judd Anticline/Monocline is interpreted to form an important, generally west-trending structure (Smallwood & Kirk 2005, fig. 15) that extends for at least 33 km within the Judd sub-basin (Figs 5 & 6(i)). However, the west-trending 'Judd Anticline' of Smallwood (2004, fig. 13) refers to a broad structural feature that comprises an amalgamation of the Judd, Westray and South Judd anticlines as described in this paper. Seismic reflection evidence suggests that there are at least two main phases of fold growth associated with the development of this anticline. Considerable depositional thinning of the lower to middle Eocene (latest Ypresian to late Lutetian) succession within the NW limb of the Judd Anticline (Fig. 6(i)) is interpreted to be indicative of the first pulse of deformation. The onset of this deformation is marked by the development of the LE (early Eocene i.e. latest Ypresian) Unconformity ⑨. This was followed by

a more protracted phase of fold growth during mid Eocene times (Fig. 3). Significant attenuation of the lower to middle Eocene succession occurs on the SE limb of the anticline in particular, at the prominent L3 (late Lutetian) Unconformity ⑦. In addition, the overlying middle Eocene to Oligocene succession is also deformed, though the age of this deformation cannot be accurately ascertained as the upper part of the interval is absent through erosion over the crest of the Judd Anticline due to the development of the Top Palaeogene Unconformity (TPU) ⑤. Notwithstanding this uncertainty, it is suggested that this latter phase of folding occurred sometime during the late Oligocene. This interpretation supports that of Smallwood (2004), who recognized several phases of deformation including Eocene (latest Ypresian and late Lutetian), Oligocene and ?mid Miocene times, associated with NE–SW orientated compressional stress.

Westray Anticline

The term Westray Anticline is informally introduced here for a generally asymmetrical, NW-trending growth fold within the Judd sub-basin (Figs 5 & 6(ii)). The axial trace of this anticline extends for approximately 45 km, and its amplitude

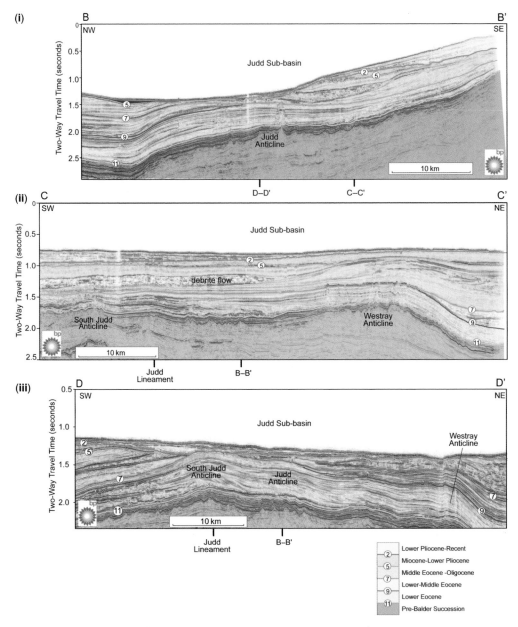

Fig. 6. (i) Seismic profile B–B′ across the Judd Anticline, (ii) Seismic profile C–C′ across the South Judd and Westray anticlines and (iii) Seismic line D–D′ across the South Judd, Judd and Westray anticlines. See Figures 3 and 5 for age of reflectors and location of profiles, respectively. Abbreviations: ②INU, Intra-Neogene (Early Pliocene) Unconformity; ⑦L3, Mid Eocene (late Lutetian); ⑨LE, Early Eocene (latest Ypresian) Unconformity; MMU, Mid Miocene Unconformity; ⑪TBF, Top Balder Formation; ⑤TPU, Top Palaeogene Unconformity.

increases markedly towards the SE where it merges with the eastern deformational margin of the 'Judd Anticline' as defined by Smallwood (2004, figs 12 & 13). At least three main phases of growth have been recognized for the Westray Anticline. Like the Judd Anticline, a significant onlap and thinning of the lower to middle Eocene (latest Ypresian–late Lutetian) succession occurs on the NE limb of the

Westray Anticline (Fig. 6(ii)) and is considered to mark a distinct phase of fold growth activity during latest early Eocene (latest Ypresian times) times (Fig. 3). This was followed by a more gradual and protracted phase of growth until mid Eocene (late Lutetian) times. The lower to middle Eocene interval is absent on the SW flank of the structure, possibly due in part to erosion associated with the development of the L3 (late Lutetian) ⑦ Unconformity. There is also evidence for depositional thinning of the upper part of the middle Eocene to Oligocene succession across the Westray Anticline. Here for example, a distinct debrite flow with chaotic seismic facies onlaps the SW flank of the structure. This suggests that the fold had significant penecontemporaneous relief, and exerted considerable influence on the distribution of the debrite. Rejuvenation of fold growth occurred during development of the TPU ⑤ (Fig. 3) and was associated with onlap of Miocene to lower Pliocene sediments, particularly on the NE limb of the anticline. This was followed by a further phase of growth associated with formation of the Neogene Unconformity (INU) ②, with onlap of Pliocene to Recent sediments onto the SW margin of the Westray Anticline. Indeed the seabed itself appears to be slightly domed over the Westray Anticline (Fig. 6ii), although this may be caused in part by differential subsidence on its flanks due to the effects of sediment loading and compaction rather than recent compression.

South Judd Anticline

The South Judd Anticline is considered to form a short, slightly asymmetrical NW-trending growth fold and occurs within the SW part of the Judd sub-basin (Figs 5 & 6(iii)). The axial trace of the anticline extends for approximately 18 km. In contrast to the Westray Anticline, its amplitude increases towards the NW, where it merges with the east-trending Judd Anticline. There is only evidence for one major phase of deformation associated with the South Judd Anticline, though its exact timing is not easily defined due to the truncation of key stratigraphic units. Generally, the parallel-bedded Palaeogene (and possibly even the Miocene to early Pliocene) succession as a whole appears deformed by a single episode of compression (Fig. 6(iii)). However, the stratigraphic succession has been truncated over the crestal part of the South Judd Anticline by a composite unconformity that combines the TPU ⑤ and INU ② (and possibly others too). The main age of the deformation is clearly post-Eocene and is probably of late Oligocene age; similar to the

proposed growth on the parallel Westray Anticline (Fig. 3).

In terms of local controls on the style and distribution of the fold structures within the Judd sub-basin, the Westray and South Judd anticlines appear to be closely spatially associated with the inferred traces of the Westray and Judd lineaments of Rumph et al. (1993) and from BGS unpublished information (Fig. 5). These NW-trending lineaments possibly originated as Proterozoic Laxfordian-style shear zones, similar to those described from the Lewisian Complex on mainland Scotland and the Outer Isles (e.g. Park et al. 2002). Offshore, these lineaments are considered to have been reactivated as Permo-Triassic, Cretaceous and Cenozoic transfer zones (e.g. Earle et al. 1989; Rumph et al. 1993; Dean et al. 1999), partitioning the NE-trending sub-basins of the Faroe–Shetland Basin. Transfer zones typically have components of strike-slip movement associated with them (e.g. Lister et al. 1986) and there is a possibility that Westray and South Judd folds represent positive flower structures. A more plausible explanation, however, is derived from the observation that the anticlines have a close spatial association with footwall blocks or ramps of the Judd and Westray highs (Fig. 5), and that the folds probably developed as a consequence of buttressing of the sedimentary succession against these relatively rigid structural highs.

The east-trending Judd Anticline has a rather anomalous orientation with regard to the mainly NE-trending Caledonian structural grain prevalent within the Faroe–Shetland Basin. A plausible explanation could be that the anticline formed in response to north–south compression during Eocene times, as a result of ridge-push associated with seafloor spreading at the Aegir Ridge to the north of the Faroe Islands (Boldreel & Andersen 1993) which persisted until Chron 12 times (earliest Oligocene) (Lundin & Doré 2005). This view is supported by Smallwood & Kirk (2005), who believe that inversion was caused by north–south compressional stress and was concentrated between the Westray Fault and the Judd and Rona highs.

The variation in the phases of fold growth of the Judd, South Judd and Westray anticlines (Fig. 3) may suggest that they should be considered as distinct (though generically-linked) structural features, and not as a single compressional structure as described by Smallwood (2004).

Margins of the Faroe–Shetland Basin

A complex area of deformation occurs within the transitional zone between the Faroe–Shetland and

Rockall basins (Figs 1 & 7). Here, Cenozoic growth folds display four main trends, namely: (1) WNW-trending e.g. Wyville Thomson Ridge; (2) NW-trending e.g. Ymir Ridge; (3) NNW-trending e.g. Munkagrunnur Ridge; and (4) west-trending e.g. the Alpin Dome. The age of the seismic horizons used in the evaluation of the timing of formation of the Wyville Thomson and Ymir ridges largely follows that of Stoker *et al.* (2001), STRATAGEM partners (2002), Johnson *et al.* (2005) and Stoker *et al.* (2005a, b). However, the calibration of these markers remains somewhat speculative due to a lack of commercial wells and shallow boreholes in the area.

Wyville Thomson Ridge

The Wyville Thomson Ridge forms a large symmetrical, WNW-trending anticline, with an axial trace that extends for more than 200 km (Figs 7 & 8). The fold has an amplitude and wavelength of approximately 2 km and 40 km, respectively, at the level of the TPL ⑫ (Fig. 8). A number of deformational phases are considered to have contributed to the evolution of the Wyville Thomson Ridge. On the NE flank of the anticline, the lower and middle parts of the Eocene succession (between the Intra Miocene Unconformity (IMU) ④ and an

intra-Eocene Unconformity (IEUb) ⑩ and possibly also the upper Paleocene to Eocene lavas) thin towards the ridge, suggesting a long-lived episode of Paleocene and Eocene growth (Johnson *et al.* 2005) (Fig. 3). The Eocene to Oligocene interval above the IEUb ⑩ event is strongly attenuated; the angular break interpreted to represent a composite unconformity that combines the effects of the C30 (late Eocene) ③, TPU ⑤ IMU ④ unconformities (e.g. Johnson *et al.* 2005). On the basis of regional evidence, the development of the IMU ④ is regarded to be the most significant of these unconformities and considered to be associated with an early to mid Miocene phase of growth on the Wyville Thomson Ridge (e.g. Johnson *et al.* 2005; Stoker *et al.* 2005a, b) (Fig. 3). According to Boldreel & Andersen (1993) and Tate *et al.* (1999), the Wyville Thomson Ridge represents part of a system of ramp-anticlines, which include the Ymir and Munkagrunnur ridges (see below) that formed above a crustal detachment that was active during latest Paleocene times and onwards as a result of mainly north–south compression associated with the spreading on the Aegir Ridge. However, a minor component of the fold growth may be due to strain partitioning associated with regional sinistral transpression along the NW European margin during Palaeogene times (e.g. Imber *et al.* 2005).

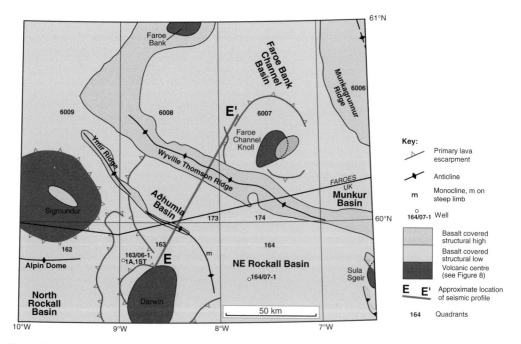

Fig. 7. Summary distribution map of the main compressional structural features within the Wyville Thomson Complex and surrounding area (modified after Johnson *et al.* 2005).

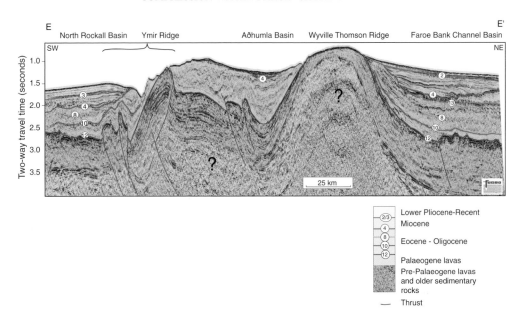

Fig. 8. Seismic profile E–E′ across the Wyville Thomson and Ymir ridges. See Figures 3 and 7 for age of reflectors and location of profile, respectively. Abbreviations: ③C10, Early Pliocene Unconformity; IEUa, ⑩b and ⑧c, Intra-Eocene unconformities; ④IMU, Intra-Miocene Unconformity; ②INU, Intra-Neogene (Early Pliocene) Unconformity; ⑫TPL, Top Palaeogene lavas. Note that ⑬Opal A – Opal C/T transformation horizon is a diagenetic reflector of late Miocene age (Davies & Cartwright 2002).

Ymir Ridge

The Ymir Ridge forms an asymmetrical, NW-trending and faulted anticlinal complex that extends for over 100 km (Figs 7 & 8). The fold amplitude and wavelength are approximately 1.4 km and 40 km respectively at the level of the TPL ⑫ (Fig. 8). The Eocene succession on the SW flank of the Ymir Ridge displays growth folds and is cut by penecontemporaneous reverse faults. The timing of this deformation is difficult to define accurately, as the Eocene succession is strongly truncated by a significant composite unconformity surface that combines the effects of the C30 (Late Eocene) ③, TPU ⑤ and IMU ④. As for the Wyville Thomson Ridge, the Miocene unconformity surface ④ is interpreted to mark the most important of the unconformity surfaces and may have formed as a result of significant pulse of compression within the Faroe–Shetland region (e.g. Johnson *et al.* 2005) (Fig. 3).

Munkagrunnur Ridge

The Munkagrunnur Ridge forms a slightly asymmetrical elongate NNW-trending anticlinal feature (Keser Neish 2003; Smallwood 2005) that extends

for at least 135 km (Figs 7 & 8), though the nature of its transition with the Faroe Platform to the NW is unclear. The nature and origin of the Munkagrunnur Ridge is poorly understood, but the results of potential field modelling suggest that it comprises a crystalline basement block, capped by less that 2 km of pre-Eocene strata and 1 km of folded Palaeogene lavas (Smallwood *et al.* 2001). Because these deformed lavas crop out at the seabed over a large proportion of the ridge (Keser Neish 2003), the age of any compressional deformation is difficult to assess, other that it must have occurred in latest Paleocene or later times. By analogy with the Wyville Thomson and Ymir ridges, this deformation may have occurred during Eocene, Oligocene and Miocene times.

Alpin Dome

The Alpin Dome forms a little surveyed, slightly asymmetrical, east-trending anticline that extends for approximately 50 km in the North Rockall Basin (STRATAGEM partners 2002; Stoker *et al.* 2005a) (Fig. 7). The timing of deformation is not fully understood as yet, but it appears that a major phase of compression may have occurred during late Eocene (C30) and mid Miocene (IMU) times on the SW flank of the anticline, with the possibility of an additional late Oligocene (TPU) phase which only significantly affected the NE flank (Stoker *et al.* 2005a) (Fig. 3). Speculatively a local causal mechanism for the formation of the anticline could be the buttressing of the post-Palaeogene lavas sedimentary section against the southern flank of the Sigmundur Seamount (Fig. 7).

SE flank of the Faroe–Shetland Basin

Little is known regarding the effects of Cenozoic compression in the hinterland area to the SE of the Faroe–Shetland Basin, mainly due to the fact that the Cenozoic strata are largely thin or absent. However, at the SW end of the Rona High that flanks the basin (Fig. 2), Booth *et al.* (1993, fig. 3) recognized a major 'mid Cenozoic' unconformity, with Pliocene sediments resting on early Paleocene rocks. They suggested that this unconformity is related to a period of inversion during late Oligocene to Miocene times, and was responsible for the removal of 1250 m of strata from the crest of the high. This could be coincident with the Miocene phases of fold growth observed over a large part of the NE Faroe–Shetland Basin. Towards the NE end of the Rona High, deep marine Late Cretaceous strata are unconformably overlain by marginal marine upper Paleocene and younger sediments (Goodchild *et al.* 1999). The formation of this unconformity is consistent with a phase of inversion during mid Paleocene times and could be associated with the effects of regional uplift associated with the development of the Iceland Plume.

Summary and conclusions

When considering the Faroe–Shetland Basin, Wyville Thomson Ridge and Ymir Ridge areas as a whole, there is considerable geographical variation in both the age and orientation of the observed growth folds, though some commonality with regard to the inferred local mechanisms of formation (see below).

Structural trends and controls

Essentially, there are six main orientations of growth fold within the study area: (1) NE-trending; (2) NNE-trending; (3) east-trending; (4) NW-trending; (5) NNW-trending; and (6) WNW-trending. The pre-existing structural architecture of the underlying sedimentary basins is likely to have exerted a considerable influence on the development of these fold trends.

The NE-trending anticlines are by far the most numerous within the study area but are mainly restricted to the NE Faroe–Shetland Basin. Here, fold generation is inferred to be linked to buttressing of strata against pre-existing basement-involved architecture that has a strong inherited Caledonian or pre-Caledonian structural grain. If pre-existing structure is a key factor in the determination of the orientations of Cenozoic growth folds, then this implies that pre-existing Caledonian structure may be much less important in the SW Faroe–Shetland Basin and Wyville Thomson areas. In these areas, the presence of Palaeogene igneous centres and generally NW-trending shear zones may be more influential in the development of growth folds. NNE-trending Cenozoic reverse faults are rare, but a single example associated with the Pilot Whale Anticline in the NE Faroe–Shetland Basin formed either by buttressing against the Brendan Volcanic Centre, or by growth associated with left-lateral strike-slip fault movement on the NW-trending Magnus Lineament or Transfer Fault. East-trending faults are also rare, but the slightly arcuate Alpin Dome in the North Rockall Basin may have formed as a result in compression of strata against the southern flank of the Sigmundur Seamount. The similarly trending Judd Anticline within the Judd sub-basin developed during phases of NE to SW compression, though the degree to which the underlying structural architecture of the area was an influence on its formation remains unclear. The Munkagrunnur and Westray anticlines form NW- to NNW-trending growth folds, with the latter considered to represent part of a system of ramp anticlines formed during phases of north–south compression associated with the development of the Aegir Ridge. The Westray Anticline lies parallel to, and in close proximity to, the Westray Lineament or Transfer Fault and extends between basement blocks that form the north and south Westray High (Fig. 2). It is probably associated with buttressing against a step in the existing basement architecture although, alternatively, it may represent a flower structure associated with lateral shear along the Westray Lineament. Similarly, the NW-trending South Judd Anticline appears to be almost coincident with the Judd Lineament or Judd Transfer Fault. The most probable cause of formation is buttressing of sedimentary strata against the basement of the juxtaposed Judd High. The NW-trending Ymir Ridge and WNW-trending Wyville Thomson Ridge are considered to form part of a series of ramp anticlines similar to that described for the Munkagrunnur Ridge. The Wyville Thomson Ridge is unlikely to have a significant component of strike-slip movement associated with its formation, as the platform margin to the SE is not offset (Kimbell *et al.* 2005).

Regional deformation history

Within the context of the NE Atlantic margin as a whole, it appears that the earliest phase of Cenozoic fold growth development occurred in late Paleocene to early Eocene times, particularly on the Hatton High, Hatton Basin, Wyville Thomson and Ymir ridges (Fig. 3). During mid to late Eocene times, significant development of anticlinal structures occurred within the SW Faroe–Shetland Basin, Hatton High and Basin, respectively. In mid Eocene to early Oligocene times, major fold growth of north- to NNW trending domes occurred within the Norwegian margin, with a second major pulse prevalent during early Miocene times (e.g. Lundin & Doré 2002). These two pulses of activity resulted in the formation of margin-wide unconformities. The early Miocene event correlates with a major episode of fold growth observed within the NE Faroe–Shetland Basin, though here, there is also a significant slightly younger mid Miocene phase too (e.g. Ritchie *et al.* 2003). There are also indications of Miocene fold development in the SW Faroe–Shetland Basin (Smallwood 2004) and particularly around the Wyville Thomson and Ymir ridge area (e.g. Johnson *et al.* 2005; Stoker *et al.* 2005a, b). The effects of localized early Pliocene deformation is observed throughout the Faroe–Shetland Basin, along the Wyville Thomson and Ymir ridges and within the Hatton High and Basin areas. However, this phase of deformation should not be confused with the effects of regional Pliocene epeirogenic uplift and continental margin tilting as described by Stoker *et al.* (2005a, b) and Praeg *et al.* (2005). Some anticlines within the Faroe–Shetland and Wyville Thomson Ridge areas have a positive topographic expression at the seabed (Fig. 8) (e.g. Johnson *et al.* 2005 figs 3 & 6) suggesting that fold growth activity may still be occurring.

Regional mechanisms causing compression

There have been many models suggested to account for the distribution, orientation and age of growth folds long the NE Atlantic margin between Norway and Greenland in the north, and the Hatton–Rockall area in the south. These include the closing of the Tethys Ocean (Roberts 1989), strike-slip fault movement and 'shuffling' along NW-trending transfer zones/lineaments (Doré & Lundin 1996), a combination of seafloor spreading geometries and ridge-push (Boldreel & Andersen 1993), intraplate stress (e.g. Cloetingh 1990), the

pulsing plume hypothesis (Lundin & Doré 2002), ridge-push and mantle drag forces (Mosar *et al.* 2002) and plume-enhanced asthenospheric flow (e.g. Kusznir 2006). As there is presently no obvious regional spatial and temporal pattern to the evolution of compressional structures throughout the NE Atlantic margin, it is considered likely that a combination of mechanisms might best account for this. However, progress regarding an assessment of the relative importance of individual mechanisms is, we believe probably substantially hindered by poor calibration (i.e. inadequate dating) of growth folds (and hence regional correlation).

This paper is published with the permission of the Executive Director, British Geological Survey (NERC). Thanks are due to BP and Fugro Multi Client Services for permission to reproduce seismic illustrations and associated maps. We are grateful for the comments of Dave Ellis and David Moy which helped to improve the manuscript.

References

ANDERSEN, M. S., NIELSEN, T., SØRENSEN, A. B., BOLDREEL, O. L. & KUIJPERS, A. 2000. Cenozoic sediment distribution and tectonic movements in the Faroe region. *Global and Planetary Changes*, **24**, 239–259.

ANDERSEN, M. S., SØRENSEN, A. B., BOLDREEL, L. O. & NIELSEN, T. 2002. Cenozoic evolution of the Faroe Platform comparing denudation and deposition. *In*: DORÉ, A. G., CARTWRIGHT, J. A., STOKER, M. S., TURNER, J. P. & WHITE, N. (eds) *Exhumation of the North Atlantic Margin: Timing, Mechanisms and Implications for Petroleum Exploration*. The Geological Society, London, Special Publication, **196**, 291–311.

BLYSTAD, P., BREKKE, H., FAERSETH, R. B., LARSEN, B. T., SKOGSEID, J. & TØRUDBAKKEN, B. 1995. Structural elements of the Norwegian continental shelf. Part II: The Norwegian Sea Region. *NPD Bulletin No 8*, Norwegian Petroleum Directorate.

BOLDREEL, L. O. & ANDERSEN, M. S. 1993. Late Pliocene to Miocene compression in the Faeroes-Rockall area. *In*: PARKER, J. R. (ed.) *Petroleum Geology of Northwest Europe, Proceedings of the 4th Conference*. The Geological Society, London, 1026–1034.

BOLDREEL, L. O. & ANDERSEN, M. S. 1994. Tertiary development of the Faeroe-Rockall Plateau based on reflection seismic data. *Bulletin of the Geological Society of Denmark*, **41**, 162–180.

BOLDREEL, L. O. & ANDERSEN, M. S. 1998. Tertiary compressional structures on the Faroe-Rockall Plateau in relation to northeast Atlantic ridge-push and Alpine foreland stresses. *Tectonophysics*, **300**, 13–28.

BOOTH, J., SWIECICKI, T. & WILCOCKSON, P. 1993. The tectono-stratigraphy of the Solan Basin, west of Shetland. *In*: PARKER, J. R. (ed.) *Petroleum Geology of*

Northwest Europe: Proceedings of the 4th Conference. The Geological Society, London, 987–998.

CLOETINGH, S., GRADSTEIN, F. M., KOOI, H., GRANT, A. C. & KAMINSKI, M. 1990. Plate reorganization: a cause of rapid late Neogene subsidence and sedimentation around the North Atlantic. *Journal of the Geological Society, London*, **147**, 495–506.

COWARD, M. P., DEWEY, J. F., HEMPTON, M. & HOLROYD, J. 2003. Tectonic evolution. *In*: EVANS, D., GRAHAM, C. G., ARMOUR, A. & BATHURST, P. (eds) *Millennium Atlas: petroleum geology of the central and northern North sea.* The Geological Society, London, 17–33.

DAVIES, R. & CARTWRIGHT, J. A. 2002. A fossilised Opal A to Opal C/T transformation on the northeast Atlantic margin: support for a significantly elevated palaeogeothermal gradient during the Neogene, *Basin Research*, **14**, 467–485.

DAVIES, R., CLOKE, I., CARTWRIGHT, J., ROBINSON, A. & FERRERO, C. 2004. Post-breakup compression of a passive margin and its impact on hydrocarbon prospectivity: An example from the Tertiary of the Faroe-Shetland Basin, United Kingdom. *American Association of Petroleum Geologists Bulletin*, **88**, 1–20.

DEAN, K., MCLAUCHLAN, K. & CHAMBERS, A. 1999. Rifting and the development of the Faeroe-Shetland Basin. *In*: FLEET, A. J. & BOLDY, S. A. R. (eds) *Petroleum Geology of Northwest Europe: Proceedings of the 5th Conference.* The Geological Society, London, 533–544.

DORÉ, A. G. & LUNDIN, E. R. 1996. Cenozoic compressional structure of the NE Atlantic margin: nature, origin and potential significance for hydrocarbon exploration. *Petroleum Geoscience*, **2**, 299–311.

DORÉ, A. G., LUNDIN, E. R., JENSEN, L. N., BIRKELAND, Ø, ELIASSEN, P. E. & FICHLER, C. 1999. Principal tectonic events in the evolution of the northwest European Atlantic Margin. *In*: FLEET, A. J. & BOLDY, S. A. R. (eds) *Petroleum Geology of Northwest Europe: Proceedings of the 5th Conference.* The Geological Society, London, 41–61.

DUINDAM, P. & VAN HOORN, B. 1987. Structural evolution of the West Shetland continental margin. *In*: BROOKS, J. & GLENNIE, K. W. (eds) *Petroleum Geology of NW Europe: Proceedings of the 3rd Conference.* Graham and Trotman, London, 765–773.

EBDON, C. C., GRANGER, P. J., JOHNSON, H. D. & EVANS, A. M. 1995. Early Tertiary evolution and sequence stratigraphy of the Faroe-Shetland Basin: implications for hydrocarbon prospectivity. *In*: SCRUTTON, R. A., STOKER, M. S., SHIMMIELD, G. B. & TUDHOPE, A. W. (eds) *The Tectonics, Sedimentation and Palaeoceanography of the North Atlantic Region.* The Geological Society, London, Special Publication, **90**, 51–69.

EARLE, M. M., JANKOWSKI, E. J. & VANN, I. R. 1989. Structural evolution of the Faeroe-Shetland Channel and northern Rockall Trough. *In*: TANKARD, A. J. & BALKWILL, H. R. (eds) Extensional tectonics and stratigraphy of the North Atlantic margins. *Memoir of the American Association of Petroleum Geologists*, **46**, 461–489.

GOODCHILD, M. W., HENRY, K. L., HINKLEY, R. J. & IMBUS, S. W. 1999. The Victory gas field, West of

Shetland. *In*: FLEET, A. J. & BOLDY, S. A. R. (eds) *Petroleum Geology of Northwest Europe: Proceedings of the 5th Conference.* The Geological Society, London, 713–724.

HAFLIDASON, H., KING, E. L., BRETT, C. P. *ET AL.* 1996. Marine geological/geophysical cruise report on the North Sea margin. Upper North Sea Fan, Miller Slide and Faeroe-Shetland Channel. *R/V Håkon Mosby cruise No.* **HM110-96**. University of Bergen.

HARLAND, W. B., ARMSTRONG, R. L., COX, A. V., CRAIG, L. E., SMITH, A. G. & SMITH, D. G. 1990. *A Geologic Time Scale 1989.* Cambridge University Press, Cambridge.

HITCHEN, K. & RITCHIE, J. D. 1987. Geological review of the West Shetland area. *In*: BROOKS, J. & GLENNIE, K. W. (eds) *Petroleum Geology of NW Europe: Proceedings of the 3rd Conference.* Graham and Trotman, London, 737–749.

HJELSTUEN, B. O., ELDHOLM, O. & SKOGSEID, J. 1997. Vøring Plateau diapir fields and their structural and depositional settings. *Marine Geology*, **144**, 33–57.

HOVLAND, M., NYGAARD, E. & THORBJØRNSEN, S. 1998. Piercement shale diapirism in the deep-water Vema Dome area, Vøring basin offshore Norway. *Marine and Petroleum Geology*, **15**, 191–201.

HUUSE, M. & MICKELSON, M. 2004. Eocene sandstone intrusions in the Tampen Spur area (Norwegian North Sea Quad 34) imaged by 3D seismic data. *Marine and Petroleum Geology*, **21**, 141–155.

IMBER, J., HOLDSWORTH, R. E., MCCAFFREY, K. J. W., WILSON, R. W., JONES, R. R., ENGLAND, R. W. & GJELDVIK, G. 2005. Early Tertiary sinistral transpression and fault reactivation in the western Vøring Basin, Norwegian Sea: Implications for hydrocarbons exploration and pre-breakup deformation in ocean margin basins. *American Association of Petroleum Geologists Bulletin*, **89**, 1043–1069.

JOHNSON, H., RITCHIE, J. D., HITCHEN, K., MCINROY, D. B. & KIMBELL, G. S. 2005. Aspects of the Cenozoic deformational history of the northeast Faroe–Shetland Basin, Wyville-Thomson Ridge and Hatton Bank areas. *In*: DORÉ, A. G. & VINING, B. (eds) *Petroleum Geology: NW Europe and Global Perspectives. Proceedings of the 6th Conference.* The Geological Society, London, 993–1007.

KESER NEISH, J. 2003. The Faroese Region: A Standard Structural Nomenclature System. Faroese Geological Survey, Tórshavn, Faroe Islands.

KIMBELL, G. S., GATLIFF, R. W., RITCHIE, J. D., WALKER, A. S. D. & WILLIAMSON, J. P. 2004. Regional three-dimensional gravity modelling of the NE Atlantic margin. *Basin Research*, **16**, 259–278

KIMBELL, G. S., RITCHIE, J. D., JOHNSON, H. & GATLIFF, R. W. 2005. Controls on the structure and evolution of the NE Atlantic margin revealed by regional potential field imaging and 3D modelling. *In*: DORÉ, A. G. & VINING, B. (eds) *Petroleum Geology: North-West Europe and Global Perspectives. Proceedings of the 6th Petroleum Geology Conference.* The Geological Society, London, 933–945.

KUSZNIR, N. 2006. The state of stress within rifted continental margin lithosphere: Geodynamic constraints. Compressional deformation within passive margins:

nature, causes and effects. Conference at the Geological Society, London, 19th–20th October 2006, p2 (abstract).

LAMERS, E. & CARMICHAEL, S. M. M. 1999. The Paleocene deepwater sandstone play West of Shetland. In: FLEET, A. J. & BOLDY, S. A. R. (eds) Petroleum Geology of Northwest Europe: Proceedings of the 5th Conference. The Geological Society, London, 645–659.

LISTER, G. A., ETHERIDGE, M. A. & SYMONDS, P. A. 1986. Detachment faulting and the evolution of passive continental margin. Geology, 14, 246–250.

LØSETH, H. & HENRIKSEN, S. 2005. A Middle to Late Miocene compression phase along the Norwegian passive margin. In: DORÉ, A. G. & VINING, B. (eds) Petroleum Geology: North-West Europe and Global Perspectives. Proceedings of the 6th Petroleum Geology Conference. The Geological Society, London, 845–859.

LUNDIN, E. R. & DORÉ, A. G. 2002. Mid-Cenozoic postbreakup deformation in 'passive' margins bordering the Norwegian-Greenland Sea. Marine and Petroleum Geology, 19, 79–93.

LUNDIN, E. & DORÉ, A. G. 2005. NE Atlantic break-up: a re-examination of the Iceland mantle plume model and the Atlantic-Arctic linkage. In: DORÉ, A. G. & VINING, B. (eds) Petroleum Geology: North-West Europe and Global Perspectives. Proceedings of the 6th Petroleum Geology Conference. The Geological Society, London, 933–945.

MOSAR, J., LEWIS, G. & TORSVIK, T. H. 2002. North Atlantic sea-floor spreading rates: implications for Tertiary development of inversion structures of the Norwegian-Greenland Sea. Journal of the Geological Society, London, 159, 503–515.

NADIN, P. A., KUZNIR, N. J. & CHEADLE, M. J. 1997. Early Tertiary plume uplift of the North Sea and Faeroe-Shetland Basins. Earth and Planetary Science Letters, 148, 109–207.

PARK, R. G., STEWART, A. D. & WRIGHT, D. T. 2002. The Hebridean terrane. In: TREWIN, N. H. (ed.) The Geology of Scotland (4th edn), The Geological Society, London, 45–80.

PRAEG, D., STOKER, M. S., SHANNON, P. M., CERAMICOLA, S., HJELSTUEN, B. O., LABERG, J. S. & MATHIESEN, A. 2005. Episodic Cenozoic tectonism and the development of the NW European 'passive' continental margin. Marine and Petroleum Geology, 22, 1007–1030.

RITCHIE, J. D., JOHNSON, H. & KIMBELL, G. S. 2003. The nature and age of Cenozoic contractional dating within the NE Faroe-Shetland Basin, Marine Geology, 20, 399–409.

ROBERTS, D. G. 1989. Basin inversion in and around the British Isles. In: COOPER, M. A. & WILLIAMS, G. D. (eds) Inversion Tectonics. The Geological Society, London, Special Publication, 44, 131–150.

ROBERTS, D. G., THOMSON, M., MITCHENER, B., HOSSACK, J., CARMICHAEL, S. & BJØRNSETH, H. M. 1999. Palaeozoic to Tertiary rift and basin dynamics: mid-Norway to the Bay of Biscay – a new context for hydrocarbon prospectivity in the deep water frontier. In: FLEET, A. J. & BOLDY, S. A. R. (eds) Petroleum Geology of Northwest Europe: Proceedings of the 5th Conference. The Geological Society, London, 7–40.

RUMPH, B., REAVES, C. M., ORANGE, V. G. & ROBINSON, D. L. 1993. Structuring and transfer zones in the Faeroe Basin in a regional tectonic context. In: PARKER, J. D. (ed.) Petroleum Geology of Northwest Europe: Proceedings of the 4th conference, The Geological Society, London, 999–1010.

SMALLWOOD, J. R. 2004. Tertiary inversion in the Faroe-Shetland Channel and the development of major erosional scarps. In: DAVIES, R. J., CARTWRIGHT, J. A., STEWART, S. S., LAPPIN, M. & UNDERHILL, J. R. (eds) 3D Seismic Technology: Application to the Exploration of Sedimentary Basins. The Geological Society, London, Memoir, 29, 187–198.

SMALLWOOD, J. R. 2005. Lithology prediction from velocity data; Paleocene sediments in the Faroe–Shetland area. In: ZISKA, H., VARMING, T. & BLOCH, D. (eds) Faroe Island Exploration Conference: Proceedings of the 1st Conference. Annales Societatis Scientarum Faeroensis Supplementum, 43, 71–81.

SMALLWOOD, J. R. & GILL, C. E. 2002. The rise and fall of the Faroe-Shetland Basin; evidence from seismic mapping of the Balder Formation. Journal of the Geological Society, London, 159, 627–630.

SMALLWOOD, J. R. & KIRK, W. 2005. Exploration in the Faroe-Shetland Basin: Disappointments and Discoveries. In: DORÉ, A. G. & VINING, B. (eds) Petroleum Geology: North-West Europe and Global Perspectives. Proceedings of the 6th Petroleum Geology Conference. Geological Society, London, 977–991.

SMALLWOOD, J. R., TOWNS, M. J. & WHITE, R. S. 2001. The structure of the Faroe-Shetland Trough from integrated deep seismic and potential field modelling. Journal of the Geological Society, London, 158, 409–412.

SØRENSEN, A. B. 2003. Cenozoic basin development and stratigraphy of the Faroes area. Petroleum Geoscience, 9, 189–207.

STOKER, M. S., HITCHEN, K. & GRAHAM, C. C. 1993. The Geology of the Hebrides and West Shetland Shelves, and adjacent Deep-Water Areas. British Geological Survey United Kingdom Offshore Regional Report, London, HMSO.

STOKER, M. S., VAN WEERING, T. C. E. & SVAERDBORG, T. 2001. A Mid-Late tectonostratigraphic framework for the Rockall Trough. In: SHANNON, P. M., HAUGHTON, P. D. & CORCORAN, D. (eds) The Petroleum Exploration of Ireland's Offshore Basins. The Geological Society of London, Special Publication, 188, 411–438.

STOKER, M. S., NIELSEN, T., VAN WEERING, T. C. E. & KUIJPERS, A. 2002. Towards an understanding of the Neogene tectonostratigraphic framework of the NE Atlantic margin between Ireland and the Faroe Islands. Marine Geology, 188, 233–248.

STOKER, M. S., HOULT, R. J., NIELSEN, T., HJELSTUEN, B. O., LABERG, J. S., SHANNON, P. M., PRAEG, D., MATHIESEN, A., VAN WEERING, T. C. E. & MCDONNELL, A. 2005a. Sedimentary and oceanographic responses to early Neogene compression on the NW European margin. *Marine and Petroleum Geology*, **22**, 1031–1044.

STOKER, M. S., PRAEG, D., SHANNON, P. M. *ET AL.* 2005*b*. Neogene evolution of the Atlantic continental margin of NW Europe (Lofoten Islands to SW Ireland): anything but passive. *In*: DORÉ, A. G. & VINING, B. (eds) *Petroleum Geology: North-West Europe and Global Perspectives. Proceedings of the 6th Petroleum Geology Conference*, Geological Society, London, 1057–1076.

STRATAGEM PARTNERS 2002. *The Neogene Stratigraphy of the Glaciated European Margin from Lofoten to Porcupine*. (Great Yarmouth, Svitzer Limited).

TATE, M. P., DODD, C. D. & GRANT, N. T. 1999. The Northeast Rockall Basin and its significance in the evolution of the Rockall – Faeroes/East Greenland rift system. *In*: FLEET, A. J. & BOLDY, S. A. R.

(eds) *Petroleum Geology of Northwest Europe: Proceedings of the 5th Conference*, Geological Society, London, 391–406.

TURNER, J. D. & SCRUTTON, R. A. 1993. Subsidence patterns in western margin basins: evidence from the Faeroe-Shetland Basin. *In*: PARKER, J. R. (ed.) *Petroleum Geology of Northwest Europe: Proceedings of the 4th Conference*. The Geological Society, London, 975–983.

VÅGNES, E., GABRIELSEN, R. H. & HAREMO, P. 1998. Late Cretaceous-Cenozoic intraplate contractional deformation at the Norwegian continental shelf: timing, magnitude and regional implications. *Tectonophysics*, **300**, 29–46.

WHITE, R S. & MCKENZIE, D. 1989. Magmatism at rift zones: The generation of volcanic continental margins and flood basalts. *Journal of Geophysical Research*, **94**, 7685–7729.

Uplift, compression and the Cenozoic Faroe–Shetland sediment budget

JOHN R. SMALLWOOD

Hess Ltd, Level 9, The Adelphi Building, 1–11 John Adam St, London WC2N 6AG, UK
(e-mail: john.smallwood@hess.com)

Abstract: Throughout the Cenozoic, the dominant sediment supply to the Faroe–Shetland Basin has been from the SE. However, the volume of sediment in the basin is greater than that supplied from the British Isles' provenance area alone. The British Isles and Faroes Platform experienced both epeirogenic and local uplift, caused by igneous underplating, mantle thermal variations and compression. A Cenozoic topographic model is presented for the British Isles' and Faroe Islands' provenance areas, from which sediment supply rates are calculated. The model includes permanent uplift from igneous underplating, which is estimated from gravity anomaly data, transient regional uplift and a simple elevation-dependent erosion term, under isostatic balance. Even using upside estimates of the British Isles' Cenozoic denudation and the documented post-Eocene contribution from the Faroe Islands, there is an apparent undersupply of sediment to the basin. The sediment volume balance suggests that around 30% of the Paleocene sediments currently in the basin were sourced from a westerly provenance area, the pre-basalt Faroes Platform terrane or East Greenland.

The Faroe Islands are positioned at the intersection of three major antiformal structures on the Northwest European Atlantic Margin (Fig. 1). The Iceland–Faroe Ridge runs oceanward to the NW of the islands, while the Fugloy Ridge runs along the continental margin to the NE, and the Munkagrunnur Ridge runs SSE. Compression has played a part in the formation of both of the landward ridges. Associated uplift and denudation has contributed to the supply of sediment into the surrounding basins. In this paper, I discuss the sediment budget of the area by comparing the material known to have been removed in the Cenozoic from the Faroes Platform and the British Isles with that mapped in the intervening sedimentary basin.

Deformational history

The three ridges forming the backbones of the Faroes continental shelf have different genetic origins. The Iceland–Faroe Ridge is composed of extremely thick oceanic crust, whereas the Fugloy Ridge and the Munkagrunnur Ridge have continental crust cores and include a thick layer of near-surface basaltic lavas dating from the time of continental breakup.

The thick crust of the Iceland–Faroe Ridge records the interaction of the proto-Iceland plume with the Mid Atlantic Ridge (Bott & Gunnarsson 1980; Smallwood et al. 1999). At the southeastern end of the Ridge the Faroes continental block received a significant quantity of igneous material, both extrusive and intrusive, at continental breakup time, around 60–55 Ma (White 1988; Ritchie et al. 1999). The extrusive products, including hyaloclastites and a basaltic lava pile, were emplaced over crystalline basement, Mesozoic and Paleocene age sediments, and the lavas outcrop both across the Faroe Islands and at or near the seabed over a wide area (Sørensen 2003; Fig. 1).

The Fugloy Ridge and the Munkagrunnur Ridge are anticlinal folds. The gravity field across the ridges is consistent with underlying thicker crust (Fig. 1; Kimbell et al. 2005), which means that their origin, along with all the structurally high areas of the Faroes continental shelf, is likely to lie partially in the differential subsidence of surrounding areas. However, compressional tectonics also plays a part. For the Fugloy Ridge, Paleocene, Eocene–Oligocene [mid-Miocene?] and more recent fold growth episodes have been recorded (Boldreel & Andersen 1993, 1995; Johnson et al. 2005).

There are no preserved post-lava sediments on the Munkagrunnur Ridge, and the offsetting stratigraphy around is poorly constrained, making growth history more difficult to ascertain. However, there is evidence that compression has played a role in the formation of the ridge in addition to the subsidence of surrounding basins. Thrust faults, or perhaps inverted normal faults, offset the uppermost lava surface immediately to the south of the ridge (Fig. 2b; Johnson et al.

From: JOHNSON, H., DORÉ, A. G., GATLIFF, R. W., HOLDSWORTH, R., LUNDIN, E. R. & RITCHIE, J. D. (eds)
The Nature and Origin of Compression in Passive Margins. Geological Society, London, Special Publications,
306, 137–152. DOI: 10.1144/SP306.6   0305-8719/08/$15.00 © The Geological Society of London 2008.

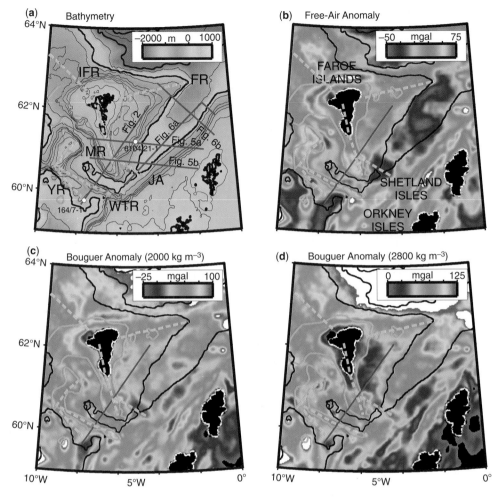

Fig. 1. Location map of study area. Pink dashed lines indicate structural highs discussed in text: FR, Fugloy Ridge; IFR, Iceland Faroe Ridge; JA, Judd Anticline; MR, Munkagrunnur Ridge; WTR, Wyville-Thomson Ridge; YR, Ymir Ridge. Orange polygons enclose areas where basalt crops out at or near seabed (Sørensen 2003). White circles indicate locations of wells mentioned in text. (**a**) Bathymetry and (**b**) Free-air gravity anomaly from compilation of satellite (Sandwell & Smith 1997) and ship track data. (**c**) Bouguer gravity anomaly using 2000 kg m^{-3} to replace water column. (**d**) Bouguer gravity anomaly using 2800 kg m^{-3} to replace water column, appropriate for identifying subsurface structure where basalt is at or near seabed.

2005). These, and similar faults south of the Wyville–Thomson Ridge (Fig. 2a) were active during deposition of the first post-lava sediments but do not offset the entire Eocene sedimentary succession, constraining their timing to pre-late Eocene. Similarly, several Eocene phases of growth have been documented on the Judd Anticline, which forms the SE extension of the Munkagrunnur Ridge (Smallwood 2004). Since these surrounding structures were undergoing compressional deformation during the Eocene it seems likely that the Munkagrunnur Ridge was also

present at this time and affected by contemporaneous deformation. In addition, Johnson *et al.* (2005) postulate a major phase of early to mid-Miocene fold growth based on onlap relationships.

Uplift and denudation

Andersen *et al.* (2002) point out that the overall strain of post-basalt NE–SW crustal shortening across the Faroes Platform is less than 1%. The NW–SE shortening is similar, but is not distributed

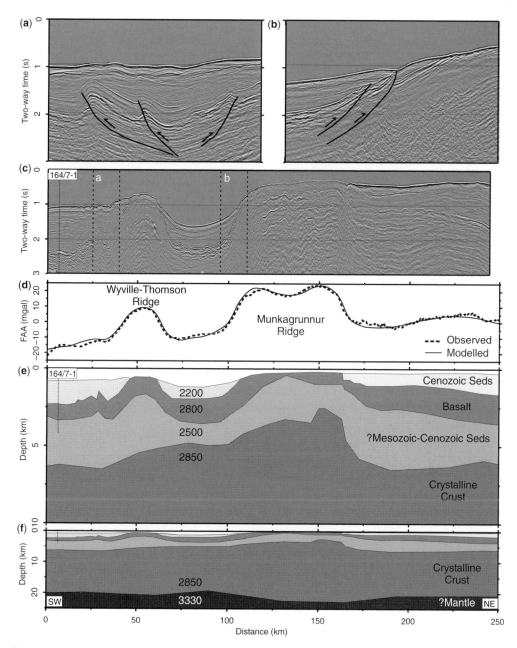

Fig. 2. Seismic line (courtesy of WesternGeco) and crustal gravity model across Wyville-Thompson and Munkagrunnur Ridges. Location shown in Figure 1. (**a**) Seismic line showing Eocene thrust faults offsetting top basalt reflector south of Wyville-Thomson Ridge. Location of panel shown in (c). (**b**) Seismic line showing Eocene thrust faults offsetting top basalt reflector south of Munkagrunnur Ridge. Location of panel shown in (c). (**c**) Regional seismic line. Top basalt reflector lies at seabed across both Ridges. (**d**) Measured (dashed) and modelled (continuous) free-air gravity anomaly along profile. (**e**) Upper 10 km and (**f**) 25 km of crustal gravity model. Densities in kg m^{-3} annotated.

uniformly. Folding on the Munkagrunnur and Fugloy Ridges may have been controlled by the position of existing basement structures (e.g. Doré et al. 1997).

On a regional scale an isostatic compensation model is instructive for considering the relationship between uplift (above base level) and subsequent denudation. Denudation is expected to be much larger than initial uplift, due to the isostatic amplification effect as the crust is unloaded as a result of erosion (see e.g. Tiley et al. (2004); Fig. 3a). The ratio of denudation to initial uplift depends on the density change at the surface and that of the asthenosphere. The Faroes is unusual in that the uppermost crust, being composed of basaltic lavas, has a relatively high density. Consequently, isostatically balanced denudation triggered by uplift will be greater than for sediment-topped crust. Andersen et al. (2002) give models based

on the Faroes in which it was shown that a few percent of shortening (pure shear case) could yield as much as a kilometre of denudation (Fig. 3a).

There is good evidence that sedimentary basins lie beneath the lavas on the Munkagrunnur Ridge. To the south, well 164/7-1 penetrated Paleocene and Cretaceous sediments beneath 1.2 km of lavas (Fig. 2; Archer et al. 2005). To the north, well 6104/21-1, drilled in 478 m of water, also established the thickness of the basalt before reaching TD at 4201 m below sea level (Figs 1, 4 & 5; Jardfeingi 2006). Secondly, wide-angle seismic experiments have detected a low-velocity zone beneath the lavas over large parts of the Faroes continental shelf (e.g. White et al. 2003). In addition, the central gravity anomaly low along the Munkagrunnur Ridge (Fig. 1) is most easily modelled with a relatively low density layer becoming shallower beneath the lavas where they are eroded

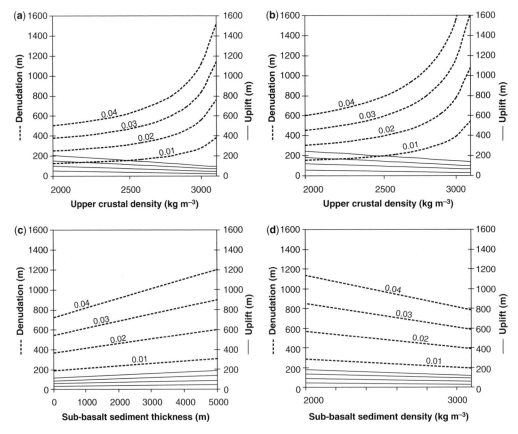

Fig. 3. Comparison of predicted denudation (dashed lines) vs. uplift (solid line) for a range of pure shear compression cases ranging from 0.01 (lowest effects) to 0.04 (highest effects). Denudation exceeds uplift above base level due to isostatic amplification effect. (**a**) Model of basalt lying directly on basement. Varying upper crustal density. Appropriate range for Faroes c. 2700–2900 kg m^{-3}. (**b**) Model of basalt over 4 km of sediments with density 2500 kg m^{-3}. (**c**) As (b), with surface basalt density 2800 kg m^{-3}, but varying sub-basalt sediment thickness. (**d**) As (b), with surface basalt density 2800 kg m^{-3}, but varying sub-basalt sediment density.

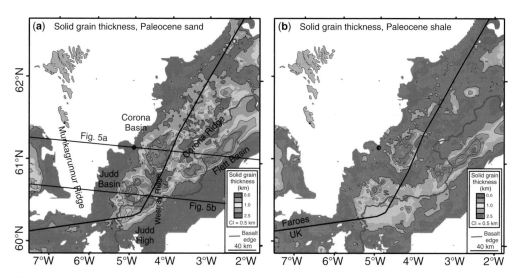

Fig. 4. Maps showing distribution of Paleocene sediments (after Smallwood 2005*b*). Map location shown in Figure 7. Blue circle indicates location of well 6104/21-1. (**a**) Solid grain thickness of sand. Main Faroe–Shetland depocentres named: Judd Basin, Corona Basin, Flett Basin. (**b**) Solid grain thickness of shale, more evenly distributed.

across the crest of the anticline (Fig. 2; Smallwood *et al.* 1999). In the model shown in Fig. 2, the base of the basalt layer (density 2800 kg m^{-3}) is positioned from migration of wide-angle reflections (method described in Fleidner & White 2001) and a velocity decrease with depth, while the thickness

of the low density (2500 kg m^{-3}) layer is constrained from weak wide-angle reflections and the gravity model. The line crosses the edge of the Munkagrunnur igneous centre at around 155 km.

If only the upper crust is considered, and a low-density (sedimentary) layer is included

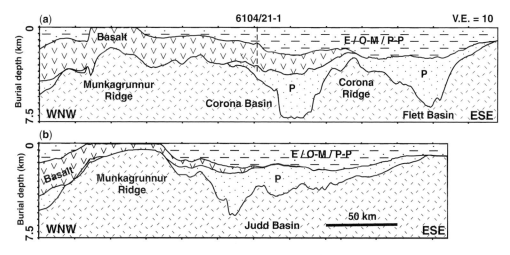

Fig. 5. Schematic cross-sections through the basin (after Smallwood 2005*b*), with depth below seabed shown (faults omitted). Line locations shown in Figures 1 & 4a. Depth conversion was made using functions described in Smallwood (2002) outside the basalt and 4.5 km s^{-1} within the lava pile layer. Main structural features named. The Top and Base Basalt surfaces and Top and Base Paleocene surfaces are shown as solid lines. P, Paleocene; E/O-M/P-P, undifferentiated Eocene, Oligo-Miocene, Plio-Pleistocene. The bottom layer includes pre-Cenozoic sediments and basement. (**a**) Line through Corona Basin and Flett Basin. Position of well 6104/21-1 indicated. (**b**) Line through northern section of Judd Basin.

beneath the lavas in a 1D isostatic uplift/denuda-tion model, the denudation is amplified, as the thickness of the sedimentary layer is increased (pure shear model) but the surface material removed has a higher density (Fig. 3b). In this case there is a linear relationship between the denu-dation and the thickness and density of the sub-basalt sedimentary layer (Fig. 3c & d). Such simple models suggest that the sub-basalt sediments could have the effect of magnifying denudation on the Faroes following a pure shear strain deforma-tional response to compression. However, the thick-ness and average density of the lithosphere is likely to be similar for columns with and without such a sub-lava sedimentary layer so that if the entire litho-sphere is thickened by pure shear, the initial uplift and total denudation will be independent of its density distribution at depth.

Material removed from the Faroes was deposited in the surrounding sedimentary basins: the Faroe Bank Channel Basin west of the Munka-grunnur Ridge (Keser Neish & Ziska 2005), the Faroe–Shetland Basin (the term used here for the collection of Cenozoic basins between the Faroe Islands and the Shetland Isles) and the basins beneath the Norwegian Sea to the north. Several wells in the Faroe–Shetland Basin have encoun-tered indications of clastic material derived from the Faroes Platform. However, most of the clastic sediment was sourced from the east of the basin, as the British Isles have provided a long-lasting emergent provenance area (Lamers & Carmichael 1999). The total volume of sediment in the Faroe–Shetland Basin has been measured through seismic mapping, in order to compare it with the volume known to have been removed from these two provenance areas during the Cenozoic.

Sediments in the Faroe–Shetland Basin

The Paleocene depocentres of the Judd, Corona, and Flett Basins and their surrounds (Figs 4 & 5) contain $4.5 \pm 1 \times 10^4$ km^3 of solid sediment, of which about half is coarse-grained (Smallwood 2005a, b). Following the eruption and emplacement of the Faroes' lavas, the basin subsided rapidly (Smallwood & Gill 2002) and clastic sediment derived from both the Faroes and the British Isles catchments was supplied to the basin.

When maps based on seismic interpretation are depth converted (Smallwood 2002) and porosity is removed (exponential porosity decay with depth, Jones et al. 2002), the total volume of post-Paleocene solid sediment is calculated to be $6 \pm 0.5 \times 10^4$ km^3. When compaction and depth con-version calculations are made, the domination of

the Eocene already apparent on the two-way time sections is further amplified (Fig. 6).

The total volume of sediment measured in the study area is $10 \pm 1 \times 10^4$ km^3, approximately 45% of which is Paleocene and 50% Eocene (Table 1). This compares with the previous estimate of Jones et al. (2002), who calculated an overall solid sediment volume ranging from 5.3 to 7.1×10^4 km^3 for Cenozoic sediment in the Faroe–Shetland area, taken as extending from approximately 59.5–61.5°N and extending to 5.5°W. This study captures a slightly larger area than that mapped by Jones et al. (2002) and includes a breakdown into three temporal intervals.

Erosion from the Faroe Islands and British Isles catchments

Throughout Cenozoic time, clastic sediments have been supplied to the Faroe–Shetland Basin from both the British Isles region and the Faroes Platform.

Erosion from the Faroes Platform

The total volume of basaltic material that has been removed from the Faroes Platform is estimated to be 4.6×10^4 km^3 (Andersen et al. 2002). This volume was calculated from the difference between the current upper surface of the Palaeogene basalt lava pile and its inferred original upper surface. The level of this original upper surface was calculated from projections of basalt dips.

Andersen et al. (2002) noted that until the Oligo-cene, the watershed on the west side of the basin lay east of the present-day Faroe Islands and most of the material derived from the basaltic plateau is believed to have been shed to the west and north, not into the Faroe–Shetland Basin.

Sediment supply from the British Isles

The overall quantity of Cenozoic denudation of the British Isles was calculated by Rowley (1998) from the compilation of estimates from sonic, apatite, vitrinite reflectance and spore colour index and reported by Jones et al. (2002). The Cenozoic denu-dation of the British Isles along with the Eocene and younger denudation of the Faroes continental shelf is shown in Figure 7.

Jones et al. (2002) calculated that between 1.8 and 3.5×10^4 km^3 of rock was eroded from the British Isles' catchment area serving the Faroe–Shetland area during the Cenozoic. The discrepancy between this figure and the observed volume of solid sediment in the basin (10×10^4 km^3) prompted the construction of a simple topographic

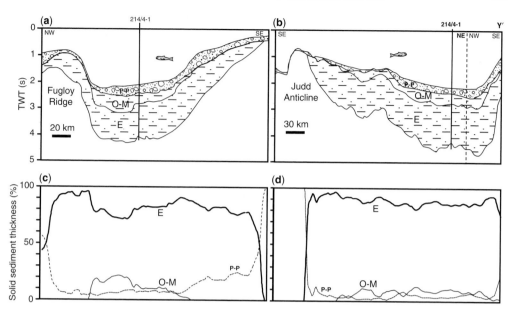

Fig. 6. (a) Longitudinal and (b) transverse interpreted seismic sections after Davies *et al.* (2001) with (c) & (d) subdivision of solid grain thickness between Eocene (E, thick solid line), Oligo-Miocene (O-M, thin line) and Plio-Pleistocene (P-P, medium dashed line) intervals. Stratigraphic control from well 214/4-1, location indicated. Line locations shown in Figure 1a. For computation of proportional solid grain thicknesses in each interval, depth conversion was made using functions described in Smallwood (2002) and removal of porosity using the generalized exponential decay function of Jones *et al.* (2002). The majority of post-Paleocene sediments in the basin are of Eocene age.

reconstruction to investigate possible changes in catchment geometry. The intention of the model was that it would also give an indication of temporal variation in sediment supply.

Constraints were placed on vertical movement of the provenance areas using methods and results from Al-Kindi *et al.* (2003) and Jones & White (2003). Jones & White (2003) favoured using the smaller of the denudation estimates of Jones *et al.* (2002) to constrain the transient uplift attributed to the proto-Iceland plume at end-Paleocene times (*c.* 57 Ma) by restoring the missing section and matching the mapped position of the palaeo-coastline (Fig. 7), and also including the effect of sea-level variation. Reconstruction of the Paleocene topography involves an additional element of uncertainty as there was significant introduction of igneous material into the lithosphere during the Paleocene (e.g. White & Lovell 1997). Clift & Turner (1998) calculated that 1–2 km of igneous underplating under the Shetland Isles and the sedimentary basins to the west could explain the observed subsidence anomalies. Although underplating has been detected by seismic techniques under the Faroe Islands, the Atlantic continent–ocean boundary, and the Irish Sea (e.g. White 1988; Smallwood *et al.* 1999; Al-Kindi *et al.*

2003), significant underplating has not been detected with similar methods around the Shetland Isles (R. England, pers. comm.) or elsewhere (Shaw-Champion *et al.* 2006). For the purposes of this paper, three underplate thickness and distribution cases were considered. Firstly, a case was tested in which no Cenozoic igneous crustal addition was included. Secondly, a 'maximum underplating' case was tested. This was estimated by computing the amount of underplated material (Fig. 8d) that would be required to explain (isostatically) the difference between sea-level and the end-Paleocene topography of Jones & White (2003), less plume uplift. The assumption behind this estimate was that no other mechanisms apart from igneous crustal addition and the transient 'plume' uplift discussed above would then have to be invoked to explain the difference between a near sea-level end-Cretaceous topography and the elevated topography present at the end of the Paleocene. The result (Fig. 8d) is inconsistent with the findings of seismic experiments which have mostly failed to detect any underplated material (see e.g. Shaw-Champion *et al.* 2006), and so this case can reasonably be taken as a maximum bound.

An intermediate underplating model was preferred, using the transform suggested by Al-Kindi

Table 1. *Volumes of solid sediment mapped within the Faroe–Shetland Basin and calculated to have been removed from British Isles' (BI) and Faroes continental shelf (FCS) catchments for Jones et al. (2002)'s (a) low and (b) high British Isles' denudation estimates. Split into the three time periods shown is from the erosion model discussed in the text. Additional material supply is required (last column) even using the high British Isles' denudation case, particularly during the Paleocene.*

a	Material in basin ($\times 10^3$ km^3)	Low case yield from BI ($\times 10^3$ km^3)	Yield from FCS post-lava ($\times 10^3$ km^3)	Difference ($\times 10^3$ km^3)
Paleocene (65–57 Ma)	45	18	—	27
Eocene (57–35 Ma)	48	15	14	19
Younger (35–0 Ma)	8	2	4	2
Total	101	35	18	48

b	Material in basin ($\times 10^3$ km^3)	High case yield from BI ($\times 10^3$ km^3)	Yield from FCS post-lava ($\times 10^3$ km^3)	Difference ($\times 10^3$ km^3)
Paleocene (65–57 Ma)	45	33	—	12
Eocene (57–35 Ma)	48	29	14	5
Younger (35–0 Ma)	8	3	4	1
Total	101	65	18	18

et al. (2003), from the 150 km low-pass filtered free-air (offshore) and Bouguer (onshore) gravity anomaly. As these authors point out, a component of the long-wavelength free-air gravity signal offshore comes from water depth variations (Fig. 1), and an overestimate of underplating thickness could result, by perhaps 50%. To attempt to improve on their method, therefore, the gravity effect of isostatically compensated bathymetry (Fig. 8b) was subtracted from the total field (Fig. 8a) to leave a smaller inferred underplating thickness around the margin's offshore basins (Fig. 8c). The method is far from satisfactory as there is little physical basis to link isostatically-corrected gravity anomalies to underplating. Variations in the isostatically-corrected gravity field can arise either from departures from local isostasy or from compensating density anomalies at different depths (which gives the signal seen in Fig. 8b). If local compensation applies to underplating then the difference between normal and underplated crust is the density difference at the base of the crust, which is spread over a few kilometres rather than being concentrated at the Moho. The difference in the gravity field will be extremely small. Where there is a correlation between underplating and gravity anomaly, and the lithosphere is inferred to be weak, the relationship is more likely to be indirect, and to relate perhaps to a deep underlying negative anomaly (residual thermal anomaly or mantle depletion).

Although not expected to be a highly accurate underplating predictor, the gravity-based method does appear to be roughly consistent with seismic observations and this has been preferred in the estimation of sediment yields. The impact on modelled sediment yield of using either the no underplating or 'maximum underplating' model is discussed below.

Temporal topography model assumptions

The ingredients of permanent uplift, transient uplift and subsidence and erosion were combined to model the topographic variation of the Faroes and British Isles sediment provenance areas during the Cenozoic. Several assumptions were required.

First, densities were assigned to the main layers of the model: sediments 2400 kg m^{-3}, basaltic upper crust 2800 kg m^{-3}, mid crust 2850 kg m^{-3}, underplating 3100 kg m^{-3}, lithospheric mantle 3330 kg m^{-3} and asthenospheric mantle 3200 kg m^{-3} (see Smallwood *et al.* 2001; Tiley *et al.* 2004).

Secondly, Airy isostasy was assumed throughout for the uplift and denudation calculations. An elastic thickness of 5 ± 2 km has been calculated for the British Isles, and underplated material under the Irish Sea is thought to be in almost complete Airy isostatic equilibrium (Tiley *et al.* 2003).

Thirdly, the total underplating inferred from long-wavelength present-day gravity anomaly highs was assumed to have been introduced in a linear manner from 65 to 57 Ma. Several studies have debated the possible multi-phase intrusion

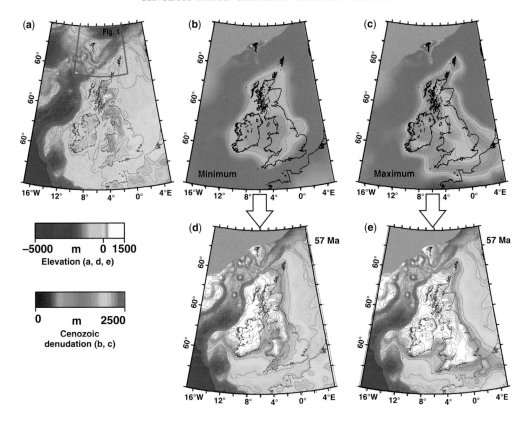

Fig. 7. (**a**) Present day topography/bathymetry. (**b**) and (**c**) Cenozoic denudation estimates from Jones *et al.* (2002)'s British Isles estimates together with those of Andersen *et al.* (2002) for the Faroes Platform. (**d**) and (**e**) consequent restored end-Paleocene topography. The restored topography includes isostatically compensated restoration of denuded section, transient uplift to match the coastline position at maximum regression and sea-level change (from method of Jones & White 2003).

process causing the deposition of the large volumes of Paleocene sediment in surrounding basins (White & Lovell 1997; Maclennan & Lovell 2002; Morton *et al.* 2002). Ar–Ar dating of intrusives, for example the suite of sills in the centre of the basin, which intrude sediments as young as the Paleocene, indicates that igneous activity finished in earliest Eocene time (Hitchen & Ritchie 1993; Smallwood & Harding in press).

Fourthly, the transient uplift associated with the proto-Iceland mantle plume was taken from Jones & White (2003), who suggested a regional uplift function circular in plan view. The uplift function ensures palaeocoastlines observed in seismic data match the model coastline at 57 Ma (Fig. 7). The uplift was assumed to arrive rapidly (again, linearly between 65 and 57 Ma) and to decay with similar rapidity: exponential decay with a half-decay time of 5 Ma was preferred. Rapid collapse of this regional uplift is attributed to the confinement of

anomalously hot asthenospheric mantle to the nascent continental rift west of the Faroe Islands (Smallwood & Gill 2002). The Balder Formation (Late Paleocene–Early Eocene) progressively onlapped basalt to the NW, as the marine transgression proceeded and deep marine conditions were re-established across the Faroe–Shetland Basin in the Early Eocene.

The final and perhaps most subjective assumption of the model was the imposition of a simplified erosion model. On such large-scale gridded models, the topographic gradient, which is an important control on erosion rate, is not well represented (e.g. Montgomery 2003), and neither climatic variations nor variability in substrate erodability were included in the model described here. Rather, to keep the model as simple as possible, all factors were combined into a single erosion rate r for each grid cell, proportional to the elevation h (in kilometres) of that cell above base level raised to

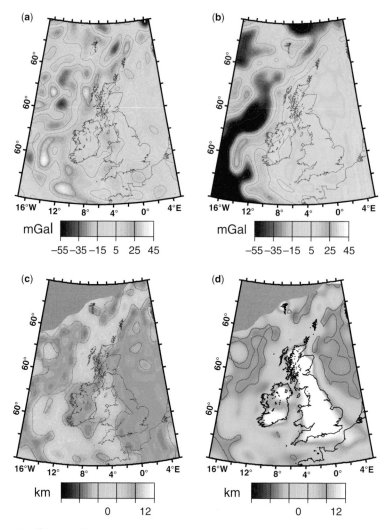

Fig. 8. (**a**) Free-air (offshore) and Bouguer (onshore) gravity anomaly filtered to highlight lower crustal underplating as described by Al-Kindi *et al.* (2003). (**b**) Modelled free-air gravity anomaly resulting from isostatically compensated bathymetry. (**c**) Difference between (a) and (b): a gravity-anomaly-based indication of crustal underplating thickness. Calibrated by observations in the East Irish Sea (see Al-Kindi *et al.* (2003). (**d**) 'Maximum' underplating thickness case: if end Paleocene topography of Jones & White (2003) (Fig. 7e) minus transient plume uplift is to be reduced to sea-level at end Cretaceous times under isostacy entirely due to removal of underplating. There is no seismic evidence of such large igneous crustal additions.

a selected power k:

$$r = Ah^k. \tag{1}$$

The coefficient A was a constant determined for each cell by inverting to match the total Cenozoic denudation (from Jones *et al.* 2002) and present day elevation. The fixed constraints were the amount of underplated material (either zero, the gravity anomaly-derived case or the maximum

shown in Fig. 8d) and the magnitude of the transient uplift (from Jones & White 2003).

The output of the model was the volume of material eroded through the Cenozoic and a reconstruction of topographic development including erosion (Fig. 9). The most obvious effect is from the transient uplift peaking at 57 Ma (Fig. 10a), raising the British Isles, particularly its western margin, and imposing a pronounced eastward tilt.

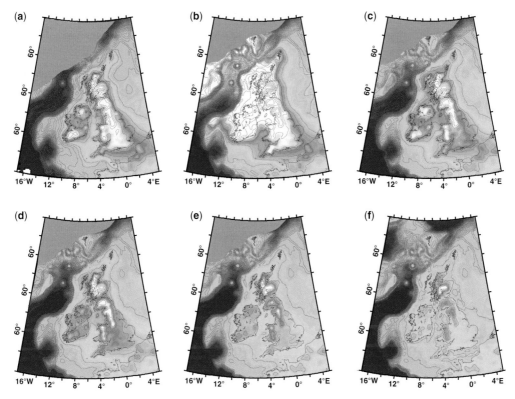

Fig. 9. Reconstructed topography of the British Isles and Faroes sediment source areas. Components included in the model are Paleocene igneous underplating, transient uplift and subsidence around continental-breakup time and erosion as a function of elevation. Constraints are the total Cenozoic denudation and present-day topography. Geometry and amount of transient uplift taken from Jones & White (2003). See discussion in the text. (**a**) 65 Ma, (**b**) 57 Ma, (**c**) 50 Ma, (**d**) 40Ma, (**e**) 20 Ma, and (**f**) 1 Ma.

The sediment supply to the Faroe–Shetland Basin was determined from the model by summing the material eroded from the onshore catchment areas (Figs 9 & 10b). The boundaries of these catchment areas did not vary very much through the Cenozoic in the model (cf. Jones *et al.* 2002), although the westward surface tilting with decay of the transient uplift increased the area supplying the basin from the east slightly. The volumes of sediment calculated to have been supplied to the basin and those mapped to lie within the basin are shown in Table 1 and Figure 10b.

Errors

A number of factors bear on the accuracy of the analysis discussed here, both in determination of the sediment supply and its temporal variation and the volume present in the basin. The errors in the sediment volumes present in the basin are discussed in Smallwood (2005*b*) and are about ±15%.

Although the post-basalt denudation of the Faroes (Andersen *et al.* 2002) is relatively well-constrained due to the consistency of the stratigraphy, the total volume of material removed from the sediment catchment area in the British Isles is subject to more uncertainty. Jones *et al.* (2002) give two estimates, the impact of which is tabulated in Table 1. There are also errors within the assumptions behind the temporal sediment supply model within this paper.

As argued by Jones & White (2003), there has been little igneous addition to the lithosphere since 57 Ma. For the temporal sediment supply model therefore, uncertainty of the exact pattern and amplitude of both intrusion and transient mantle thermal anomalies during the Paleocene appears to be of secondary importance. Furthermore, elevation changes are not significantly affected by the introduction of the underplated material as this is probably thin to absent under most of the British Isles (the preferred underplating

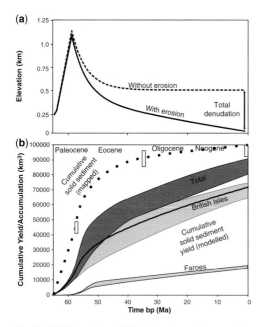

Fig. 10. (a) Example modelled elevation trajectory of a point in the north of England from the erosion model. Transient and permanent uplift (assumed linear) occurs from 65 to 57 Ma. From 57 Ma transient uplift decays exponentially. Erosion as function of elevation continues throughout. Inputs to the model are present day topography, crustal underplating (from gravity, Fig. 9), amount of transient uplift (from Jones & White 2003) and total Cenozoic denudation (from Rowley 1998, reported by Jones *et al.* 2002). (**b**) Output of solid sediment from the British Isles and Faroes catchments (using larger denudation of Jones *et al.* 2002) serving the Faroe–Shetland Basin during the Cenozoic (shaded bands). Grey bands show the range of yields when the exponent *k* in the erosion model (1) is varied from $k = 2$ (lower bound) to $k = 5$ (upper bound). The solid line at $k = 4$ is included to show the shape of yield from the British Isles. Mapped sediment volumes for Paleocene, Eocene and Oligocene–present are shown with error boxes, joined by arbitrary dotted line.

model, Fig. 8), and the uplift effect of intrusion is partly as brief as the intrusion's liquid period (Maclennan & Lovell 2002). The regional transient uplift is more significant, but this is an element of the model relatively well-constrained by the matching of the end-Paleocene coastline (Jones & White 2003).

The exact decay pattern of the transient uplift remains poorly constrained and the resulting erosion patterns similarly await improved constraints. However, the overall decrease in sediment accumulation rate in the basin is consistent with a decreasing topography in the

hinterlands. There may have been Neogene uplift events as, for example, documented in West Greenland (Japsen *et al.* 2006), but as these remain relatively obscure and hard to quantify they have not been included in the model discussed here.

The bands shown in Figure 10 indicate the effect of varying the exponent *k* (eq 1) in the erosion model from $k = 2$ to $k = 5$. Increasing *k* changed the erosion within the model from no dependence on elevation ($k = 0$) to very aggressive erosion at the higher altitudes ($k = 5$). At low values of *k*, sediment supply is fairly linear with time, as topographic variation is less important, whereas when high dependence on elevation is included the sediment supply curves indicate the highest rates occured between 60 and 50 Ma, broadly in agreement with the rate of accumulation measured in the basin (Fig. 10b). The three underplating cases tested did not strongly affect the outputs of the modelling and the yield curves fell within the grey bands on Figure 10. Although the inversion to match the denudation and present day elevation of each cell yielded different *A* values for the three underplating cases, the relative variation of elevation with time, and therefore the yield, was, in each case, dominated by the transient uplift and subsidence effect.

The non-convergence at present day of the sediment yield curves calculated for varying *k* is due to the trade-off in the fit to the two constraints on *A* for each cell of the model, the present-day elevation and the total denuded thickness. If the inversion for *A* was forced to fit the total denuded thickness exactly then the curves converged but this was achieved at the expense of fitting the present day elevation which is much better constrained. The catchment area did not vary very much though the period examined or with varying *k*.

There was minor horizontal tectonic movement during the Cenozoic and consequently this was neglected from the model (a.k.a. Jones & White 2003). Post-rift subsidence in the Faroe–Shetland Basin continued throughout the Cenozoic (Turner & Scrutton 1993), punctuated by multiple but minor compressional phases, possibly associated with relocations in the oceanic spreading centre to the west of the Faroe Islands and its interaction with the Iceland mantle plume (Boldreel & Andersen 1993; Sørensen 2003; Davies *et al.* 2004; Smallwood 2004). The effects of such pulses on the onshore areas are poorly understood, but their inclusion may be important for a refined understanding of sediment supply to be developed. No account is made in this study of sediment storage on the shelves.

Andersen *et al.* (2002) comment that throughout the Eocene, erosion products from the Faroe

Platform were deposited in Norwegian Sea Basin and Faroe Bank Channel (Basin) but only to a limited extent in the Faroe–Shetland Basin. The platform may therefore have been subject to additional tilting not included in the model under discussion here, perhaps associated with rift-flank development as continental rifting proceeded. In the absence of an additional tilt, the model discussed in this paper suggests that c. 40% of erosion product from the Faroes continental shelf would move downslope to the east. The contribution from the Faroes, shown in Figure 10 and Table 1 is likely to be an overestimate.

The model presented here is clearly a simplification of a complex system, but offers a first-order attempt to match the mapped sediment accumulation with supply from the onshore catchments. Many refinements could be made to the model suggested here, for instance lithospheric flexural rigidity, Pliocene climatic change, surface erodability variations, and Neogene uplift events (e.g. Tiley et al. 2004; Japsen et al. 2006) although the imposition of further assumptions may not add to the insight gained, without further constraint. The important observation is that as Table 1 and Figure 10 indicate, even when the upper denudation estimate of Jones et al. (2002) is used, there is still an overall shortfall of supply compared to the sediment volumes mapped within the basin.

Discussion

Although compressional strain values were very low across the Faroe–Shetland area, the mechanical stratigraphy of the upper crust that was affected by Eocene and later compressional episodes consisted of the relatively strong lava pile and surrounding sediments that would be expected to be relatively weak. The shortening appears to have been accommodated locally by folding of the upper crust, with the relatively strong basalt lava package likely to have been dominating the mechanical stratigraphy. Even if the sediments beneath the basalts were able to act as a mobile detachment layer, then the low ratio of their thickness (2–5 km) to the fold wavelength (50–100 km) makes it unlikely they could accommodate the deformation and thrust faults would be expected in spite of the low strains (Stewart 1996). To date, major through-going thrust faults have not been well-imaged on the Munkagrunnur and Fugloy Ridges and the pure shear model of uplift and denudation may be at least partly appropriate. Sub-basalt sediment presence may therefore amplify the denudation for a particular compressional strain (Fig. 3).

Cenozoic uplift was not only caused by compression. The thick crust under the Faroe Islands is believed to include a component of igneous underplating (e.g. Smallwood et al. 1999). Such underplated material is widespread along the continent–ocean transition and has also been reported beneath the Irish Sea (Al-Kindi et al. 2003). Emplacement is thought to have occurred at the time of continental breakup and caused regional permanent uplift and resulting increase in erosion rates. Associated transient uplift peaked at end Paleocene/Early Eocene time (Smallwood & Gill 2002), causing regional regression (Jones & White 2003) and accelerated erosion rates onshore (Fig. 10).

The volume of Cenozoic sediment mapped in the Faroe–Shetland Basin in this study, $10 \times 10^4 \ km^3$, is, in common with Jones et al. (2002)'s smaller estimate, much larger than the 1.8 to $3.5 \times 10^4 \ km^3$ of material estimated by Jones et al. (2002) to have been denuded from the relevant catchment area in the British Isles. Jones et al. (2002) offered three possible contributions to explain the volume discrepancy; incoming axially transported sediment, a sediment source to the west and temporal variation in drainage divides onshore UK. This study partly resolves the discrepancy by identifying a much larger palaeo-drainage area serving the Faroe–Shetland area (Fig. 9), yielding a total up to $6.5 \pm 0.5 \times 10^4 \ km^3$ of material. This study also confines the main volumetric discrepancy to the Paleocene (Table 1), thereby downplaying the importance of the introduction of material into the system by axial transport, which followed the initiation of deep-water currents between the Faroe Islands and the Shetland Isles in the Oligocene (Davies et al. 2001).

Even using the maximum Cenozoic denudation of Jones et al. (2002), the amount of sediment supplied to the basin from both west and east catchments is insufficient to match the volume mapped within the basin (Table 1). Dissolution of any soluble material eroded from the hinterland, for example carbonates, would only make the mismatch worse. The shortfall lies mainly within Paleocene times, which was prior to and during the development of the bulk of the Faroes' flood basalt province. The missing provenance area therefore is likely to be the pre-basalt terrain beneath the Faroes lava pile, and perhaps emergent hyaloclastites of the early eruptive system.

Heavy mineral studies, which allow links to be made between sediment provenance areas and sand-grade sediments, suggest that the vast majority of the Paleocene sandstone encountered in the UK sector has been sourced from the British Isles (Morton et al. 2002; Clarke 2002). However, there are several emerging qualitative indicators of Paleocene sediment input from the west. The Faroes area was adjacent to southern East Greenland before the NE Atlantic Ocean basin rifted open (e.g. Smallwood & White 2002). Similar characteristic heavy mineral suites from Cretaceous–Paleocene sandstones from East Greenland and the Mid-Norwegian continental shelf have indicated that sand was supplied from NE Greenland to western areas of the Vøring Basin to the north of the Faroe–Shetland area (Morton & Grant 1998). Low rutile : zircon ratios, characteristic of Greenlandic provenance (Whitham *et al.* 2004) have been detected in some recent wells from the Faroes sector. A Paleocene 'Greenland Flora' (Jolley & Whitham 2004) has also been identified from palynomorphs, and this fingerprint of input from a western provenance area has been detected in wells 'west of the Corona Ridge' (Jolley *et al.* 2005; Fig. 4). Additionally, results from radiometric dating of detrital white micas, zircon fission track and U/Pb dating are techniques which show promise in establishing the extent of cross-rift sediment transport from eastern Greenland to the Faroe–Shetland area (Carter *et al.* 2002; Pickles, pers. comm. 2002; Whitham *et al.* 2004). One possible sediment input point has been identified in the Kangerlussuaq area of southern East Greenland (Larsen *et al.* 1999; Larsen & Whitham 2005). This study adds quantitatively to these methods, in suggesting that perhaps 30% of the Paleocene solid sediment may have been sourced from this area.

Conclusions

Strain related to compression is responsible for at least some of the uplift experienced by the Faroe Islands, and the presence of sub-basalt sediments may cause additional amplification of denudation wherever a pure shear response to compression is experienced. Both igneous underplating and transient mantle thermal anomaly have also caused Cenozoic uplift around the Faroes Platform. These latter factors have been incorporated into a model of topographic variation together with an erosion term to model clastic sediment yield from the Faroes and British Isles catchments.

The end-Paleocene British Isles reconstruction of Jones & White (2003) indicates a sediment catchment area much bigger than that at the present day, and contributions from this catchment area partly explain the large mismatch between mapped sediment volume in the Faroe–Shetland Basin and the volumes of material eroded from provenance areas. However, even with this larger catchment area and using the maximum Cenozoic denudation of Jones *et al.* (2002), and a generous allowance from Eocene times onwards from the Faroes Platform, there is still a volumetric requirement for

material to have been derived from additional areas. If minimum denudation estimates from the British Isles are taken, then the problem is exacerbated. Conversely, although stretching the error bars in sediment mapping and sediment supply to barely credible levels could resolve the imbalance, it seems likely that as much as 30% of the Paleocene solid sediment in the Faroe–Shetland Basin may have been sourced from a pre-basalt Faroes Platform terrane or terranes currently located beneath the Cenozoic lavas in East Greenland.

The data in Figure 2 are shown by kind permission of Western Geco. The wide-angle depth migration of these data that was used to constrain the gravity model was made by Steve Checkles, Hess Geophysical Technology. Gravity compilation was made by ARK Geophysics. Geoff Kimbell pointed out the lack of physical basis for using isostatically-corrected gravity anomalies to position crustal underplated material, and his and Howard Johnson's reviews also allowed additional improvements to be made to an earlier version of the paper. Thanks to Hess for permission to publish, although the opinions expressed herein do not necessarily represent theirs.

References

AL-KINDI, S., WHITE, N., SINHA, M., ENGLAND, R. & TILEY, R. 2003. Crustal trace of a hot convective sheet. *Geology*, **31**, 207–210.

ANDERSEN, M. S., SØRENSEN, A. B., BOLDREEL, L. O. & NIELSEN, T. 2002. Cenozoic evolution of the Faroe Platform: comparing denudation and deposition. *In*: DORÉ, A. G., CARTWRIGHT, J. A., STOKER, M. S., TURNER, J. P. & WHITE, N. (eds) *Exhumation of the North Atlantic Margin: Timing, Mechanisms and Implications for Petroleum Exploration*. Geological Society, London, Special Publications, **196**, 291–311.

ARCHER, S. G., BERGMAN, S. C., ILIFFE, J., MURPHY, C. M. & THORNTON., M. 2005. Paleogene igneous rocks reveal new insights into the geodynamic evolution and petroleum potential of the Rockall Trough, UK Atlantic margin. *Basin Research*, **17**, 171–201.

BOLDREEL, L. O. & ANDERSEN, M. S. 1993. Late Paleocene to Miocene compression in the Faeroe-Rockall area. *In*: PARKER, J. R. (ed.) *Petroleum Geology of Northwest Europe: Proceedings of the 4th Conference*. Geological Society, London, 1025–1034.

BOLDREEL, L. O. & ANDERSEN, M. S. 1995. The relationship between the distribution of Tertiary sediments, tectonic processes and deep-water circulation around the Faeroe Islands. *In*: SCRUTTON, R. A., STOKER, M. S., SHIMMIELD, G. B. & TUDHOPE, A. W. (eds) *The Tectonics, Sedimentation and Palaeoceanography of the North Atlantic Region*. Geological Society, London, Special Publications, **90**, 145–158.

BOTT, M. H. P. & GUNNARSSON, K. 1980. Crustal structure of the Iceland-Faroe Ridge. *Journal of Geophysics*, **47**, 221–227.

CARTER, A., SHERLOCK, S., KELLEY, S., PICKLES, C., WHITHAM, A. & MORTON, A. 2002. A geochronological approach to reconstructing sediment pathways and detecting sediment recycling in Palaeocene sediments from the Faroes-Shetland region. *Geophysical Research Abstracts*, **4**, A02803.

CLARKE, B. J. 2002. *Early Cenozoic Denudation of the British Lsles: A Quantitative Stratigraphic Approach.* Ph.D. dissertation, University of Cambridge, UK.

CLIFT, P. & TURNER, J. 1998. Paleogene igneous underplating and subsidence anomalies in the Rockall-Faeroe-Shetland area. *Marine and Petroleum Geology*, **15**, 223–243.

DAVIES, R., CARTWRIGHT, J., PIKE, J. & LINE, C. 2001. Early Oligocene initiation of North Atlantic Deep Water formation. *Nature*, **410**, 917–920.

DAVIES, R. J., CLOKE, I. R., CARTWRIGHT, J. A., ROBINSON, A. M. & FERRERO, C. 2004. Post break-up compression of a passive margin and its impact upon hydrocarbon prospectivity: An example from the Tertiary of the Faeroe-Shetland Basin, UK. *Bulletin of the American Association of Petroleum Geologists*, **88**, 1–20.

DORÉ, A. G., LUNDIN, E. R., FICHLER, C. & OLESEN, O. 1997. Patterns of basement structure and reactivation along the NE Atlantic margin. *Journal of the Geological Society of London*, **154**, 85–92.

FLEIDNER, M. M. & WHITE, R. S. 2001. Sub-basalt imaging in the Faeroe-Shetland Basin with large-offset data. *First Break*, **19**, 247–252.

HITCHEN, K. & RITCHIE, J. D. 1993. New K-Ar ages, and a provisional chronology, for the offshore part of the British Tertiary Igneous Province. *Scottish Journal of Geology*, **29**, 73–85.

JAPSEN, P., BONOW, J. M., GREEN, P. F., CHALMERS, J. A. & LIDMAR-BERGSTRÖM, K. 2006. Elevated, passive continental margins: Long-term highs or Neogene uplifts? New evidence from West Greenland, *Earth and Planetary Science Letters*, **248**, 315–324.

JARDFEINGI 2006. Statoil exploration well 6104/21-1 completed, *Faroese Earth and Energy Directorate Press Release* 17th October 2006.

JOHNSON, H., RITCHIE, J. D., HITCHEN, K., McINROY, D. B. & KIMBELL, G. S. 2005. Aspects of the Cenozoic deformational history of the Northeast Faroe-Shetland Basin, Wyville-Thomson Ridge and Hatton Bank areas. *In*: DORÉ, A. G. & VINING, B. (eds) *Petroleum Geology: North-West Europe and Global Perspectives. Proceedings of the 6th Petroleum Geology Conference.* Geological Society, London, 993–1007.

JOLLEY, D. W. & WHITHAM, A. G. 2004. A stratigraphical and palaeoenvironmental analysis of the sub-basaltic sediments of East Greenland. *Petroleum Geoscience*, **10**, 53–60.

JOLLEY, D. W., MORTON, A. & PRINCE, I. 2005. Volcanogenic impact on phytogeography and sediment dispersal patterns in the NE Atlantic. *In*: DORÉ, A. G. & VINING, B. (eds) *Petroleum Geology: Northwest Europe and Global Perspectives. Proceedings of the 6th Petroleum Geology Conference.* Geological Society, London, 969–975.

JONES, S. M. & WHITE, N. 2003. Size and shape of the starting Iceland swell. *Earth and Planetary Science Letters*, **216**, 271–282.

JONES, S. M., WHITE, N., CLARKE, B. J., ROWLEY, E. & GALLAGHER, K. 2002. Present and past influence of the Iceland Plume on sedimentation. *In*: DORÉ, A. G., CARTWRIGHT, J. A., STOKER, M. S., TURNER, J. P. & WHITE, N. (eds) *Exhumation of the North Atlantic Margin: Timing, Mechanisms and Implications for Petroleum Exploration.* Geological Society, London, Special Publications, **196**, 13–25.

KESER NEISH, J. & ZISKA, H. 2005. Structure of the Faroe Bank Channel Basin, offshore Faroe Islands. *In*: DORÉ, A. G. & VINING, B. (eds) *Petroleum Geology: North-West Europe and Global Perspectives. Proceedings of the 6th Petroleum Geology Conference.* Geological Society, London, 873–885.

KIMBELL, G. S., RITCHIE, J. D., JOHNSON, H. & GATLIFF, R. W. 2005. Controls on the structure and evolution of the NE Atlantic margin revealed by regional potential field imaging and 3D modelling. *In*: DORÉ, A. G. & VINING, B. (eds) *Petroleum Geology: North-West Europe and Global Perspectives. Proceedings of the 6th Petroleum Geology Conference.* Geological Society, London, 933–945.

LAMERS, E. & CARMICHAEL, S. M. M. 1999. The Paleocene deepwater snadstone play west of Shetland. *In*: FLEET, A. J. & BOLDY, S. A. R. (eds) *Petroleum Geology of Northwest Europe: Proceeedings of the 5th Conference*, Geological Society, London, 645–659.

LARSEN, M. & WHITHAM, A. J. 2005. Evidence for a major sediment input into the Faroe-Shetland Basin from the Kangerlussuaq region of southern East Greenland. *In*: DORÉ, A. G. & VINING, B. (eds) *Petroleum Geology: North-West Europe and Global Perspectives. Proceedings of the 6th Petroleum Geology Conference.* Geological Society, London, 913–922.

LARSEN, M., HAMBURG, L., OLAUSSEN, S., NØRGAARD-PEDERSEN, & STEMMERIK, L. 1999. Basin evolution in southern East Greenland: An outcrop analog for Cretaceous-Paleogene basins on the North Atlantic Volcanic Margin. *Bulletin of the American Association of Petroleum Geologists*, **83**, 1236–1261.

MACLENNAN, J. & LOVELL, B. 2002. Control of regional sea level by regional uplift and subsidence caused by magmatic underplating of earth's crust. *Geology*, **30**, 675–678.

MONTGOMERY, D. R. 2003. Predicting landscape-scale erosion rates using digital elevation models. *Comptes Rendus Geosciences*, **335**, 1121–1130.

MORTON, A. C. & GRANT, S. 1998. Cretaceous depositional systems in the Norwegian Sea: heavy mineral constraints. *Bulletin of the American Association of Petroleum Geologists*, **82**, 274–290.

MORTON, A. C., BOYD, J. D. & EWEN, D. F. 2002. Evolution of Paleocene sediment dispersal systems in the Foinaven Sub-basin, west of Shetland. *In*: JOLLEY, D. W. & BELL, B. R. (eds) *The North Atlantic Igneous Province: Stratigraphy, Tectonics, Volcanic and Magmatic Processes*, Geological Society, London, Special Publications, **197**, 69–93.

RITCHIE, J. D., GATLIFF, R. W. & RICHARDS, P. C. 1999. Early Tertiary Magmatism in the offshore Northwest U.K. margin and surrounds. *In*: FLEET,

A. J. & BOLDY, S. A. R. (eds) *Petroleum Geology of Northwest Europe: Proceedings of the 5th Conference*, Geological Society, London, 573–584.

ROWLEY, E. J. 1998. *Quantifying Cenozoic Exhumation Across the British Isles*. PhD dissertation, University of Cambridge.

SANDWELL, D. T. & SMITH, W. H. F. 1997. Marine gravity anomaly from Geosat and ERS 1 satellite altimetry. *Journal of Geophysical Research*, **102**, 10,039–10,054.

SHAW-CHAMPION, M. E., WHITE, N. J., JONES, S. M. & PRIESTLEY, K. F. 2006. Crustal velocity structure of the British Isles; a comparison of receiver functions and wide-angle seismic data. *Geophysical Journal International*, **166**, 795–813.

SMALLWOOD, J. R. 2002. Use of V_0-K depth conversion from shelf to deep water: How deep is that brightspot? *First Break*, **20**, 99–106.

SMALLWOOD, J. R. 2004. Tertiary inversion in the Faroe-Shetland Channel and the development of major erosional scarps. *In*: DAVIES, R. J., STEWART, S. A., CARTWRIGHT, J. A., LAPPIN, M. & UNDERHILL, J. R. (eds) *3D Seismic Technology: Application to the Exploration of Sedimentary Basins*. Geological Society, London, Memoirs, **29**, 187–198.

SMALLWOOD, J. R. 2005*a*. Lithology prediction from velocity data: Paleocene sediments in the Faroe-Shetland area. *In*: ZISKA, H., VARMING, T. & BLOCH, D. (eds) *Faroe Islands Exploration Conference 2004 Proceedings*. Annales Societatis Scientiarum Færoensis Suppl., Torshavn, Faroe Islands, 70–81.

SMALLWOOD, J. R. 2005*b*. Quantity, distribution and provenance of Paleocene sediments in the Faroe-Shetland area. *In*: ZISKA, H., VARMING, T. & BLOCH, D. (eds) *Faroe Islands Exploration Conference 2004 Proceedings*. Annales Societatis Scientiarum Færoensis Suppl., Torshavn, Faroe Islands, 82–95.

SMALLWOOD, J. R. & GILL, C. E. 2002. The rise and fall of the Faroe-Shetland Channel: Evidence from seismic mapping of the Balder Formation. *Journal of the Geological Society of London*, **159**, 627–630.

SMALLWOOD, J. R. & HARDING, A. M. (in press). New seismic imaging methods, dating, intrusion style and effects of sills: A drilled example from the Faroe–Shetland Basin. *In*: ZISKA, H. & VARMING, T. (eds) *2nd Faroe Islands Exploration Conference 2006 Proceedings*. Annales Societatis Scientarum Faroensis Supplement, Torshavn, Faroe Islands.

SMALLWOOD, J. R. & WHITE, R. S. 2002. Ridge-plume interaction in the North Atlantic and its influence on continental break-up and seafloor spreading. *In*: JOLLEY, D. W. & BELL, B. R. (eds) *The North Atlantic Igneous Province: Stratigraphy, Tectonics, Volcanic and Magmatic Processes*. Geological Society, London, Special Publications, **197**, 15–37.

SMALLWOOD, J. R., STAPLES, R. K., RICHARDSON, K. R. & WHITE, R. S. 1999. Crust generated above the Iceland mantle plume: From continental rift to oceanic spreading center. *Journal of Geophysical Research*, **104**, 22885–22902.

SMALLWOOD, J. R., TOWNS, M. J. & WHITE, R. S. 2001. The structure of the Faroe-Shetland Trough from integrated deep seismic and potential field modelling. *Journal of the Geological Society of London*, **158**, 409–412.

SØRENSEN, A. B. 2003. Cenozoic basin development and stratigraphy of the Faroes area. *Petroleum Geoscience*, **9**, 189–207.

STEWART, S. A. 1996. Influence of detachment layer thickness on style of thin-skinned shortening. *Journal of Structural Geology*, **18**, 1271–1274.

TILEY, R., MCKENZIE, D. P. & WHITE, N. J. 2003. The elastic thickness of the British Isles. *Journal of the Geological Society of London*, **160**, 499–502.

TILEY, R., WHITE, N. J. & AL-KINDI, S. 2004. Linking Paleogene denudation and magmatic underplating beneath the British Isles. *Geological Magazine*, **141**, 345–351.

TURNER, J. D. & SCRUTTON, R. A. 1993. Subsidence patterns in western margin basins: evidence from the Faeroe-Shetland Basin. *In*: PARKER, J. R. (ed.) *Petroleum Geology of Northwest Europe: Proceedings of the 4th Conference*. Geological Society, London, 975–983.

WHITE, N. & LOVELL, B. 1997. Measuring the pulse of a plume with the sedimentary record. *Nature*, **387**, 888–891.

WHITE, R. S. 1988. A hot-spot model for early Tertiary volcanism in the N Atlantic. *In*: MORTON, A. C. & PARSON, L. M. (eds) *Early Tertiary Volcanism and the Opening of the NE Atlantic*. Geological Society, London, Special Publications, **39**, 3–13.

WHITE, R. S., SMALLWOOD, J. R., FLIEDNER, M. M., MARESH, J., FRUEHN, J. & BOSLAUGH, B. 2003. Imaging and regional distribution of basalt flows in the Faroe-Shetland Basin. *Geophysical Prospecting*, **51**, 215–231.

WHITHAM, A. G., MORTON, A. C. & FANNING, C. M. 2004. Insights into Cretaceous-Paleocene sediment paths and basin evolution in the North Atlantic from a heavy mineral study of sandstones from southern East Greenland. *Petroleum Geoscience*, **10**, 61–72.

Palaeogene evolution of the Ymir and Wyville Thomson ridges, European North Atlantic margin

H. ZISKA & T. VARMING

Jarðfeingi, Brekkutún 1, P. O. Box 3059, FO-110 Tórshavn, Faroe Islands
(e-mail: hziska@jf.fo)

Abstract: The region to the SW of the Faroe Islands is an enigmatic area where the structural trends of the Faroe–Shetland and North Rockall basins meet. The Munkagrunnur, Wyville Thomson and Ymir ridges are major tectonic features within the area and arc approximately perpendicular to the primary Caledonian structural trend. Previous studies have suggested that these ridges formed as a result of compressive forces during the Eocene, Oligocene and Miocene. However, this study suggests that these ridges were initiated by a transient rifting event in the early Paleocene. This rifting event was accompanied by an igneous phase which emplaced large volumes of intrusive and extrusive igneous rocks. The igneous centres within the study area are located on older structural features, indicating exploitation of pre-existing structural weaknesses. The same structural weaknesses were later exploited by compressive events, which resulted in the generation of Ymir Ridge South, and also influenced the orientation and shape of the other segments of Ymir Ridge and the Wyville Thomson Ridge.

The area between the northern edge of the North and North East Rockall basins and the southern edge of the Faroe–Shetland Basin and the Faroese Platform is an enigmatic region where different structural trends meet. This area is referred to as the 'study area' throughout this paper (Figs 1 & 2).

The study area has undergone little hydrocarbon exploration and there are only two wells in the area (Fig. 1): Well 164/7-1 drilled approximately 1.2 km of flood basalts and 121 m of Paleocene tuffs and tuff breccias before being terminated within heavily intruded Upper Cretaceous shales (Archer *et al.* 2005). An unconformity spanning 33 Ma was found between the Paleocene volcanic rocks and the Upper Cretaceous shales. The well was terminated above a modelled igneous pluton (Archer *et al.* 2005). The seismic data available to this study do not extend as far as well 164/7-1 (Fig. 1), but extrapolation of the interpreted basalt thickness does support the interpretation presented here. Well 163/6-1 was drilled NW of the Darwin Igneous Centre in a water depth of 1374 m. The well penetrated 1267 m of Palaeogene and Neogene sediments before penetrating the Palaeogene basalt. According to the composite log the well was terminated in dacite after drilling through 689 m of flood basalt and 356 m of acidic volcanic rocks.

One reason for the lack of exploration within the study area has been the inability to map units below the volcanic unit confidently. However, this is, becoming less complicated (e.g. Gallagher & Dromgoole 2005; Keser Neish 2005; White *et al.* 2005), leading to a better understanding of the timing of mapped structures, source distribution and maturity, potential reservoir rocks, etc.

Several large scale structures are mapped within the study area e.g. the Ymir, Wyville Thomson and Munkagrunnur ridges, and currently, the causal mechanisms for these structures are poorly understood, with transfer zones and/or compression being proposed (e.g. Kimbell *et al.* 2005; Boldreel & Andersen 1993). The implications for hydrocarbon exploration are significant in both instances, because the timing of strike-slip and compression differ significantly, with the transfer zones becoming inactive during late volcanism and compression being most pronounced in the Oligocene and Miocene times (Boldreel & Andersen 1993). Evidence from new seismic data indicates a simpler evolutionary history for the study area than has previously been proposed, with Paleocene rifting possibly playing a key role in the location and orientation of the major structural features.

Regional geology

The study area is thought to lie stratigraphically within the Caledonides (Doré *et al.* 1999). This orogeny induced steeply-dipping NE–SW trending shears within the crystalline basement rocks. Subsequent extensional phases in Triassic, late Jurassic to early Cretaceous and Paleocene resulted in the present day location of the main basins in the study area (Doré *et al.* 1999). However, the Mesozoic and older structure is generally obscured by the presence of thick Palaeogene lavas.

From: JOHNSON, H., DORÉ, A. G., GATLIFF, R. W., HOLDSWORTH, R., LUNDIN, E. R. & RITCHIE, J. D. (eds)
The Nature and Origin of Compression in Passive Margins. Geological Society, London, Special Publications,
306, 153–168. DOI: 10.1144/SP306.7   0305-8719/08/$15.00 © The Geological Society of London 2008.

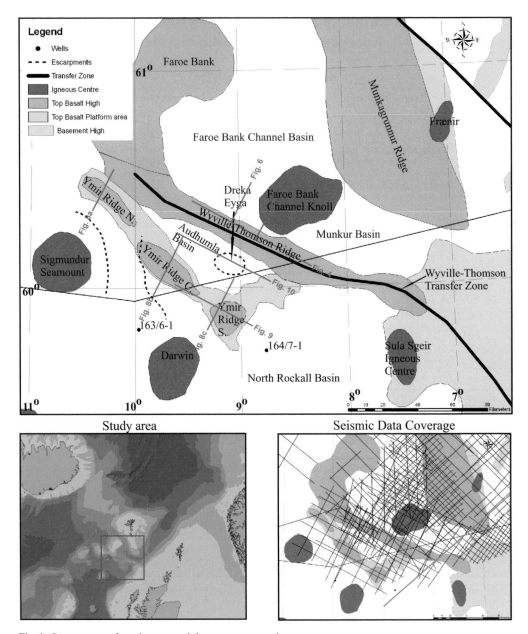

Fig. 1. Structure map. Location map and data coverage map inset.

Rumph *et al.* (1993) speculated that a series of transfer faults segment the sub-basins in the Faroe–Shetland Basin by offsetting ridges and providing for differential subsidence and hence differential sediment deposition on adjacent sides of such transfer zones. Several authors (e.g. Kimbell *et al.* 2005) have proposed that movement

along the Wyville Thomson Transfer Zone is involved, at least in part, in the genesis of the Wyville Thomson and Ymir ridges.

Breakup of the North Atlantic was preceded and followed by a series of magmatic events which resulted in the extrusion of flood basalts across the entire study area, and also the emplacement of a

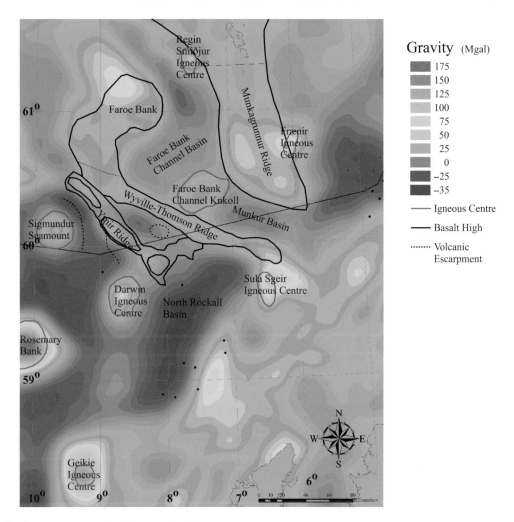

Fig. 2. Free air gravity data. Courtesy of BGS.

series of igneous complexes. The source of the excessive volume of volcanic rocks is thought to be either a mantle plume (e.g. Smallwood & White 2002) or fertile mantle (Foulger 2002). Lundin & Doré (2005) suggested that extrusion of the oldest lavas of the North Atlantic Igneous Province (NAIP) was associated with a failed attempt to separate NW Europe and Greenland along a NW–SE axis.

The igneous rocks in the study area are typified by thick flood basalts, extensive sills and dykes, and igneous centres. In addition, large volumes of tuffs were encountered in well 164/7-1 (Archer *et al.* 2005). The ages of these flood basalts are speculated by Keser Neish & Ziska (2005) to be equivalent to the Beinisvørð Formation (formerly: Lower Basalt Formation) known from onshore Faroe Islands.

The same authors propose that the Faroe Bank Channel Knoll is a shield volcano which developed contemporaneously with the Malinstindur Formation (formerly: Middle Basalt Formation) known from onshore Faroe Islands.

The study area was relatively flat-lying towards the end of the volcanic activity, as exemplified by the plane-parallel bedded character of the wide-spread basalt units imaged on seismic data and by exposures on the Faroe Islands. This implies that the present-day structure, although possibly initiated by or affected by early events, is primarily a result of events which post-date the Palaeogene volcanism.

The study area is segmented by a series of high amplitude ridges that have general NW, NNW and

WNW trends (Fig. 1). Boldreel & Andersen (1993) proposed that these ridges originated from Oligocene and Miocene compression. However, Keser Neish & Ziska (2005) suggested that the Wyville Thomson Ridge had a positive relief at least as early as Paleocene, which Johnson *et al.* (2005) suggested may be indicative of compression in the Paleocene.

Observations

Wyville Thomson Ridge

The Wyville Thomson Ridge (Figs 1 to 7) is a WNW/ESE elongated sub-symmetrical structural high, both at seabed and top basalt levels. The ridge extends from the Outer Hebrides High in the SE until its termination just beyond its SW/NE abutment against Faroe Bank in the NW (Fig. 1). The North and North East Rockall basins and Audhumla Basin are located on its southwestern margin, whereas the Munkur Basin, Faroe Bank Channel Knoll and Faroe Bank Channel Basin are found to the NE. The total length of the ridge is 180 km, and its width varies between 6 km and 18 km. Gravity data (Fig. 2) show the ridge as a high amplitude feature exhibiting similar spatial characteristics as the top basalt depth map (Fig. 3). The widest point on the ridge coincides with a slight change in the orientation of the ridge axis from a westerly trend in the south to a more WNW trend in the north. The location of the widest point of the ridge is where the Faroe Bank Channel Knoll flanks the ridge on the NE side and the southern

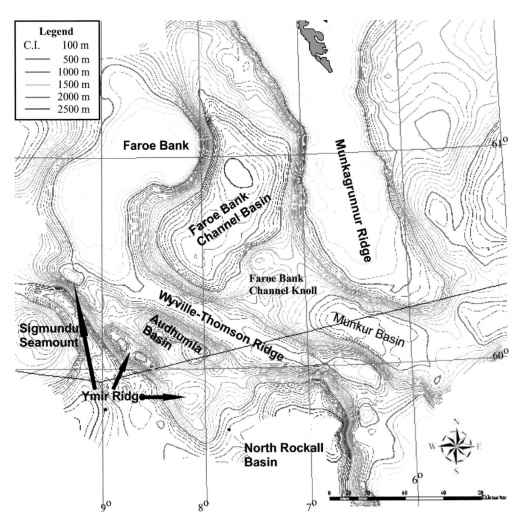

Fig. 3. Top basalt depth map.

segment of the Ymir Platform flanks the ridge on the SW side (Figs 1, 2 & 3). There is a depression in the interpreted base basalt reflection at this location (Fig. 4). No onlap of the basalt is seen in the depression, whereas in a similar depression to the NW, clear onlap of the basalt onto a pre-existing structure is observed.

The crest of the ridge has been subjected to erosion, as demonstrated by the truncated reflectors seen at seabed on Figures 4 and 6. Extrapolation of the basalt thickness at the point where the basalt intersects the seabed across the ridge (assuming no pre-erosion thickness change) reveals that in excess of 500 m of basalt has been removed due to erosion in some locations. Erosion of post-lava sedimentary sequences is also evident on the seismic data (Fig. 6). The area where the basalt outcrops at seabed is shown with a red outline on Figure 5, whereas the structural crest on top basalt level is shown with a black outline. There is a close relationship between basalt outcrop and structural crest along on the Wyville Thomson Ridge. The flood basalts become progressively thinner from the Faroe Bank Channel Basin and Audhumla Basin towards the present day outcrop of the basalts at the crest of the ridge (Fig. 5). The style of thinning in the Faroe Bank Channel Basin is pinch-out. Underlying formations also thicken into the basin (Fig. 6).

Wide aperture seismic data across the southern part of the ridge have been modelled by Klingelhofer et al. (2005) (Fig. 1). The results show the presence of a basement block below the Wyville Thomson Ridge which is elevated relative to the Munkur and North East Rockall basins on adjacent sides. According to the model, younger strata

appear to drape over this elevated basement block. However, no such fault block is evident on conventional seismic data, although this may be due to the poor quality of the seismic data. There are a few indications of faulting under, and even within, the flood basalts, as seen in Figure 7, where a normal offset at sub-basalt level appears changed to a reversed offset at base-basalt level.

Ymir Ridge

Bathymetric data show a broad flat area west of the northern half of the Wyville Thomson Ridge (Fig. 1). This area encompasses the Ymir Ridge and Audhumla Basin. The depth to top Palaeogene basalt map (Fig. 3) shows the relationship between these two structural features quite clearly. The extent of the Ymir Ridge is defined on top basalt level, and the mapped structure is shown on Figure 1. The total length of the ridge is 110 km, and the width, at the platform level varies between 6–16 km.

The areal extent of the Ymir Ridge has been interpreted differently in various studies; for example Keser Neish (2004) defined it as extending from the Faroe Bank in the north and through the Faroes/UK boundary to the south. Johnson et al. (2005), Kimbell et al. (2005) and others suggested the ridge terminates prior to it reaching the Faroe Bank in the north. We suggest the introduction of the term Ymir Platform for the generally elevated area around the Ymir Ridge (Figs 1 & 3). The NW termination of the Ymir Platform also defines the northern termination of the Audhumla Basin, which is located between the Wyville Thomson

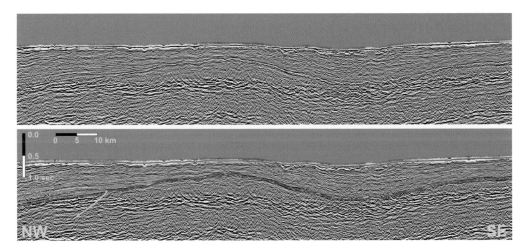

Fig. 4. Seismic line along the Wyville Thomson Ridge. Green, top basalt; red, base basalt; blue, intra-basalt; yellow, fault. Seismic data courtesy of Fugro Multi Client Services (UK) Ltd. For location of seismic profile, see Figure 1.

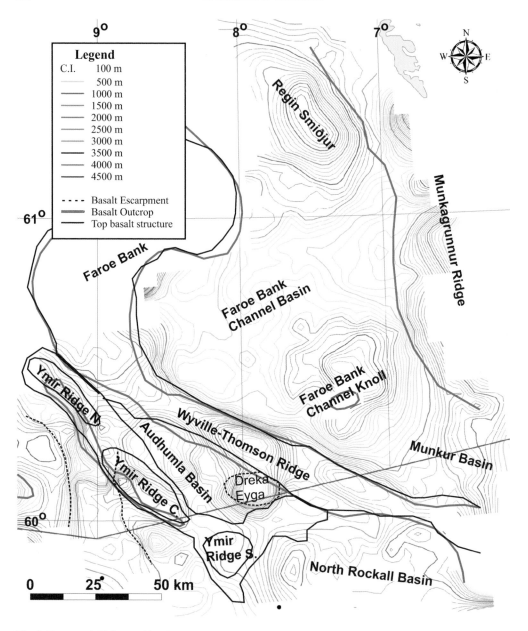

Fig. 5. Interpreted thickness of basalt.

Ridge and the Ymir Ridge. The Ymir Ridge is flanked to the SW by the North Rockall Basin.

The Ymir Platform exhibits substantial wavelength and amplitude variation along its length (Figs 1 & 8). These variations are seen as three separate structural culminations. The northern culmination exhibits a relatively short wavelength and high amplitude; the central culmination has a longer wavelength and high amplitude, whereas

the southern culmination has a long wavelength and small amplitude. These variations along the ridge provide the criteria for recognizing ridge segments that are here termed Ymir Ridge North, Ymir Ridge Central and Ymir Ridge South.

The northern segment (Figs 1 & 8a) is an asymmetric NNW/SSE-trending feature, with a steep slope on the southwestern flank. The slope on the northeastern flank of this segment is characterized

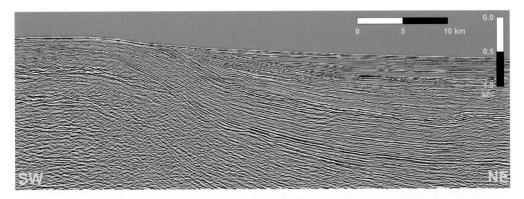
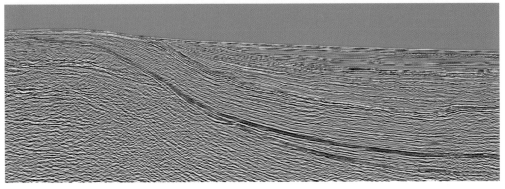

Fig. 6. Seismic line from Wyville Thomson Ridge (SW) to Faroe Bank Channel (NE). Green, top basalt; red, base basalt; purple, sub basalt reflection. Seismic data courtesy of Fugro Multi Client Services (UK) Ltd. For location of seismic profile, see Figure 1.

by an uneven top basalt surface which is paralleled by reflections within the basalt. The shape of the uneven top basalt surface could be indicative of faulting, although the traces of any faults are difficult to define confidently. Gravity data (Fig. 2) show a gravity high, which conforms with the top basalt structure.

The central segment (Figs 1 & 8b) is also an asymmetric NNW/SSE-trending feature with a steeper dip on the southwestern side compared to the northeastern side. There are indications of thrust faults at the crest, and reverse faults are also seen on the NE flank (Fig. 8b). However, it is not possible to map the areal extent of this faulting due to the limited data coverage. The volcanic section thickens from the crest of the segment into the Audhumla Basin (Fig. 8b). Gravity data (Fig. 2) show a gravity high, which conforms with the top basalt structure.

The southern segment of the ridge (Figs 1 & 8c) is a broader, lower amplitude feature, which is more equant in outline compared with the northwesterly part of the ridge and there is a slight extension to the SE. This segment of the ridge is asymmetric

with the structural culmination offset towards the SW. There is no gravity anomaly associated with Ymir Ridge South (Fig. 2).

Seismic data (Fig. 9) demonstrate that the basalt section thickens off the Ymir Ridge Central and reaches a maximum just NW of the crest of Ymir Ridge South, before it thins towards the SW. Flattening the seismic on the top basalt, shows a symmetrical basin which has been filled with subaerially erupted lavas. This infilling was probably from a northerly direction, as indicated by the onlap onto the southern flank of the basin.

Transfer zones

The term transfer zone is used in the same context as commonly found in literature concerning the Faroe–Shetland Basin, where it is used in connection with lineaments, lineament terminations and basin/basement segmentation (e.g. Rumph *et al.* 1993; Doré *et al.* 1999; Kimbell *et al.* 2005).

Transfer zones have been described in connection with the location and generation of both the Wyville Thomson Ridge and Ymir Ridge

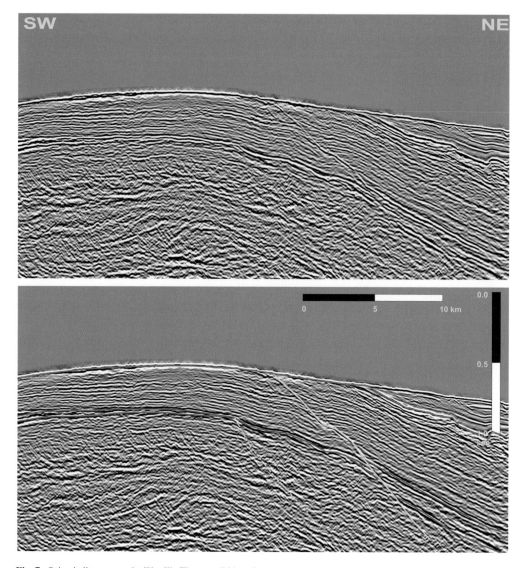

Fig. 7. Seismic line across the Wyville Thomson Ridge. Green, top basalt; red, base basalt; purple, sub basalt; yellow, faults. Seismic data courtesy of Fugro Multi Client Services (UK) Ltd. For location of seismic profile, see Figure 1.

(e.g. Rumph *et al.* 1993; Kimbell *et al.* 2005). No faults with a measurable strike-slip component are observed at top basalt level at the speculated location of either the Wyville Thomson Transfer Zone nor the Ymir Transfer Zone. It was not possible to map faults confidently under the flood basalts on the available seismic data. The lack of well calibration means that it is not possible to demonstrate if there is differential subsidence across either structural feature, as has been observed in connection with transfer zones in the Faroe–Shetland Basin (Rumph *et al.* 1993).

Palaeogene magmatism

The entire study area is covered by a sequence of flood basalts in addition to the presence of a number of igneous centres (e.g. Ritchie *et al.* 1999). Variations in thickness of the different volcanic units relative to present day structures is believed to reflect the infilling of pre-existing topography. The location of igneous centres and volcanic escarpments may also give an insight into the structure of the area prior to and during volcanism.

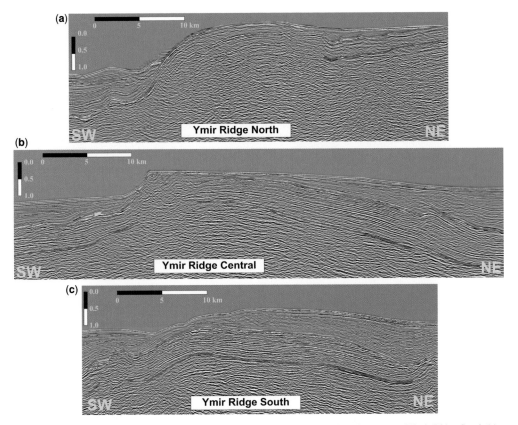

Fig. 8. Seismic lines across Ymir Ridge North. (**a**) Ymir Ridge Central (**b**) and northern part of Ymir Ridge South (**c**). Green, top basalt; red, base basalt. Seismic data courtesy of Fugro Multi Client Services (UK) Ltd. For location of seismic profiles, see Figure 1.

Flood basalts. The top of the flood basalts is defined as a strong seismic reflector which is found on all seismic data in the area (e.g. Fig. 4). However, the lack of wells in the study area prevents a confident definition of a reflector which represents the base of the lava flows.

The red reflector on Figures 4 and 6–10 is, in most of the area, the lowermost of the parallel high amplitude reflectors. This reflector is therefore interpreted to represent the base of the subaerial lava flows. Mapping this reflector in the study area has allowed the generation of a basalt thickness map (Fig. 5). It is not possible to conclude on the presence or, indeed, absence of older flood basalt units, or other volcanic units, at deeper levels.

There are indications of deeper igneous units in the Audhumla Basin, where intra- to sub-basalt structures have been interpreted to be an igneous intrusive feature (Keser Neish 2004). This could, potentially, be of a nature similar to the pluton modelled below the terminal depth reached in well 164/7-1 (Archer *et al.* 2005). Figure 10 shows an erosive

escarpment at top basalt level on both sides of the suggested intrusive feature. This erosive escarpment encircles the Dreka Eyga intrusion (Fig. 1). Here the interpreted base basalt reflector is truncated, and older units are thus exposed under the post-volcanic sediments. Truncations of older units under the basalt are visible on either side of another potentially similar feature called 'Hitt Eyga' on Figure 10. These features, interpreted here as associated with igneous intrusions, are probably of limited areal extent compared to the extrusive basalts, which cover the entire study area.

Two other volcanic escarpments have been mapped in the study area (Figs 1, 2 & 5), and others have been mapped in adjacent areas, particularly around volcanic centres such as Darwin (Abraham & Ritchie 1991; Johnson *et al.* 2005). These volcanic escarpments represent the rapid cooling and brecciation of flood basalts as they reached the palaeoshoreline. The height of the escarpment represents the water depth at the time of basalt extrusion (e.g. Kiørboe 1999; Smythe 1983).

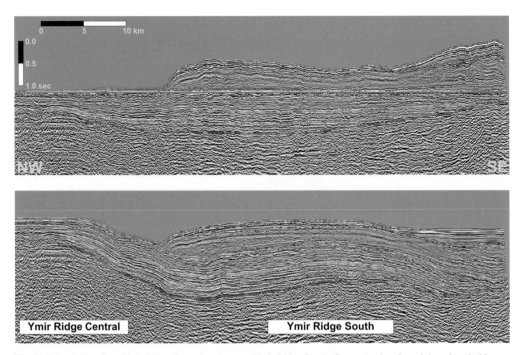

Fig. 9. Seismic line from Ymir Ridge Central and across Ymir Ridge South. Green, top basalt; red, base basalt; blues, intra basalts. Seismic data courtesy of CGGVeritas. For location of seismic profile, see Figure 1.

One of the volcanic escarpments is located around the Sigmundur seamount (Fig. 1), with lava flows originating on the Sigmundur seamount. The escarpment is located in the deepest part of the area between the Sigmundur Seamount and the Ymir Ridge and its full extent is mapped by Ritchie *et al.* (1997). The lava flow direction, indicated by the escarpment, is outwards from the central parts of Sigmundur Seamount.

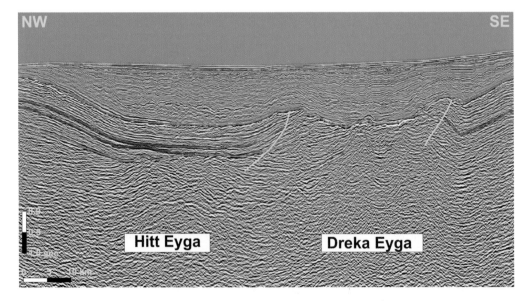

Fig. 10. Seismic line in the Audhumla Basin. Green, top basalt; red, base basalt; purple/blue, sub basalt. Seismic data courtesy of Fugro Multi Client Services (UK) Ltd. For location of seismic profile, see Figure 1.

The second volcanic escarpment, which was mapped by Ritchie *et al.* (1997), is located SE of the Sigmundur Seamount volcanic escarpment and runs in a SW–NE to SSW–NNE direction from the North Rockall Basin across the crest of the Ymir Ridge and into the Audhumla Basin. The lava flow direction is from the SE. Data density precludes a full understanding of the extent and style of termination of these escarpments.

Igneous centres. There are a number of igneous centres in the study area (Figs 1, 2 & 5). These are, Regin Smiðjur (Keser Neish 2004), Faroe Bank Channel Knoll (Roberts *et al.* 1983), Sigmundur Seamount (Ritchie *et al.* 1997), Darwin (Abraham & Ritchie 1991), Rosemary Bank (Hitchen & Ritchie 1993), Geikie Volcanic Centre (Evans *et al.* 1989; Ernst *et al.* 2005), and the Sula Sgeir Igneous Centre. Frænir (Keser Neish 2004) is an igneous centre, which lies just outside the study area.

The Faroe Bank has previously been speculated to be an igneous centre, primarily based on the gravity and magnetic anomalies associated with the feature (Dobinson 1970; Keser Neish 2004). The gravity anomaly associated with the Faroe Bank (Fig. 2) shows a varying response, with a relative low in the westernmost part and a gravity high in the north. This differs from the other igneous centres in the area (Fig. 2) and the response is hard to reconcile with the understanding of an igneous centre as a feature which typically, has a high density igneous core and a distinct circular gravity anomaly associated with it.

Well 164/7-1 was drilled into heavily intruded upper Cretaceous shales, and was terminated above a modelled igneous pluton (Archer *et al.* 2005). Within the Audhumla Basin, the top basalt reflectors are truncated (Fig. 10), and this truncation can be mapped into an ellipsoid shape (Figs 1, 2 & 5). Keser Neish (2004) suggested that this was due to an intrusion and named it 'Dreka eyga'. Seismic data (Fig. 10) suggest another similar feature, subcropping the flood basalts, adjacent to the Dreka Eyga intrusion. The truncations here could represent a similar hiatus as observed in the 164/7-1 well.

Figure 2 shows the free air gravity data for the study area with the outlines of the igneous centres drawn on. A positive gravity anomaly is observed between the Geikie and Darwin Igneous Centres and seems to form part of an extension of a trend that links the Dreka Eyga Intrusion, Faroe Bank Channel Knoll and Frænir Igneous Centre. Wide aperture data are available across this anomaly. However, modelling of these data by Klingelhofer (2005) resulted in a final model which does not account for the presence of this gravity anomaly.

Analysis

The study area has had a very complex genesis, as demonstrated by the presence of intersecting structural trends, reverse and normal faults, compressive elements alongside evidence for subsidence and igneous centres above and below the flow basalts.

Transfer zones

It has been suggested that both the Wyville Thomson Ridge and Ymir Ridge are underlain by transfer zones (e.g. Rumph *et al.* 1993; Archer *et al.* 2005; Kimbell *et al.* 2005). Archer *et al.* (2005) suggest that their Ymir Ridge lineament, is a long lived feature that has been influential in the location of the igneous centres in the study area, including the modelled pluton below the base of well 164/7-1. Kimbell *et al.* (2005) clearly demonstrate that there is an offset between the Faroe–Shetland Basin and the North Rockall Basin, although this does not demonstrate strike-slip movement, but suggests that the zone is a major structural partition between the two basins.

Pure strike-slip and transpressive movements along strike transverse fault zones is known to result in a complex set of en-echelon folds at an angle to the fault zone (e.g. Lowell 1985), where the aspect ratio of the folds produced is between 1:5 and 1:10 (Sattarzadeh *et al.* 2000). The associated fault pattern is highly complex with both normal and reverse faulting potentially occurring in each fold (e.g. Lowell 1985). We are not aware of any such transverse movements along a fault which have resulted in an elongated high amplitude short wavelength ridge similar to the present day expression of the Wyville Thomson Ridge or Ymir Ridge.

No evidence is found on seismic data to support the presence, or indeed absence, of transfer zone strike-slip movement. This could be related to the timing of transfer zone movement, as in the Faroe–Shetland Basin. Large variations in the thickness of Cretaceous strata across the transfer zones have been observed in the Faroe–Shetland Basin (Rumph *et al.* 1993), indicating that they are primarily associated with the Cretaceous rifting event. No conclusive evidence for any such activity along these zones during the Paleocene or later has been observed. It can be assumed that the possible transfer zone movements in the Faroe–Shetland Basin had ceased by the early Paleocene.

Rifting is speculated to have occurred in the study area in the early Paleocene (Lundin & Doré 2005), and such movement is likely to have exploited pre-existing structural weaknesses, including fault zones originating from Cretaceous rifting.

Palaeogene magmatism

The most prominent features on seismic data in the study area are the Palaeogene flood basalts, which cover the entire area, and a number of associated igneous centres. The flood basalts are speculated to be contemporaneous with the classic tabular lava flows of the Beinisvørð Formation (Keser Neish & Ziska 2005) known from onshore Faroe Islands (Passey & Bell 2007). Observations onshore of marine to marginal marine sediments between the lava flows indicate that subsidence kept pace with extrusion (Ellis *et al.* 2002). The parallel bedded character of the interpreted basalt unit suggests that most of the area was relatively flat lying towards the end of volcanism. However, there are volcanic escarpments observed at top basalt level within the study area (Figs 1, 2 & 5; Ritchie *et al.* 1997; Archer *et al.* 2005). This demonstrates that at least parts of the area were below sea level during the extrusion of the later basalts in the area. One such volcanic escarpment has been found within the basaltic unit. The existence of these basalt escarpments suggests that there was differential subsidence during volcanism. The volcanic escarpments do not correlate to the present day structure of Ymir Ridge Central, or even the top basalt structure of the same Ridge segment, indicating that the current structural configuration post-dates the eruption of the lavas. The generally parallel bedded nature of the basalt succession suggests that the pre-volcanic landscape had been drowned by the flood basalts, as is often the case in large igneous provinces (e.g. Jerram & Widdowson 2004).

Mapping the thickness of the flood basalt on seismic data shows that the basalt thickens from the point where the top basalt reflector is truncated at the seabed on the Wyville Thomson Ridge towards the central part of the Faroe Bank Channel and Audhumla Basin (Fig. 5). The amount of thickening varies along the ridge, and thus indicates that the Wyville Thomson Ridge was a relatively positive feature of varying magnitude prior to and during early basalt extrusion, with a more rapidly subsiding basin developing at the location of the present day Faroe Bank Channel and Audhumla Basins. Figure 4 shows a seismic line along the Wyville Thomson Ridge and the onlap of the basalt onto a pre-existing structure is supporting evidence in favour of the presence of a structural feature where the Wyville Thomson Ridge is today prior to the extrusion of the basalt, as has previously been suggested by Waddams & Cordingley (1999). The ridge was then buried by

the encroaching basalt section. The depression towards the SE of Figure 4 is of the same magnitude as the one the NW and discussed above. There are no onlaps of the basalt section associated with this depression, suggesting that the depression is a post-depositional fold feature. The location of the depression is where the Ridge changes orientation slightly to a more NW–SE direction towards the south. The Faroe Bank Channel Knoll and Dreka Eyga are located adjacent to this depression.

Lundin & Doré (2005) suggest that the study area was in the centre of an early Paleocene transient rift, providing a potential mechanism for basin development. Such transient rifting was originally proposed by Waagstein (1988), who suggested that the rift orientation was NE–SW, or roughly perpendicular to the rift proposed by Lundin & Doré. Geochemical evidence led Waagstein to suggest that the oldest lavas on Greenland were sourced through a similar transient rift in Greenland.

Paleocene rifting is further supported by the 1100 m of volcaniclastic material observed in the Lopra well which was all deposited in less than 200 m of water (Ellis *et al.* 2002), suggesting significant subsidence during the Paleocene. Ziska & Morgan (2005) suggested that a basement fault was active during the extrusion of the Beinisvørð Formation.

Evidence from orientations of faults and dykes at outcrop on the Faroe Islands shows a significant difference in strike in the Beinisvørð Formation compared to the Malinstindur and Enni Formations. The dominant trend in the Beinisvørð Formation is NNW–SSE, whereas the trend in the Malinstindur and Enni Formations is east–west. The older trend is thus parallel to the proposed transient rift in the early Paleocene (Lundin & Doré 2005) and the younger trend is parallel to the rift which led to continental breakup in the Eocene.

The Faroe Bank Channel Knoll Igneous Centre (Figs 1, 2 & 5) is located in the southern part of the Faroe Bank Channel Basin. The appearance of a thickening section of basalt towards the central part and a depression in the centre of the Faroe Bank Channel Knoll suggests that the igneous centre is the remains of a shield volcano as suggested by Keser Neish & Ziska (2005). The extrusives associated with the Faroe Bank Channel Knoll are emplaced onto earlier flood basalts, and clearly postdate the emplacement of the flood basalt covering the area. Onshore observations show that the Malinstindur Formation, which is the basalt unit overlying the Beinisvørð Formation, is most likely erupted from shield volcanoes (Rasmussen & Noe-Nygaard 1969). Regin Smiðjur Igneous Centre (Figs 2 & 5) shows many of the same characteristics as Faroe Bank Channel Knoll.

As mentioned previously, the Faroe Bank Channel Knoll lies on a slightly curving SSW–NNE to WSW–ENE trend with the Frænir Igneous centre, Drega Eyga intrusion, Darwin Igneous Centre and Geikie Igneous Centre (Fig. 2). The intersection of this trend also lines up with a gravity anomaly between Ymir Ridge Central and South (Fig. 2), and the post volcanic depression on the Wyville Thomson Ridge (Fig. 4).

The trend which connects these features is the same as the general trend in the area, broadly orthogonal to the Wyville Thomson Ridge. The results of this study suggest that a pre-existing structural weakness has been exploited by magma during the creation of the igneous centres. The existence of a structural feature connecting the aforementioned igneous centres is suggested by the observation of a gravity anomaly connecting the Darwin and Geikie igneous centres (Fig. 2). Klingelhofer et al. (2005) modelled wide aperture data across this gravity anomaly between the Geikie and Darwin igneous centres. However, forward gravity modelling of the output model of Klingelhofer et al. (2005)'s does not account for this gravity anomaly.

Compression/extension

Both the Wyville Thomson Ridge and the Ymir Ridge have been ascribed a compressive ramp anticline origin (e.g. Boldreel & Andersen 1993; Johnson et al. 2005) in the Eocene, Oligocene and Miocene. Potential field modelling has resulted in contradictory results with Tate et al. (1999) concluding that there is relatively shallow basement under the ridge, whereas Waddams & Cordingley (1999) concluded that there is an underlying deeper, inverted sedimentary basin. Klingelhofer et al. (2005) analysed wide aperture data across the Wyville Thomson Ridge, and their final model shows a basement high with the overlying layers draping over it, which leads the authors to conclude that the ridge is of compressive origin.

The premise of a compressive origin for the Wyville Thomson and Ymir ridges was originally based on observations of sedimentary sequences overlying the flood basalts (Boldreel & Andersen 1993). Observation of basalt and potential pre-basalt units, which thicken away from the Wyville Thomson Ridge, led Johnson et al. (2005) to conclude that compression may have been initiated in the Paleocene. In contrast, Lundin & Doré (2005) suggest the presence of an early Paleocene transient rift from Scotland to Greenland. This postulated rift transects the study area and the suggested width extends from the Munkagrunnur Ridge in the NE to the Darwin and Sigmundur igneous centres in the SW. This rifting event was accompanied by

the extrusion of large volumes of volcanic material. Geochemical signatures of these basalts and basalts on Greenland led Waagstein (1988) to suggest that these basalts were extruded through two parallel transient rifts, one across the Faroese Platform and one in Greenland. Waagstein also suggested that these rifts were parallel to the final continental breakup, and thus at right angles to the rift that is proposed by Lundin & Doré (2005).

Flood basalts are known to fill in depressions first, and, if the extruded volume is large enough, the flows will cover all pre-existing structures (Jerram & Widdowson 2004) and create a flat lying plateau of basalt, hence the name plateau basalts. The flood basalts have covered the entire study area, but there are variations in thickness which relate to present-day structure; the most notable example is the observed thinning of the flood basalts across the Wyville Thomson Ridge and Ymir Ridge Central (Fig. 5). The seismic data show onlap onto the pre-existing Wyville Thomson Ridge along the ridge, whereas such onlap is not seen perpendicular to the ridge. The implication of these observations is twofold. The first is that there was limited relief when basalt extrusion started, which is why the thinning is in the shape of pinchout rather than onlap, but the subsidence was not sufficient to channel all the extruded basalt into the developing depressions, and thus prevent the basalt from regularly flowing over the ridge. Evidence from other volcanic rifts shows that volcanism may post-date the initial rift by tens of millions of years (Jerram & Widdowson 2004) meaning that the sag basin geometry seen on e.g. Figure 6 is a likely outcome of such a rifting event.

The volcanic section thickens off the central segment of the Ymir Ridge (Figs 5, 8 & 9). Figure 9 also shows that there is no such thickness variation which conforms to the present day structure of Ymir Ridge South. However, a basin seems to have developed at this location during volcanism. These observations suggest that the central segment of the Ymir Ridge may have undergone an evolutionary history similar to the Wyville Thomson Ridge, while the southern segment has a different evolutionary history, which did not involve any relief prior to or during volcanism.

The post-basalt sedimentary section within the study area shows evidence of later compressive phases (Boldreel & Andersen 1993). Such compressive phases are bound to have influenced the deeper section, either on a crustal scale (Tate et al. 1999) or as basin inversion (Waddams & Cordingley 1999).

The lineament that links Frænir, Faroe Bank Channel Knoll, Darwin and Geikie igneous centres has a positive gravity anomaly associated with it (Fig. 2). We suggest that this lineament is linked to a deep seated feature, which transects the Ymir Ridge between the central and southern segments and cuts the Wyville Thomson Ridge north of the section where the ridge is widest (Fig. 3). Seismic data along the Wyville Thomson Ridge reveal a depression in the pre-basalt section at the location where the gravity anomaly crosses the ridge. This depression is of similar magnitude as the one which has resulted in the onlap of the basalt further towards the NW on the ridge. No onlap is observed in this depression (Fig. 4), indicating that this depression postdates volcanism.

Gravity data (Fig. 2) show a positive gravity anomaly along the Wyville Thomson Ridge and along Ymir Ridge Central, supporting the basement core modelled by Klingelhofer *et al.* (2005). No such gravity anomaly is associated with Ymir Ridge South. This suggests that the southern segment of Ymir Ridge is not underlain by an elevated basement block. However, there is a gravity high between Ymir Ridge Central and South. This high lines up with a gravity anomaly that connects the NE trending line of igneous centres (Fig. 2).

Discussion

This study suggests a new evolutionary history for the study area. Although no firm evidence has been observed supporting the presence of a transfer fault associated with the Wyville Thomson Ridge, the orientation of the ridge approximately perpendicular to the maximum tensile stress direction during the Cretaceous, may indicate the possible presence of a transfer fault. However, no direct evidence has been found, which suggests that any such transfer fault played an active role in the generation of the Wyville Thomson or Ymir Ridges.

It has previously been suggested that Oligocene and Miocene compressional events resulted in the generation of the Wyville Thomson and Ymir ridges. It has been shown here that the Wyville Thomson Ridge and the central segment of the Ymir Ridge were relatively positive features prior to the extrusion of the basalt. This means either that the compressive phases started a lot earlier then originally suggested by Boldreel & Andersen (1993), as suggested by e.g. Johnson *et al.* (2005), or alternatively that the ridges are created in connection with rifting events, including possible early Paleocene rifting as suggested by Lundin & Doré (2005).

Firm evidence in the shape of deep-seated normal faults on the flanks of the ridge and in the basin has not been found. Neither have any other fault patterns been confidently mapped under the flood basalts. This is due to relatively poor imaging of the sub-basalt layers, although Figure 7 shows a small normal fault under the

basalt section. However, the fault was reactivated as a reverse fault after the emplacement of the basalt, which was probably linked to later compressive phases. There are indications of a possible similar fault further updip, but the offset is negligible.

Further evidence in favour of an extension model for the initiation of the Wyville Thomson Ridge is found in the orientation of the fractures in the Beinisvørð Formation onshore Suðuroy, which are parallel to the proposed rift, and predate the emplacement of the overlying Malinstindur Formation, and are thus unlikely to be related to later compressive phases. The fractures show small-scale fault displacement, but there is a consistent direction of the throw on the faults, which leads to fairly substantial, though unquantified, displacement (Rasmussen & Noe-Nygaard 1969).

The evidence presented in this paper supports the ideas proposed by Lundin & Doré (2005), that a transient rifting event transected the study area in the early Paleocene. This rifting episode resulted in the generation of the Wyville Thomson Ridge and the central segment of the Ymir Ridge.

Figures 5 and 9 show that there is no correlation between the thickness of the basalt and the location of the present day structure of the Ymir Ridge South. Thus this segment of the ridge had a different genetic history compared to the Ymir Ridge Central and the Wyville Thomson Ridge, and the event that formed the ridge postdates the extrusion of the basalt. This is also supported by gravity data (Fig. 2) which shows positive gravity anomalies associated with the features that have been shown to predate volcanism, although no such gravity anomaly is observed in connection with Ymir Ridge South. However, there is a gravity anomaly that crosses the Ymir Ridge between the central and southern segments. This same anomaly crosses the Wyville Thomson Ridge where it is widest and where the previously mentioned post-basalt induced depression is observed at the crest of the ridge. The most likely causative tectonic event of the southern segment of the Ymir Ridge is therefore likely to be found in the later compressive phases, as suggested by Boldreel & Andersen (1993) to be the cause of all segments of both ridges.

A number of igneous centres are located within the research area, with all but one located west of Munkagrunnur Ridge. This is taken as further evidence for an active rift system to the west of Munkagrunnur Ridge. The lineament that links the Geikie, Darwin, Dreka Eyga, Faroe Bank Channel Knoll and Frænir igneous centres (Figs 1, 2 & 5) may indicate that the location of these centres is to some degree controlled by pre-existing structural weaknesses. The gravity lineament, which lines up with the primary tectonic trends in the area, and the location of the igneous centres may indicate that there is a deep fault zone that has been exploited by magma during the volcanic phases, and then reactivated with a reverse movement during the later compressive phases. This reactivation is interpreted as strike-slip or transpressive movement and caused the generation of Ymir Ridge South as it inverted the basin which was filled by basalt during volcanism (Fig. 9). The reactivation also induced the change in orientation of the Wyville Thomson Ridge, and the depression which was subsequently peneplaned through erosion. Other evidence for the effect of compression on pre-existing structures is seen on Figure 8, where reverse faults and 'pop up' features are seen at the crest and flank of Ymir Ridge Central.

Conclusion

The presented work leads us to conclude that Wyville Thomson Ridge and the central segment of the Ymir Ridge predate the Palaeogene volcanism. The likely cause of these segments of the ridge is most likely associated with a transient rifting event in the early Paleocene. This rifting event resulted in the extrusion of the flood basalts, which today cover the study area. The southern segment of Ymir Ridge postdates the extrusion of the basalt, and has a different genetic history compared to the central segment and the Wyville Thomson Ridge. The author's preferred model is that this segment of the ridge was created by compressive forces, which inverted a basin that was filled by basalt during volcanism.

Eocene and younger compressive phases have clearly also had a significant influence on the other discussed structures within the study area, as documented by e.g. (Boldreel & Andersen 1998; Johnson et al. 2005).

I would like to acknowledge Fugro Multi Client Services (UK) Ltd, CGGVeritas and WesternGeco for the use of seismic data, and BGS for the help in obtaining satellite gravity data. I would like to thank the two reviewers John Smallwood and Neil T. Grant for helpful reviews which improved the final manuscript significantly.

References

ABRAHAM, D. A. & RITCHIE, J. D. 1991, The Darwin Complex, a Tertiary igneous centre in the Northern Rockall Trough. *Scottish Journal of Geology*, **27**, 113–125.

ARCHER, S. G., BERGMAN, S. C., ILIFFE, J., MURPHY, C. A. & THORNTON, M. 2005. Palaeogene igneous rocks reveal new insights into the geodynamic evolution and petroleum potential of the Rockall Trough, NE Atlantic Margin. *Basin Research*, **17**, 171–201.

BOLDREEL, L. O. & ANDERSEN, M. S. 1993. Late Paleocene to Miocene compression in the Faeroe-Rockall area. *In*: PARKER, J. R. (ed.) *Petroleum Geology of Northwest Europe: Proceedings of the 4th Conference*. Geological Society, London, 1025–1034.

BOLDREEL, L. O. & ANDERSEN, M. S. 1998. Tertiary compressional structures on the Faeroe-Rockall Plateau in relation to northeast Atlantic ridge-push and Alpine foreland stresses. *Tectonophysics*, **300**, 13–28.

DOBINSON, A. A. 1970. *A Magnetic Survey of the Faroe Bank*. Ph.D. thesis, University of Durham.

DORÉ, A. G., LUNDIN, E. R., JENSEN, L. N., BIRKELAND, Ø., ELIASSEN, P. E. & FICHLER, C. 1999. Principal tectonic events in the evolution of the northwest European Atlantic margin. *In*: FLEET, A. J. & BOLDY, S. A. R. (eds) *Petroleum Geology of Northwest Europe: Proceedings of the 5th Conference*. Geological Society, London, 41–61.

ELLIS, D., BELL, B. R., JOLLEY, D. W. & O'CALLAGHAN, M. 2002. The stratigraphy, environment of eruption and age of the Faroes Lava Group, NE Atlantic Ocean. *In*: JOLLEY, D. W. & BELL, B. R. (eds) *The North Atlantic Igneous Province: Stratigraphy, Tectonic, Volcanic and Magmatic Processes*. Geological Society, London, Special Publication, 253–269.

ERNST, R. E., BUCHAN, K. L. & CAMPBELL, I. H. 2005. Frontiers in large igneous province research. *Lithos*, **79**, 271–297.

EVANS, D., ABRAHAM, D. A. & HITCHEN, K. 1989. The Geikie igneous centre, west of Lewis: its structure and influence on Tertiary Geology. *Scottish Journal of Geology*, **25**, 339–352.

FOULGER, G. 2002. Plumes, or plate tectonic processes? *Astronomy and Geophysics*, **43**, 19–23.

GALLAGHER, J. W. & DROMGOOLE, P. 2005. Seeing Below the Basalt, Offshore Faroes, EAGE 67th Conference & Exhibition, June 4, Madrid, Spain, 1–4. Extended Abstracts G038.

HITCHEN, K. & RITCHIE, J. D. 1993. New K-Ar ages, and a provisional chronology, for the offshore part of the British Tertiary Igneous Province. *Scottish Journal of Geology*, **29**, 73–85.

JERRAM, D. A. & WIDDOWSON, M. 2004. The anatomy of Continental Flood Basalt Provinces: geological constraints on the processes and products of flood volcanism. *Lithos*, **79**, 385–405.

JOHNSON, H., RITCHIE, J. D., HITCHEN, K., McINROY, D. B. & KIMBELL, G. S. 2005. Aspects of the Cenozoic deformational history of the Northeast Faroe-Shetland Basin, Wyville-Thomson Ridge and Hatton Bank areas. *In*: DORÉ, A. G. & VINING, B. A. (eds), *Petroleum Geology: North-West Europe and Global Perspectives, Proceedings of the 6th Petroleum Geology Conference*. Geological Society, London, 993–1007.

KESER NEISH, J. 2004. *A Standard Structural Nomenclature System*, Faroese Geological Survey.

KESER NEISH, J. 2005. Faroese Area: Structural Interpretation of Seismic Data in a Basalt Enviroment. *In*: ZISKA, H., VARMING, T. & BLOCK, D. (eds) *Faroe Islands Exploration Conference Proceedings of the 1st Conference*. Tórshavn, Føroya Fróðskaparsetur, 131–145.

KESER NEISH, J. & ZISKA, H. 2005. Structure of the Faroe Bank Channel Basin, offshore Faroe Islands.

In: DORÉ, A. G. & VINING, B. A. (eds) *Petroleum Geology: North-West Europe and Global Perspectives: Proceedings of the 6th Petroleum Geology Conference*. Geological Society, London, 873–885.

KIMBELL, G. S., RITCHIE, J. D., JOHNSON, H. & GATLIFF, R. W. 2005. Controls on the structure and evolution of the NE Atlantic margin revealed by regional potential field imaging and 3D modeling. *In*: DORÉ, A. G. & VINING, B. A. (eds) *Petroleum Geology: North-West Europe and Global Perspectives: Proceedings of the 6th Petroleum Geology Conference*. Geological Society, London, 933–945.

KIØRBOE, L. 1999. Stratigraphic relationships of the Lower Tertiary of the Faroe Basalt Plateau and the Faeroe-Shetland Basin. *In*: FLEET, A. J. & BOLDY, S. A. R. (eds) *Petroleum Geology of Northwest Europe: Proceedings of the 5th Conference*. Geological Society, London, 559–572.

KLINGELHOFER, F., EDVARDS, R. A. & HOBBS, R. W. 2005. Crustal structure of the NE Rockall Trough from wide-angle seismic data modeling. *Journal of Geophysical Research*, **110**, B11105; doi:10.1029/2005JB003763.

LOWELL, J. D. 1985. Structural Styles in Petroleum Exploration, OGCI Publications. Tulsa, Oil and Gas Consultants International Inc.

LUNDIN, E. R. & DORÉ, A. G. 2005. NE Atlantic break-up: a re-examination of the Iceland mantle plume model and the Atlantic–Arctic linkage. *In*: DORÉ, A. G. & VINING, B. A. (eds) *Petroleum Geology: North-West Europe and Global Perspectives: Proceedings of the 6th Petroleum Geology Conference*. Geological Society, London, 739–754.

PASSEY, S. R. & BELL, B. R. 2007. Morphologies and emplacement mechanisms of the lava flows of the Faroe Islands Basalt Group, Faroe Islands, NE Atlantic Ocean. *Bulletin of Volcanology*, **70**, 139–156.

RASMUSSEN, J. & NOE-NYGAARD, A. 1969. *Beskrivelse til Geologisk Kort over Færøerne i målestok 1:50 000*. Geological Survey of Denmark I. Series: København, C. A. Reitzels Forlag (Jørgen Sandal).

RITCHIE, J. D., HITCHEN, K. & EDWARDS, J. W. F. 1997. The Sigmundur Complex, a ?Tertiary igneous centre in the northern Rockall Trough. *Scottish Journal of Geology*, **33**, 97–103.

RITCHIE, J. D., GATLIFF, R. W. & RICHARDS, P. C. 1999. Early Tertiary magmatism in the offshore NW UK margin and surrounds. *In*: FLEET, A. J. & BOLDY, S. A. R. (eds) *Petroleum Geology of North-West Europe: Proceedings of the 5th Conference*. Geological Society, London, 573–584.

ROBERTS, D. G., BOTT, M. H. P. & URUSKI, C. 1983. Structure and origin of the Wyville-Thomson Ridge. *In*: BOTT, M. H. P., SAXOV, S., TALWANI, M. & THIEDE, J. (eds) *Structure and Development of the*

Greenland-Scotland Ridge. Nato Conference Series. Plenum Press, London, 133–158.

RUMPH, B., REAVES, C. M., ORANGE, V. G. & ROBINSON, D. L. 1993. Structuring and transfer zones in the Faeroe Basin in a tectonic context. *In*: PARKER, J. R. (ed.) *Petroleum Geology of Northwest Europe: Proceedings of the 4th Conference*. Geological Society, London, 999–1009.

SATTARZADEH, Y., COSGROVE, J. W. & VITA-FINZI, C. 2000. The interplay of faulting and folding during the evolution of the Zagros deformation belt. *In*: COSGROVE, J. W. & AMEEN, M. S. (eds) *Forced Folds and Fractures*. Geological Society, London, Special Publications, **169**, 187–196.

SMALLWOOD, J. R. & WHITE, R. S. 2002. Ridge-plume interaction in the North Atlantic and its influence on continental breakup and seafloor spreading. *In*: JOLLEY, D. W. & BELL, B. R. (eds) *The North Atlantic Igneous Province: Stratigraphy, Tectonic, Volcanic and Magmatic Processes*. Geological Society, London, Special Publications, 15–37.

SMYTHE, D. K. 1983. Faeroe-Shetland Escarpment and continental margin north of the Faeroes. *In*: BOTT, M. H. P., SAXOV, S., TALWANI, M. & THIEDE, J. (eds) *Structure and Development of the Greenland-Scotland Ridge*. New Methods and Concepts. Plenum Press, New York, 109–119.

TATE, M. P., DODD, C. D. & GRANT, N. T. 1999. The northeast Rockall Basin and its significance in the evolution of the Rockall-Faeroes/East Greenland rift system. *In*: FLEET, A. J. & BOLDY, S. A. R. (eds) *Petroleum Geology of Northwest Europe: Proceedings of the 5th Conference*. Geological Society, London, 391–406.

WAAGSTEIN, R. 1988. Structure, composition and age of the Faeroe basalt plateau. *In*: MORTON, A. C. & PARSON, L. M. (eds) *Early Tertiary Volcanism and the Opening of the NE Atlantic*. Geological Society, London, Special Publications, 225–238.

WADDAMS, P. & CORDINGLEY, T. 1999. The regional geology and exploration potential of the NE Rockall Basin. *In*: FLEET, A. J. & BOLDY, S. A. R. (eds) *Petroleum Geology of Northwest Europe: Proceedings of the 5th Conference*. Geological Society, London, 379–390.

WHITE, R. S., SPITZER, R., CHRISTIE, P. A. F., ROBERTS, A., LUNNON, Z., MARESH, J. & GROUP, i. w. 2005. Seismic imaging through basalt flows on the Faroe Shelf. *In*: ZISKA, H., VARMING, T. & BLOCK, D. (eds) *Faroe Islands Exploration Conference Proceedings of the 1st Conference*. Tórshavn, Føroya Fróðskaparsetur, 11–31.

ZISKA, H. & MORGAN, R. 2005. Can Paleomagnetism be used as a mapping tool in basalt provinces? *In*: EAGE 67th Conference & Exhibition, Madrid, Spain. Extended Abstracts G039.

Compressional structures on the West Iberia rifted margin: controls on their distribution

G. PÉRON-PINVIDIC[1], G. MANATSCHAL[1], S. M. DEAN[2] & T. A. MINSHULL[2]

[1]*IPGS/CGS-EOST, 1 rue Blessig, 67084 Strasbourg, France*
(e-mail: gwenn.peron-pinvidic@eost.u-strasbg.fr)

[2]*NOC, European Way, Southampton, SO14 3ZH, UK*

Abstract: The West Iberia margin is a magma-poor rifted margin that resulted from Jurassic to Cretaceous polyphase rifting leading to the opening of the North Atlantic Ocean. The Mesozoic rift structures were overprinted by two compressive tectonic events during Eocene and Miocene times resulting from collision between Iberia, Europe and Africa. The effects of these compressive tectonic events are expressed by faults and folds within the post-rift sedimentary sequence. We mapped and studied these Cenozoic deformation structures throughout the Southern Iberia Abyssal Plain (40°–41°N, 11°–13°W) on the basis of an extensive dataset of time migrated seismic profiles acquired by various academic institutions. Acoustic basement has also been analysed on the basis of its seismic aspect, in order to test potential relationships with the distribution of the post-rift sedimentary deformation.

Our observations lead to three major conclusions concerning the deformation affecting the post-rift sediments in the Southern Iberia Abyssal Plain: (1) the deformation occurs within the zone of exhumed continental mantle and not at its transition to continental or oceanic crust; (2) it is localized within a zone overlying basement with well-defined seismic characteristics; and (3) it is closely related to the major topographic features observed in the ocean–continent transition. The localization of the deformation within the zone of exhumed continental mantle and not at its boundaries to the adjacent oceanic and continental crust suggests that the limits between the different types of crust are transitional rather than sharp. Our results show that the zone of exhumed continental mantle represents the weakest zone within the margin that is preferentially deformed during initial convergence. At higher convergence rates, this zone may coincide with the location of a future subduction.

Post-rift compressional structures are well known from the NW European margins and their formation has been attributed to various causes, such as changes in seafloor-spreading geometry, ridge-push forces affecting pre-existing crustal weaknesses, major changes in plate motions, influence of the Alpine collision, or influence of the Iceland Plume (Lundin & Doré 2002). In contrast, compressional structures on the West Iberia margin have received less attention, despite the extensive investigations of this margin over the last three decades. Seismic surveys and deep sea drilling (e.g. ODP Legs 103, 149 and 173) along this margin and in particular in the Southern Iberia Abyssal Plain, have revealed the existence of a transitional domain up to 160 km wide that formed at the end of magma-poor and polyphase rifting during late Jurassic to early Cretaceous time. However, because all ODP drill sites (897, 899, 1068, 1069, 1070) targeted structural highs, and because the interpretation of geophysical data is often ambiguous, the internal structure and composition of the ocean–continent transition is at present still debated.

An alternative approach to the analysis of the internal structure of the ocean–continent transition is to study how this zone behaved during Cenozoic compression. Inherited heterogeneities within the basement, defined either by compositional, thermal and/or structural variations, are likely to control the distribution of deformation during compression and would tend to localize deformation. Thus, the distribution of deformation structures related to reactivation can give insights into the rheological behaviour and indirectly into the internal structure and nature of the ocean–continent transition and its boundaries with the adjacent continental and oceanic crusts. In order to test this conceptual idea, deformation structures related to the Cenozoic compression in the post-rift sediments were mapped and their distribution compared with the distribution of basement domains, distinguished by specific seismic character. Our results show an interesting correlation between the distribution of deformation structures in the post-rift sediments and the mapped basement domains, which will be discussed later.

From: JOHNSON, H., DORÉ, A. G., GATLIFF, R. W., HOLDSWORTH, R., LUNDIN, E. R. & RITCHIE, J. D. (eds)
The Nature and Origin of Compression in Passive Margins. Geological Society, London, Special Publications,
306, 169–183. DOI: 10.1144/SP306.8   0305-8719/08/$15.00 © The Geological Society of London 2008.

Tectonic setting

The Iberia margin is a magma-poor passive margin situated offshore Spain and Portugal. It extends over 800 km from Cap Finistere in the North (*c.* 43°N) to Cap Sao Vincente in the south (*c.* 37°N). It results from continental rifting and early Cretaceous breakup of North America and Iberia/Europe which led to the opening of the southern North Atlantic Ocean. Three segments, easily identifiable on a bathymetric map (Fig. 1), can be identified through the Iberia margin: the Galicia Margin (or Deep Galicia Margin) in the north, the Tagus Abyssal Plain in the south and the Southern Iberia Abyssal Plain in the centre.

The tectonic history of the Iberia margin is complex. Following the tectonics of the Variscan orogeny, the area underwent the effects of three major episodes of rifting and two phases of post-rift compression. Although the compressional events are well dated (Eocene and Miocene), the precise ages of the rifting episodes are less well constrained. Pinheiro *et al.*(1996) proposed a late Triassic to early Jurassic age for the first phase of rifting, followed by an Oxfordian to early Kimmeridgian

phase and finally a Valanginian/Hauterivian to late Aptian phase. The structural architecture acquired by the margin during these events is characterized by series of tilted basement blocks bounded by normal faults and by zones of more irregular, flat topography and by peridotite ridges, referred to here as the ocean–continent transition. The nature of this domain has been studied by numerous geophysical and geological surveys (magnetic, gravity, and seismic surveys; ODP Legs 103, 149 and 173). Despite all the available data, the origin, formation and nature of the ocean–continent transition basement remains controversial. In the past, three hypotheses have been discussed:

Ultra-slow spreading oceanic crust. Sawyer (1994) and Whitmarsh & Sawyer (1996) suggested that the ocean–continent transition in the Southern Iberia Abyssal Plain is oceanic crust formed in an ultra-slow spreading environment, with an accretion rate of about 6.3 to 5 mm a^{-1} (half spreading rate). They argued that none of the rocks drilled during Leg 149 was of continental origin, an argument subsequently proved wrong, since the

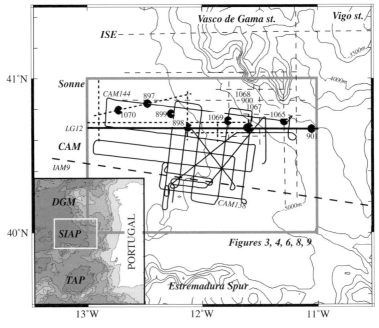

Fig. 1. Bathymetric map of the Southern Iberia Abyssal Plain (contours are drawn every 250 m) with time migrated seismic reflection profiles used in the study. Thin lines mark the CAM profiles (Cambridge University; Discovery 215 Working Group 1998). Dashed lines mark the SONNE profiles (Roeser *et al.* 1992), the ISE'97 profiles (Henning *et al.* 2004) and the IAM9 profile (Pickup *et al.* 1996). The bold line marks the Lusigal12 profile (Groupe Galice 1979). Circles represent boreholes of the Ocean Drilling Program Legs 149 and 173. The inset in the lower left corner shows a bathymetric map of the whole Iberia margin and the location of the study area (DGM, Deep Galicia Margin; SIAP, Southern Iberia Abyssal Plain; TAP, Tagus Abyssal Plain).

gabbros drilled at Site 900 are of Palaeozoic age and therefore continental (Manatschal *et al.* 2001). Whitmarsh & Sawyer (1996) compared the common occurrence of drilled serpentinized mantle peridotites with ultra-slow spreading systems, where mantle rocks are exposed at the seafloor (Cannat 1993). The hypothesis of ultra-slow spreading oceanic crust is also incompatible with magnetic data. In the Southern Iberia Abyssal Plain, the magnetic anomalies are weak and very few linear anomalies are identified; Whitmarsh & Miles (1995) were unable to model these as seafloor-spreading anomalies.

Thinned, disrupted and intruded continental crust. Other studies suggested that the ocean–continent transition is thin continental crust that has been faulted and intruded by magmatic bodies during rifting (Whitmarsh *et al.* 1990*a*; Whitmarsh & Miles 1995; Whitmarsh & Sawyer 1996). The development of this hypothesis came from the analysis of magnetic anomalies. Based on a suggestion that breakup propagated northwards, Whitmarsh & Miles (1995) proposed that the magnetic anomalies can be explained by syn-rift magmatic intrusions into highly thinned continental crust. This model was able to explain the wide-angle seismic observations of Whitmarsh *et al.* (1990*b*). However, more recent seismic refraction experiments revealed that the ocean–continent transition is made of a *c.*4 km thick lower layer with high velocities (*c.* 7.6 km s^{-1}) and a 2–4 km thick upper layer with lower velocities (4.5–7 km s^{-1}) (Chian *et al.* 1999; Dean *et al.* 2000), neither of which is interpreted as continental in origin.

Exhumed serpentinized peridotites. The third hypothesis is that the ocean–continent transition consists of serpentinized peridotite resulting from the exhumation of lithospheric mantle, perhaps accompanied by melt intrusions (Beslier *et al.* 1996; Pickup *et al.* 1996; Discovery 215 Working Group 1998; Chian *et al.* 1999; Dean *et al.* 2000). This hypothesis arises from the analysis of seismic velocity models and from drilling results (Legs 103, 149, 173). The ocean–continent transition has particular seismic velocity patterns that are interpreted as representative of serpentinized peridotites: the upper *c.* 2–4 km layer is interpreted to represent highly serpentinized peridotites (up to 100%) and the underlying velocity gradient suggests a decrease in degree of serpentinization with depth (Discovery 215 Working Group 1998; Chian *et al.* 1999; Dean *et al.* 2000).

At present, the scientific community favours the third hypothesis. Whitmarsh *et al.* (2001) introduced the term 'zone of exhumed continental

mantle' to describe the most likely nature of the deep Iberia ocean–continent transition. However, for the conjugate Newfoundland margin the composition of the basement in transition zone is still debated (see Hopper *et al.* 2004; Shillington *et al.* 2006; Lau *et al.* 2006).

Deformation structures in the post-rift sediments

In the Southern Iberia Abyssal Plain, six seismic units have been defined by Wilson *et al.* (1996) and partly redefined by Péron-Pinvidic *et al.* (2007). The six units are characterized by reflectors and packages of reflectors that present the same seismic characteristics through the area. Correlations with lithological units defined at the boreholes of ODP Legs 149 and 173 (Sawyer *et al.* 1994; Whitmarsh *et al.* 1998) were made in order to define the lithologies, their depositional environments and the age of the units (Péron-Pinvidic 2006). Figure 2 illustrates the six seismic units and shows their distributions in a schematic transect across the Southern Iberia Abyssal Plain.

Mapped deformation structures

Deformation structures such as folds and faults are observed within seismic Units C and D in the Southern Iberia Abyssal Plain but do not affect Unit E, which dates the deformation as approximately mid to late Miocene (Péron-Pinvidic 2006). This age suggests that the deformation was contemporaneous with the compression of the Betic domain in southern Spain and the Gulf of Cadiz (Maldonado *et al.* 1999) that resulted from the collision with the African plate. Another older event is dated as Eocene (Masson *et al.* 1994) and is linked with the formation of the Pyrenean–Cantabrian chain forming the northern limit of the Iberian microplate. However, this event is better recorded in the Deep Galicia Margin, whereas in our study area, the Miocene event is more dominant.

Three types of deformation structures can be seen in the post-rift sediments. These are shown in Figure 3 and consist of faults (mainly reverse faults, but normal faults occur as well), folds above basement highs and folds above flat basement.

Among the mapped deformation structures, normal faults were observed in some seismic sections (CAM142, CAM151 and CAM153). Unless these normal faults were formed by sedimentary compaction, this observation may be surprising in the context of compressional tectonics. However, we believe that their presence indicates that the direction of compression was oblique to the

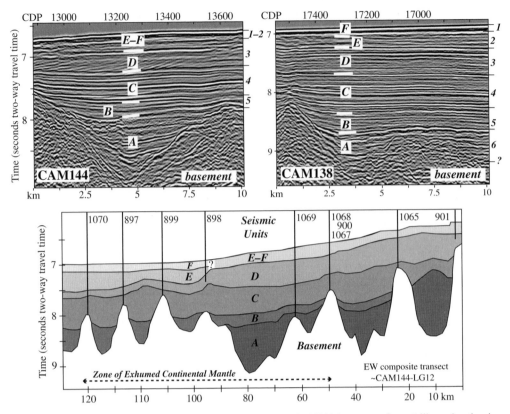

Fig. 2. Details of the time migrated seismic profiles CAM138 and CAM144 (upper two figures) illustrating the six seismic units determined in the Southern Iberia Abyssal Plain. Lower figure shows a schematic representation of the distribution of the six seismic units in an east–west composite transect across the Southern Iberia Abyssal Plain. Also shown are the location of the ODP sites drilled during Legs 149 and 173.

margin rather than strictly perpendicular. De Paola *et al.* (2005) investigated inversion structures traditionally analysed as being due to local or regional crustal shortening. They found that such compressional structures might also be formed by progressive and partitioned transtension. Therefore, the post-rift compressive structures observed within the Southern Iberia Abyssal Plain may have formed by an oblique convergence that might also lead to local normal faulting.

Distribution of deformation structures

On the basis of the Sonne and Lusigal seismic lines, Masson *et al.* (1994) described the sedimentary deformation within the Southern Iberia Abyssal Plain as 'series of en-echelon segments, with a consistent eastward offset between segments towards the south'. However, such en-echelon structures are not evident in our more comprehensive dataset. Two zones of deformation can be

distinguished, one west and the other east of profile CAM132 (Fig. 3). To the west, numerous deformation structures are observed, spanning all the defined categories, and can be followed along strike between profiles (e.g. faults in the western parts of profiles CAM142, 151 and 153; Fig. 3). The 010°–025°N strike of these faults mimics the trend of the underlying basement highs (Fig. 4). In contrast, deformation structures in the eastern zone are rare and less well developed and cannot be traced over large distances.

Comparing the locations of deformation structures with a basement contour map allows seven zones to be identified. They are labelled 1 to 5, PR3 and PR4 in Figure 4. The zones labelled PR3 and PR4 correspond to the peridotite ridges R3 and R4 described by Beslier *et al.* (1993), Pickup *et al.* (1996) and Dean *et al.* (2000).

Zones PR3 and PR4 (peridotite ridges). Peridotite ridge PR3 has been described as an almost north–south linear continuous basement structure (Beslier *et al.* 1993). However, our observations do not support such a continuous structure. In reality this zone corresponds to an alignment of different independent basement morphologies, linking an elevated symmetrical block in the north to flatter and more massive structures towards the south. Each block of PR3 is associated with deformation structures.

Peridotite ridge PR4 has been described as extending from the basement high drilled at ODP Site 898 in the north to the southwestern part of the Southern Iberia Abyssal Plain (Pickup *et al.* 1996; Dean *et al.* 2000) (Fig. 4). However, as in the case of PR3, this structure does not correspond to a continuous feature. Sedimentary wedges of Unit E above Unit D are observed to occur in the north.

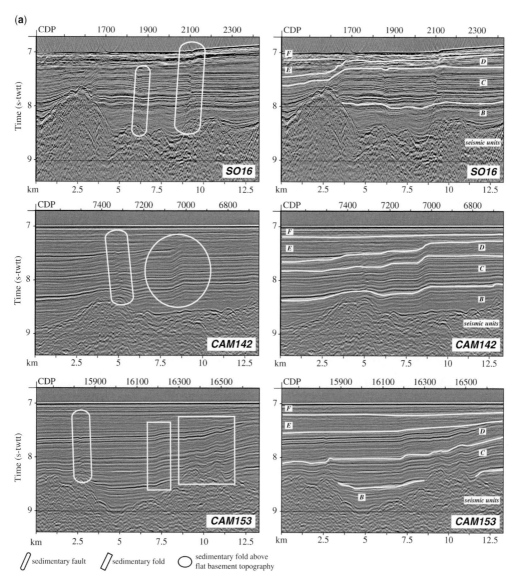

(a)

sedimentary fault   sedimentary fold   sedimentary fold above flat basement topography

Fig. 3. (a) Three details of time migrated seismic profiles CAM142, 153, and Sonne16 (s-twtt, seconds two-way travel time) illustrating on the left the three types of deformation structures observed in the post-rift sediments, and on the right the dated reflectors marking limits between the different seismic units.

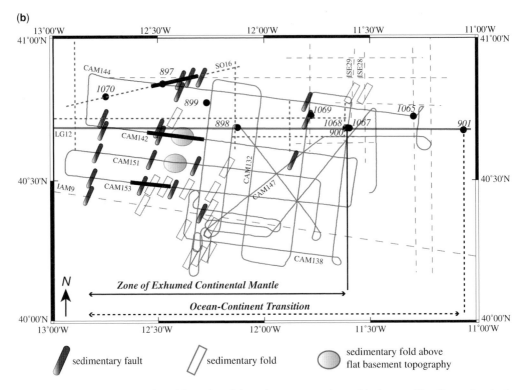

Fig. 3. (*Continued*) (**b**) Distribution of the various deformation structures observed in the post-rift sediments in seismic profiles in a map of the Southern Iberia Abyssal Plain. The bold segments refer to the seismic extracts presented in Figure 3a.

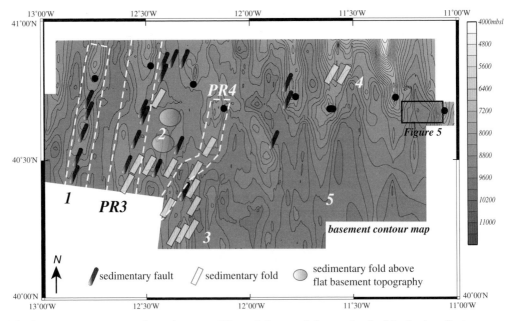

Fig. 4. Basement contour map (interval contour, 200 m; mbsl, metres below sea-level) of the Southern Iberia Abyssal Plain on which the deformation structures observed in the post-rift sediments are superposed. PR3 and PR4 refer to the peridotite ridges R3 and R4. 1, 2, 3, 4 and 5 refer to particular zones of deformation (cf. text for details).

Zones 1 to 5

- Zone 1 is comparable to PR3. In our study area, it corresponds to a topographic alignment of different basement highs, from a symmetrical structure likely to be a peridotite ridge on profile CAM144 to flatter and more massive highs to the south. Fault structures are consistently observed to be associated with these basement highs.
- Zone 2 is located between PR3 and PR4. It displays widespread deformation structures including faults and folds of varying amplitude. This deformation is associated with particularly irregular basement topography. In profiles CAM142 and CAM151 there are large folds that are not directly linked with a basement structure occurring over an almost flat basement.
- Zone 3 located to the south of PR4 displays numerous fold structures of variable length and shape above irregular basement morphology.
- Zone 4 corresponds to the northeastern part of the Southern Iberia Abyssal Plain where basement topography is characterized by major tilted blocks, deep basins and strong reflectors within the basement. Here, deformation structures are rare. However, within the basin bordering the basement block at ODP Site 901 (Fig. 5), strong reflections corresponding to the base of Unit C and to the upper part of Unit B are folded and onlapped by reflectors belonging to

the upper part of Unit C and to the overlying Unit D. Because deeper reflectors are not affected, we prefer to interpret this structure as the result of deep currents that were localized at the foot of the margin within fault bounded grabens, an interpretation which is compatible with more regional studies of this structure (Reston, pers. comm. 2005).

- Zone 5 corresponds to the southeastern part of our study area. In this zone the basement deepens towards the south without marked topography and deformation structures.

A correspondence between basement topography and the distribution of deformation structures is clear within the western zone where the major alignments of basement highs seem to control the distribution of the deformation structures (zones 1 and PR3). West of profile CAM132 almost all basement highs are associated with sedimentary deformation. This observation suggests that these structures were reactivated during the compressive Cenozoic phase and caused folding and/or faulting of the overlying sediments. Sibuet *et al.* (1996) described a normal fault bordering the eastern flank of PR3 on profile Lusigal04. They interpreted this structure to be reactivated as a reverse fault during lower Miocene, leading to deformation of the overlying sedimentary sequences. We were not able to identify such a reactivated structure through our dataset: in the western Southern

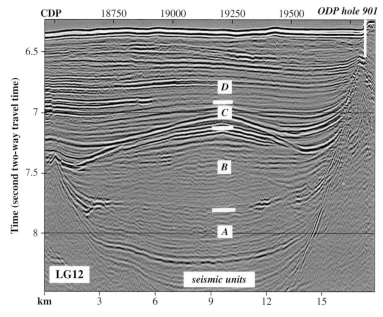

Fig. 5. Extract of the time migrated seismic profile LG12 illustrating a large fold-like structure in the post-rift sedimentary sequence, interpreted as a depositional structure related to deep currents.

Iberia Abyssal Plain no clear reflectors have been identified that either bound these highs or underlie them. Within the central and the eastern part of the area, the distribution of deformation structures is less widespread. There is no deformation above each basement high, like that seen in the western zone. The key question is, therefore, what controls the distribution of the deformation in the Southern Iberia Abyssal Plain.

Sedimentary deformation in the Bay of Biscay and Porcupine Basin

Deformation structures similar to those observed in the Southern Iberia Abyssal Plain are also described from other areas along the NW European Atlantic margin. Montadert *et al.* (1979) and Masson & Parson (1983) studied the northern continental margin of the Bay of Biscay and the southern Porcupine Basin respectively. They described complex zones of faulting and folding confined to elongated narrow belts more or less coincident with the location of the ocean–continent transition. These observations suggest that the occurrence of deformation structures in the post-rift sediments overlying the zone of exhumed continental mantle, as observed in the Southern Iberia Abyssal Plain, may be a more general feature of magma-poor rifted margins and ultimately may be used as a finger print to localize the zone of exhumed continental mantle within the ocean–continent transition.

Seismic character of the acoustic basement

The broad coverage and consistent acquisition and processing parameters of the CAM seismic profiles enabled us to analyse the variation of the seismic reflection character of acoustic basement across the Southern Iberia Abyssal Plain. In this study, basement corresponds to the acoustic domain underlying the layered sedimentary cover. It may correspond to either crustal, mantle or magmatic material, potentially covered by pre-rift sediments in the continental part.

An initial study by Dean (1999) defined three distinct reflective characters ('unreflective', 'layered reflective' and 'reflective' basement) that led him to identify four regions within the Southern Iberia Abyssal Plain. We have refined his approach by adding more criteria to define five acoustic basement domains (named I to V; Fig. 6). The criteria used in our study are: (1) seismic character of top of basement (chaotic, continuous or not, easily identifiable or not); (2) sedimentary onlaps onto top basement and clarity of these onlap

relationships; (3) topography (flat or characterized by tilted blocks); (4) the presence of reflectors within the basement; (5) the dimensions of the tilted basement blocks if present; and (6) the seismic character of the underlying basement (transparent or chaotic, more or less reflective). These domains were mapped through the CAM seismic lines (Fig. 6). We then interpolated the domain boundaries between these profiles, checking them on the Sonne, ISE, IAM9 and LG12 lines.

Basement domains identified in the Southern Iberia Abyssal Plain

Basement domain I is characterized mainly by large angular tilted basement blocks bordered by high amplitude, continuous listric reflectors interpreted as detachment faults. Basement reflectivity is chaotic and dominated by the presence of numerous reflectors of varying length, depth, dip and amplitude. Some of these are interpreted as faults and detachment faults. The top of the basement is difficult to define precisely: it is marked by a chaotic and discontinuous reflector with low amplitude. Sedimentary onlaps are also poorly imaged and difficult to identify.

Basement domain II also displays basement blocks, but with a distinct geometry from those of domain I. They are smaller and flatter. Unlike domain I, no clear reflectors are observed bordering the blocks and penetrating the basement. Numerous reflectors are observed within the basement, but they are not obviously linked with the formation of the blocks. The top of basement is better defined than in domain I. It corresponds to a discontinuous reflector with moderate to high amplitude. Sedimentary onlaps are clearly identifiable where the top basement reflector is continuous. The reflection character of the basement is still chaotic and cut by numerous reflections.

Basement domain III is characterized by irregular basement topography. No large blocks or tilted blocks are observed. Reflectors are still present within the basement but far less numerous and are often close to the surface. The top of basement is very difficult to define and is often difficult to distinguish from the overlying sediments. Therefore, the identification of sedimentary onlaps poses problems. The seismic character of the basement is chaotic and transparent.

Basement domain IV is defined by uniform basement reflection character, rough with medium amplitude and with rare reflections which are always located close to top basement. There are blocks, but without any bordering or underlying reflectors. The top of basement is clear, marked by high amplitude, relatively continuous reflector.

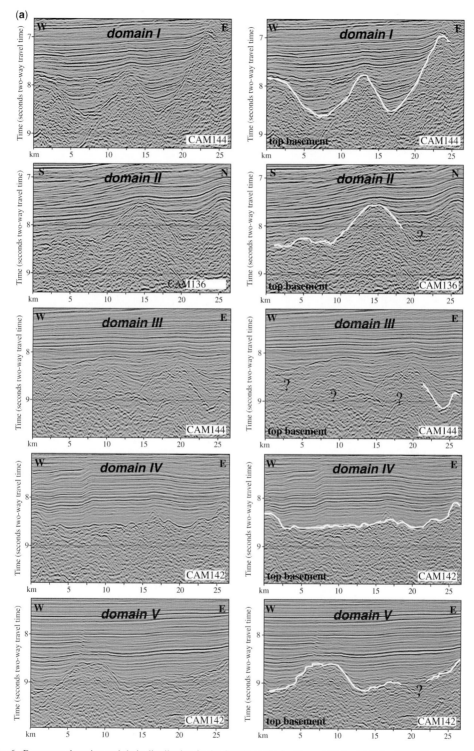

Fig. 6. Basement domains and their distribution in the Southern Iberia Abyssal Plain. (**a**) Seismic profiles illustrating the five basement domains distinguished in this study with on the right the interpreted basement limit.

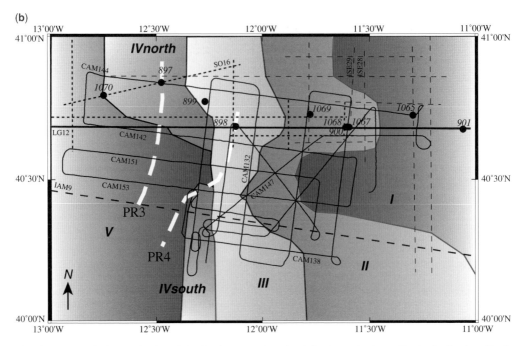

Fig. 6. (*Continued*) (**b**) Distribution of the five basement domains defined on seismic profiles in the Southern Iberia Abyssal Plain. PR3 and PR4 refer to the peridotite ridges R3 and R4.

Sedimentary onlaps are well defined. Two sub-domains are seen, a northern one (IV$_{north}$) and a southern one (IV$_{south}$).

Basement domain V is characterized by a discontinuous and chaotic top basement reflector often poorly defined. Sedimentary onlaps are also difficult to identify. Basement blocks are observed, from elevated symmetrical structures to lower, larger and asymmetrical ones. No internal reflections were identified. The basement in this domain is more reflective than in domain IV.

Relationship between basement domains and geophysical and geological attributes

Seismic refraction. Wide-angle seismic profiles (Chian *et al.* 1999; Dean *et al.* 2000) have revealed strong lateral variations in the velocity and velocity gradient at the top of basement across the Southern Iberia Abyssal Plain. These variations appear to correspond well with variations in acoustic basement character (Fig. 7). The velocity at the top of basement is *c.* 4.5 km s^{-1} in domain I, *c.* 5.0–5.3 km s^{-1} in domain II, *c.* 3.8–4.7 km s^{-1} in domain III, and *c.* 5 km s^{-1} in domains IV and V.

Reduced to the pole magnetic anomalies. Russell & Whitmarsh (2003) published a reduced-to-the-pole magnetic anomalies chart revealing various magnetic features through the West Iberia margin.

Correlations between basement domains limits and the reduced-to-the-pole magnetic anomalies chart are not obvious. The southern part of Southern Iberia Abyssal Plain does not exhibit any clear correlation, except domain V that corresponds to the largest negative magnetic anomaly of the area (−250nT). However, in the northern part, along the drilled transect, the limits of the basement domains correspond to some of the magnetic features (Fig. 8). Relatively high amplitude anomalies (+150nT) characterize domain I. Domain II is associated with low anomalies (−100nT). Domain III corresponds to a positive large anomaly (+50nT) over drilled Sites 899 and 898, and domains IV$_{north}$ and V correspond to the first magnetic anomaly commonly identified as oceanic (M3; Whitmarsh & Miles 1995).

Drilled lithologies. The comparison between defined basement domains and drilled lithologies shows that continental and exhumed mantle domains can be distinguished: the pre-rift sediments underlain by upper continental rocks (Site 1065) correspond to domain I; exhumed crust (Sites 900 and 1067) and continental allochthons overlying exhumed mantle (1068 and 1069) correspond to domain II; and serpentinized peridotites (Site 1070, 897 and 899) correspond to basement domains III, IV and V. The mantle rocks drilled at ODP Site 1070, 897 and 899 are quite different in

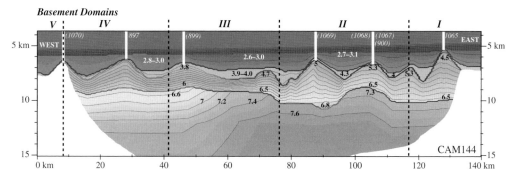

Fig. 7. Velocity model for the CAM144 seismic profile established by Chian *et al.* (1999). The contour interval is 0.2 km s^{-1}. Basement domains limits and ODP drill sites are also indicated.

detail. At Site 897 the entire ultramafic section is extensively serpentinized and exhibits a transition from carbonate-rich serpentinite associated with serpentinite breccias at the top (e.g. ophicalcite) to massive serpentinized peridotite, locally displaying plagioclase and clinopyroxene enriched zones down hole. At Site 899 ultramafic rocks were found in breccias and as olistoliths of serpentinized peridotite several tens of metres across, intercalated with sediments. The ultramafic clasts and olistoliths that may derive from the adjacent basement have a large compositional range from plagioclase-bearing peridotites to pyroxene- and olivine-rich

peridotites. Up to 30% plagioclase occurs in patches or veinlets in the peridotites or rims the spinel. At Site 1070 massive serpentinized mantle rocks containing gabbro pegmatites are overlain by a poorly sorted, clast-supported breccia which consists of serpentinized peridotite and gabbro clasts that are cemented by blocky calcite. At the contact between these 'ophicalcites' and the massive serpentinized mantle, serpentine gouge was observed. The underlying serpentinized peridotite varies in composition between pyroxene-rich and -poor layers and has a weak, shallowly dipping high-T foliation. It remains unclear

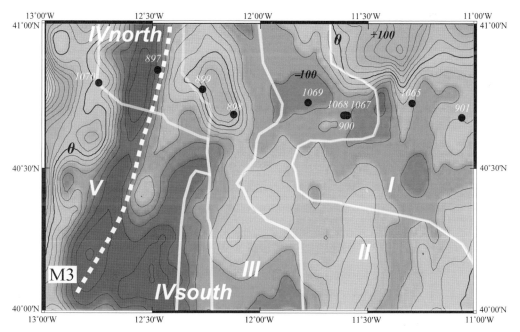

Fig. 8. Reduced to the pole magnetic anomalies established by Russell & Whitmarsh (2003). The contour interval is 25 nT. Basement domains limits and ODP drill sites are indicated on the map.

whether compositional variations, (plagioclase-bearing lherzolite occurs at Sites 897 and 899 but is absent at Site 1070) or the occurrence of a tectono-sedimentary cover sequence formed by breccias and/or ophicalcite can explain the seismic facies differences between basement domains III, IV and V. In any case, the mantle drilled in the Southern Iberia Abyssal Plain appears to be heterogeneous throughout the zone of exhumed continental mantle.

Discussion

The internal structure of the ocean–continent transition at magma-poor rifted margins is at present poorly known. The aim of this paper was to explore how this zone behaved during subsequent Cenozoic compression based on mapping of basement domains and of the distribution of deformation structures in the overlying post-rift sediments. We believe that inherited heterogeneities within the basement, defined either by compositional, thermal and/or structural variations, may control the distribution of deformation during compression. Therefore, we expected to see localization of the deformation in the case of strong heterogeneities and more distributed deformation in the case of a very homogeneous zone of exhumed continental mantle. Moreover, in the case of abrupt lithological

contacts at the boundaries between this zone and the adjacent continental and oceanic crust, deformation structures would be expected to occur at the limits of the zone, whereas if the boundaries correspond to gradual transitions, the deformation would not necessarily coincide with these limits.

The results of our mapping show an interesting correlation between the distribution of deformation structures in the post-rift sediments and mapped basement domains corresponding to lithologically defined parts of the margin. Domain I corresponds to the thinned continental distal margin; domains III to V to the zone of exhumed continental mantle; and domain II to a transition between these regions. This correspondence between the mapped basement domains and the location of post-rift sedimentary deformation is suggested by a comparison of Figures 3 and 6. Deformation structures in the post-rift sediments occur mainly within basement domains III, IV and V, with a clear concentration within IV and V (Fig. 9). Deformation structures that occur outside of these domains are rare. These are reverse faults that slightly affect some reflectors of Unit C above Site 1069 basement block and above another block along profile CAM147 (domain II) together with an asymmetrical fold north of Hobby High visible on ISE lines 28 and 29 at the limit between domains I and II.

The observed correlation between basement domains and deformation structures in the overlying

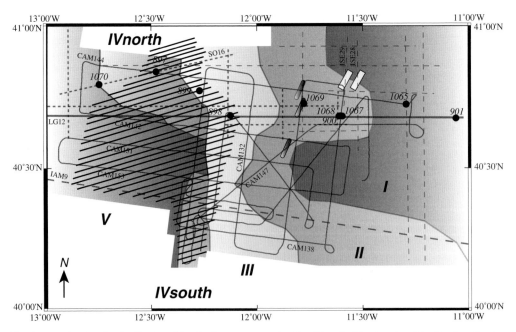

Fig. 9. Map showing the distribution of the five basement domains (I to V) and of the domain of the Southern Iberia Abyssal Plain where the deformation localized preferentially (dashed area) (for legend see Fig. 3).

post-rift sediments illustrates that deformation is localized in the zone of exhumed continental mantle and not at its boundaries. Therefore the boundaries between the zone of exhumed continental mantle and the adjacent continental and oceanic crust are likely to be transitional and strong relative to the zone itself. The concentration of deformation along aligned basement highs indicates that the highs correspond to regions of crustal weakness that are related to inherited structures and/or lithological variations. These observations have two major implications: one concerns the characterization and description of the zone of exhumed continental mantle in magma-poor margins and the second the reactivation and onset of subduction during the transition from passive to active margins:

Characterization of the zone of exhumed continental mantle in magma-poor margins

Although the existence of a zone of exhumed continental mantle has only been confirmed for the Iberia margin (the only deep magma-poor margin where drilling penetrated basement), geophysical evidence suggests that such zones are more widespread and may occur at many margins. Thinon (1999) suggested the existence of exhumed mantle in the Amorican margin and Bullock & Minshull (2005) for the Goban Spur. Deformation structures similar to those observed in the Southern Iberia Abyssal Plain are also described from the NW European Atlantic margins. As mentioned above, Montadert et al. (1979) and Masson & Parson (1983) studied the northern continental margin of the Bay of Biscay and the southern Porcupine Basin where they identified post-rift deformations more or less coincident with an area showing the seismic characteristics of a zone of exhumed continental mantle. These observations suggest that the occurrence of deformation structures in the post-rift sediments in this zone, as observed in the Southern Iberia Abyssal Plain, may be a more general feature of magma-poor rifted margins and may be used as an indicator for locating exhumed mantle within an undrilled ocean–continent transition.

Reactivation and onset of subduction during the transition from passive to active margins

How passive margins are reactivated and ultimately evolve into an active margin with a subduction zone is poorly understood. The Southern Iberia Abyssal Plain shows the incipient stage of compression, which allows us to see where deformation was first localized and consequently to define the weakest zone within the margin. In the case of the Southern Iberia Abyssal Plain, if convergence had continued, shortening would have localized in the zone of exhumed continental mantle and finally led to the formation of a subduction zone. Unfortunately, we cannot test this hypothesis for the Iberia margin. However, we can look for evidence of this process in the ancient margins in the Alps that are commonly considered to be analogues for Iberia type margins (see Manatschal 2004 and references therein). In the case of the Alpine margins, the remnants of the distal margins and the zone of exhumed continental mantle are well preserved and may correspond, like the Iberia margin, to the lower plate margin (based on the terminology of Lister et al. 1986). In the reconstruction of the former rifted margins in the Alps, the transition to more oceanward parts of the zone of exhumed continental mantle are however not preserved except for some particular examples (e.g. Chenaillet massif, French Alps). Most of the ophiolites in the Alps that show some more oceanic characteristics (Lagabrielle & Lemoine 1997) are overprinted by high pressure metamorphism (blueschist to eclogite facies) indicating subduction pathways. Thus, in the Alps, the subduction had to start in the zone of exhumed continental mantle, so that the more continental parts of this zone are still preserved, belonging to the hanging wall of the subduction (e.g. Platta and Err nappes; Manatschal & Nievergelt 1997) whereas more oceanward parts together with the oceanic crust were subducted. Based on observations from the Alps and Iberia, we believe that the zone of exhumed continental mantle is the weakest part in magma-poor margins and represents the location where the subduction may have localized at the transition from a passive to an active margin.

Conclusions

The aim of this study was to investigate whether there is a direct relationship between the distribution of compressional structures in post-rift sediments in the Southern Iberia Abyssal Plain and the nature of underlying basement domains that were defined using a number of geophysical and geological attributes. The results show that deformation structures are localized preferentially within the zone of exhumed continental mantle and not at the boundaries with continental or oceanic crust. This key observation enables us to draw three major conclusions.

1. The boundaries of the zone of exhumed continental mantle with the adjacent continental and oceanic crust are not reactivated,

suggesting that they are transitional rather than sharp lithological contacts.

2. The zone of exhumed continental mantle is heterogeneous and represents the weakest part of the distal margin and therefore a preferred location for the initiation of subduction.

3. Mapping of deformation structures in post-rift sediments is an indirect way to determine the nature of the underlying basement and may be used as a fingerprint to locate the exhumed mantle in the deep parts of weakly reactivated magma-poor rifted margins.

This work was supported by the Royal Society through a Joint Project Grant. GM and GPP thank the GDR Marges. GPP thanks the EU and the Marie Curie grant program. We also wish to thank I. Walker and R. Gatliff for comments, suggestions and constructive reviews.

References

BESLIER, M. O., ASK, M. & BOILLOT, G. 1993. Ocean-continent boundary in the Iberia Abyssal Plain from multichannel seismic data. *Tectonophysics*, **218**, 383–393.

BESLIER, M. O., CORNEN, G. & GIRARDEAU, J. 1996. Tectono-metamorphic evolution of peridotites from the ocean/continent transition of the Iberia Abyssal Plain margin. *In*: WHITMARSH, R. B., SAWYER, D. S., KLAUS, A. & MASSON, D. G. (eds) *Proceedings of the Ocean Drilling Program, Scientific Results*, **149**, 397–412.

BULLOCK, A. D. & MINSHULL, T. A. 2005. From continental extension to seafloor spreading: crustal structure of the Goban Spur rifted margin, southwest of the UK. *Geophysical Journal International*, **163–2**, 527–546.

CANNAT, M. 1993. Emplacement of mantle rocks in the seafloor at Mid-Ocean Ridges. *Journal of Geophysical Research*, **98-B3**, 4163–4172.

CHIAN, D., LOUDEN, K., MINSHULL, T. A. & WHITMARSH, R. B. 1999. Deep structure of the ocean-continent transition in the southern Iberia Abyssal Plain from seismic refraction profiles: Ocean Drilling Program (Legs 149 and 173) transect. *Journal of Geophysical Research*, **104-B4**, 7443–7462.

DE PAOLA, N., HOLDSWORTH, R. E., MCCAFFREY, K. J. W. & BARCHI, M. R. 2005. Partitioned transtension: an alternative to basin inversion models. *Journal of Structural Geology*, **27**, 607–625.

DEAN, S. M. 1999. *Structure of the ocean–continent transition in the southern Iberia Abyssal Plain*. PhD thesis, University of Cambridge.

DEAN, S. M., MINSHULL, T. A., WHITMARSH, R. B. & LOUDEN, K. E. 2000. Deep structure of the ocean-continent transition in the southern Iberia Abyssal Plain from seismic refraction profiles: the IAM-9 transect at 40°20′N. *Journal of Geophysical Research*, **105-B3**, 5859–5885.

Discovery 215 Working Group (MINSHULL, T. A., DEAN, S. M., WHITMARSH, R. B., RUSSELL, S. R., LOUDEN, K. E. & CHIAN, D.) 1998. Deep structure in the vicin-ity of the ocean-continent transition zone under the southern Iberia Abyssal Plain. *Geology*, **26**, 743–746.

Groupe Galice 1979. The continental margin off Galicia and Portugal : acoustical stratigraphy, dredge stratigraphy, and structural evolution. *In*: SIBUET, J. C., RYAN, W. B. F. *ET AL. Initial Reports DSDP*, 47 (Pt.2). Washington (U.S. Govt. Printing Office), 633–662.

HENNING, A. T., SAWYER, D. S. & TEMPLETON, D. C. 2004. Exhumed upper mantle within the ocean-continent transition on the northern West Iberia margin: evidence from prestack depth migration and total tectonic subsidence analyses. *Journal of Geophysical Research*, **109-B5**, B05103, doi:10.1029/2003JB002526.

HOPPER, J. R., FUNCK, T., TUCHOLKE, B. E., LARSEN, H. C., HOLBROOK, S., LOUDEN, K., SHILLINGTON, D. & LAU, H. 2004. Continental breakup and the onset of ultra-slow seafloor spreading off Flemish Cap on the Newfoundland rifted margin. *Geology*, **32**, 93–96.

LAGABRIELLE, Y. & LEMOINE, M. 1997. Alpine, Corsican and Apennine ophiolites: the slow-spreading ridge model. *Comptes Rendus de l'Académie des Sciences, Series IIA, Earth and Planetary Science*, **325**, 909–920.

LAU, H. K. W., LOUDEN, K. E., FUNCK, T., TUCHOLKE, B. E., HOLBROOK, W. S., HOPPER, J. R. & LARSEN, H. C. 2006. Crustal structure across the Grand Banks - Newfoundland Basin Continental margin - I. Results from a seismic refraction profile. *Geophysical Journal International*, **167**, 127–156.

LISTER, G. S., ETHERIDGE, M. A. & SYMONDS, P. A. 1986. Detachment faulting and the evolution of passive continental margins. *Geology*, **14**, 246–250.

LUNDIN, E. & DORE, A. G. 2002. Mid-Cenozoic post-breakup deformation in the 'passive' margins bordering the Norwegian–Greenland Sea. *Marine and Petroleum Geology*, **194**, 79–93.

MALDONADO, A., SOMOZA, L. & PALLARES, L. 1999. The Betic orogen and the Iberian – African boundary in the gulf of Cadix: geological evolution (central North Atlantic). *Marine Geology*, **155**, 9–43.

MANATSCHAL, G. 2004. New models for evolution of magma-poor rifted margins based on a review of data and concepts from West Iberia and the Alps. *International Journal of Earth Sciences*, **93**, 432–466.

MANATSCHAL, G. & NIEVERGELT, P. 1997. A continent-ocean transition recorded in the Err and Platta nappes (Eastern Switzerland). *Eclogae Geologicae Helvetiae*, **904**, 3–27.

MANATSCHAL, G., FROITZHEIM, N., RUBENACH, M. & TURRIN, B. D. 2001. The role of detachment faulting in the formation of an ocean-continent transition: insights from the Iberia Abyssal Plain. *In*: WILSON, R. C. L., WHITMARSH, R. B., TAYLOR, B. & FROITZHEIM, N. (eds) *Non-Volcanic Rifting of Continental Margins: A Comparison of Evidence from Land and Sea*. Geological Society, London, Special Publications, **187**, 1–24.

MASSON, D. G. & PARSON, L. M. 1983. Eocene deformation on the continental margin SW of the British Isles. *Journal of the Geological Society, London*, **140**, 913–920.

MASSON, D. G., CARTWRIGHT, J. A., PINHEIRO, L. M., WHITMARSH, R. B., BESLIER, M. O. & ROESER, H. 1994. Compressional deformation at the ocean-continent transition in the NE Atlantic. *Journal of the Geological Society, London*, **151**, 607–613.

MONTADERT, A., ROBERTS, D. G., DE CHARPAL, O. & GUENNOC, P. 1979. Rifting and subsidence of the northern continental margin of the Bay of Biscay. *In*: MONTADERT, L. & ROBERTS, D. G. (eds) *Initial Reports of the Deep Sea Drilling Project, 48*. Washington (U.S. Government Printing Office), 1025–1060.

PERON-PINVIDIC, G., MANATSCHAL, G., MINSHULL, T. A. & SAWYER, D. S. 2007. Tectonosedimentary evolution of the deep Iberia-Newfoundland margins: Evidence for a complex breakup history. *Tectonics*, **26**, doi:10.1029/2006TC001970.

PICKUP, S. L. B., WHITMARSH, R. B., FOWLER, C. M. R. & RESTON, T. J. 1996. Insight into the nature of the ocean-continent transition off West Iberia from a deep multichannel seismic reflection profile. *Geology*, **24**, 1079–1082.

PINHEIRO, L. M., WILSON, R. C. L., PENA DOS REIS, R., WHITMARSH, R. B. & RIBEIRO, A. 1996. The western Iberia margin: a geophysical and geological overview. *In*: WHITMARSH, R. B., SAWYER, D. S., KLAUS, A. & MASSON, D. G. (eds) *Proceedings of the Ocean Drilling Program, Scientific Results*, **149**, 3–21.

ROESER, H. A., BARGELOH, H. O., EILERS, G. *ET AL*. 1992. *SONNE Cruise S0-75 : Geophysical investigations of the crustal structure of the North Atlantic off Portugal, final report of the geophysical legs of the SONNE cruise SO-75, 14 October 1991–12 November 1991*. Cruise report 109.997, Bundesanstalt für Geowissenschaften und Rohstoffe, Hannover.

RUSSELL, S. M. & WHITMARSH, R. B. 2003. Magmatism at the west Iberia non-volcanic rifted continental margin: evidence from analyses of magnetic anomalies. *Geophysical Journal International*, **154**, 706–730.

SAWYER, D. S. 1994. The case for slow-spreading oceanic crust landward of the peridotite ridge in the Iberia Abyssal Plain. *Eos*, **75**, 616.

SAWYER, D. S., WHITMARSH, R. B., KLAUS, A. *ET AL*. 1994. Proceedings of the Ocean Drilling Program, Initial Reports 149. College Station, TX.

SHILLINGTON, D. J., HOLBROOK, W. S., AVENDONK, H. V. *ET AL*. 2006. Evidence for asymetric nonvolcanic rifting and slow incipient seafloor spreading from seismic reflection data on the Newfoundland margin.

Journal of Geophysical Research, **111**, B09402, doi:10.1029/2005JB003981.

SIBUET, J. C., THOMAS, Y., MARSSET, B., NOUZE, H., LOUVEL, V., SAVOYE, B. & LE FORMAL, J. P. 1996. Detailed relationship between tectonics and sedimentation from PARISAR deep-tow seismic data acquired in the Iberia Abyssal Plain. *In*: WHITMARSH, R. B., SAWYER, D. S., KLAUS, A. & MASSON, D. G. (eds) *Proceedings of the Ocean Drilling Program, Scientific Results*, **149**, 649–657.

THINON, I. 1999. *Structure profonde de la marge de Gascogne et du Bassin Armoricain*. Ph.D. thesis, Bretagne Occidentale University of Brest, France.

WHITMARSH, R. B. & MILES, P. R. 1995. Models of the development of the West Iberia rifted continental margin at 40°30′N deduced from surface and deep-tow magnetic anomalies. *Journal of Geophysical Research*, **100-B3**, 3789–3806.

WHITMARSH, R. B., MILES, P. R. & MAUFFRET, A. 1990*a*. The ocean–continent boundary off the western continental margin of Iberia - I. Crustal structure at 40°30′N. *Geophysical Journal International*, **103**, 509–531.

WHITMARSH, R. B., MILES, P. R. & PINHEIRO, M. 1990*b*. The seismic velocity structure of some NE Atlantic continental rise sediments; a lithification index? *Geophysical Journal International*, **101**, 367–378.

WHITMARSH, R. B. & SAWYER, D. S. 1996. The ocean-continent transition beneath the Iberia Abyssal Plain and continental rifting to seafloor spreading processes. *In*: WHITMARSH, R. B., SAWYER, D. S., KLAUS, A. & MASSON, D. G. (eds) *Proceedings of the Ocean Drilling Program, Scientific Results*, **149**, 713–733.

WHITMARSH, R. B., BESLIER, M. O., WALLACE, P. J. *ET AL*. 1998. Proceedings of the Ocean Drilling Program, Initial Reports, **173**. College Station, TX.

WHITMARSH, R. B., MANATSCHAL, G. & MINSHULL, T. A. 2001. Evolution of magma-poor continental margins from rifting to seafloor spreading. *Nature*, **413**, 150–154.

WILSON, R. C. L., SAWYER, D. S., WHITMARSH, R. B., ZERONG, J. & CARBONELL, J. 1996. Seismic stratigraphy and tectonic history of the Iberia Abyssal Plain. *In*: WHITMARSH, R. B., SAWYER, D. S., KLAUS, A. & MASSON, D. G. (eds) *Proceedings of the Ocean Drilling Program, Scientific Results*, **149**, 617–630.

Elastic flexure and distributed deformation along Australia's North West Shelf: Neogene tectonics of the Bonaparte and Browse basins

MYRA KEEP[1] & MATHEW HARROWFIELD[1,2]

[1]*School of Earth and Geographical Sciences, The University of Western Australia, M004, 35 Stirling Highway, Nedlands, 6009, WA (e-mail: myra.keep@uwa.edu.au)*

[2]*Current address: Woodside Energy, 240 St George's Terrace, Perth, 6000*

Abstract: Neogene collision between Australia and the Banda Arc modified the adjacent Bonaparte and Browse basins of the North West Shelf of Australia. Modification comprised both continuous long-wavelength amplification of Permo-Carboniferous basement topography and flexure and normal faulting of Triassic–Recent sedimentary cover. Deformation was continuous across the Browse and Bonaparte basins, despite the basins being separated by a rupture-barrier style accommodation zone, the Browse–Bonaparte Transition. The degree of basement control and mechanisms of fault linkage vary significantly across this transition, and reflect differences in the structural relief, amplitude and depth of rifted basement either side of the transition. Neogene collision amplified the architectural divide. Amplification of basement topography over wavelengths of several hundred kilometres was associated with negligible horizontal length change. The transcurrent component of Neogene deformation was partitioned outboard of any continuous flexural amplification.

Australia's North West Shelf formed originally as part of an intra-continental rift that commenced during the early stages of Gondwana breakup in the Devonian, and defined several thousand kilometres of the future Australian margin (Yeates *et al.* 1987). Additional rift events in the Devonian to Permian, Late Carboniferous and Late Triassic to Jurassic created the regional basement architecture and controlled the distribution of source and reservoir horizons of the local hydrocarbon province (e.g. Australian Geological Survey Organisation (AGSO) North West Shelf Study Group 1994; Etheridge & O'Brien 1994). During the Jurassic–Cretaceous, the punctuated separation of the West Burma blocks resulted in dramatic changes in palaeogeography along the northern and southern parts of the future North West Shelf, resulting in the passive margin that would become the North West Shelf (Etheridge & O'Brien 1994; Longley *et al.* 2002). Diachronous collision between Australian continental crust and the Banda Arc from the early Miocene reactivated and modified the Devonian–Cretaceous architecture of the North West Shelf (Fig. 1) (e.g. Baillie & Jacobsen 1995; Keep *et al.* 2002).

Despite the currently convergent plate-margin setting, Neogene deformation on the North West Shelf is dominated by normal faults and depocentres rather than by shortening structures (Fig. 2) (Woods 1988; Shuster *et al.* 1998). Three mechanisms have been proposed to explain this paradox:

(1) localized extension in pockets of the North West Shelf (e.g. Woods 1988); (2) flexural tension of Australia's partially subducted leading edge (O'Brien *et al.* 1999); and (3) penetrative strike-slip modification of the Timor Sea region (Shuster *et al.* 1998). Although such models provide a plausible explanation of some depocentre shapes, they are inconsistent with the style and distribution of Neogene deformation.

The adjacent Browse and Bonaparte basins (Fig. 1), thought to represent upper- and lower-plate Lister-style rift compartments (Lister *et al.* 1991) respectively of the North West Shelf (O'Brien *et al.* 1999), are separated by a lineament known as the Browse–Bonaparte Transition (Fig. 1) (O'Brien *et al.* 1993, 1999; Etheridge & O'Brien 1994; Struckmeyer *et al.* 1998). The Bonaparte Basin, with its broad outer margin plateau and a narrow margin-parallel graben (Fig. 3a), represents a salient upper-plate rift margin (UPRM), whereas the deeper and more extensive Browse Basin (Fig. 3b) is interpreted as a lower-plate rift margin (LPRM) embayment (O'Brien *et al.* 1993, 1999). Despite this asymmetry, basement faults trend consistently NE–SW on both sides of the Browse–Bonaparte Transition (Fig. 2) (Pattillo & Nicholls 1990; Struckmeyer *et al.* 1998; de Ruig *et al.* 2000).

The NW–SE trending Browse–Bonaparte Transition coincides with deep linear geophysical anomalies (Elliott 1994) and with present-day bathymetry, including dramatic bathymetric

From: JOHNSON, H., DORÉ, A. G., GATLIFF, R. W., HOLDSWORTH, R., LUNDIN, E. R. & RITCHIE, J. D. (eds)
The Nature and Origin of Compression in Passive Margins. Geological Society, London, Special Publications,
306, 185–200. DOI: 10.1144/SP306.9   0305-8719/08/$15.00 © The Geological Society of London 2008.

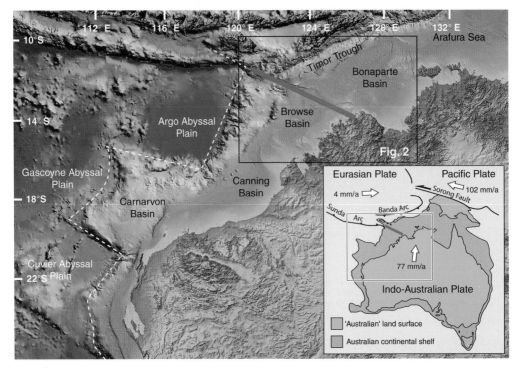

Fig. 1. Bathymetry (AGSO) and tectonic setting of NW Australia. Basement compartmentalization corresponds to basin subdivisions and rectilinear steps in the modern continent/ocean boundary (dashed). Position and geophysical expression of the Browse–Bonaparte Transition is indicated (red). Ongoing collision between Australia and the Eurasia/Pacific Arc system (inset) occurred from the Miocene onward.

changes across the lineament (O'Brien *et al.* 1993, 1999; AGSO 1994). This transition is interpreted as the accommodation zone across which polarity of the Permo-Carboniferous rift reversed (O'Brien *et al.* 1993; Etheridge & O'Brien 1994). Whether the structure represents a fault-bound 'transfer' style (e.g. Hayward & Ebinger 1996) or continuous 'rupture-barrier' style (e.g. Faulds & Geissman 1992) feature of basement architecture remains unclear. The Browse–Bonaparte division reflects compartmentalization of the wider North West Shelf over length scales of 600–700 km, corresponding to the Carnarvon, Browse/Canning and Bonaparte basins (Fig. 1) (O'Brien *et al.* 1993, 1999).

We present a synthesis of Neogene tectonism in the Browse and Bonaparte basins and attempt to reconcile the growth of major Neogene depocentres with brittle normal faults in a convergent plate boundary setting. In particular, we relate apparent Neogene subsidence to modification of the basement architecture. Structural and stratigraphic data from the Bonaparte and Browse basins are presented and we examine differences in the style and intensity of the Neogene deformation across

the Browse–Bonaparte Transition. In addition we describe the nature of the Browse–Bonaparte Transition and relate long-lived compartmentalization of the North West Shelf to weak episodic tectonic modification.

Geological framework and tectonostratigraphy

A 2D two-way-time (TWT) seismic grid spanning the Browse and Bonaparte basins was mapped and tied using around 40 wells for which Tertiary picks were determined (Fig. 4). This grid, comprising more than 4000 open-file lines with an average line spacing of around 5–10 km, was used to construct structural cross-sections and to correlate fault projections across the area. Stratigraphic mapping of the Bonaparte Basin (Fig. 5) shows detailed isochores at selected intervals from the Permian to the seafloor. Similar maps for the Browse Basin (Fig. 6) appear courtesy of Woodside Energy Ltd, after Longley *et al.* (2002).

Although basement on this part of the North West Shelf, especially coring the underlying

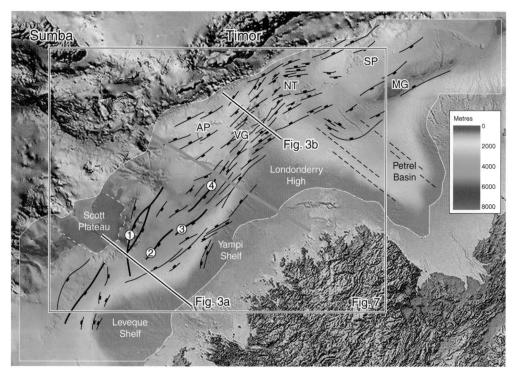

Fig. 2. Basement fault trends across the Browse and Bonaparte basins after Pattillo & Nicholls (1990), Struckmeyer *et al.* (1998) and de Ruig *et al.* (2000), superimposed upon the Oxfordian isochore (after Longley *et al.* 2002). The Bonaparte upper-plate is marked by the outer-margin highs of the Ashmore (AP) and Sahul (SP) platforms, separated from the Londonderry High (LH) by the Vulcan (VG) and Malita (MG) grabens and Nancar Trough (NT). The Browse–Bonaparte Transition is shown by the red line. Major basement faults of the Browse Basins (bold) after Struckmeyer *et al.* (1998): (1) Scott Reef Fault Trend, (2) Caswell Fault, (3) Brewster Fault and (4) Bassett Fault. The earlier structural grain of the Petrel Basin (dashed) reflects failed Devonian–Carboniferous rifting (O'Brien *et al.* 1993).

structural highs, is thought to be Precambrian in age, the oldest and deepest horizon that can be correlated across the Bonaparte and Browse basins is the regional Oxfordian (JO) unconformity (Fig. 7a). However, locally in the Bonaparte Basin the top Permian surface can also be identified (Fig. 5a). Within this local top Permian surface the basement architecture of the Bonaparte Basin, including major troughs and highs, can be identified (Fig. 5). Above this surface the top Permian–Aptian isochore (Fig. 5b) reflects both Permo-Triassic infill and more localized syntectonic Jurassic–Cretaceous sedimentation.

The Oxfordian (JO) horizon map clearly illustrates changes in Mesozoic structural relief between the Browse and Bonaparte basins. In the southern Bonaparte Basin, the amount of Oxfordian structural relief (Fig. 7a) is virtually identical to that of the top Permian (syn-rift) surface (Fig. 5a). By comparison, Oxfordian (JO) structural relief in the Browse Basin was probably of lesser amplitude

than the underlying syn-rift architecture (Fig. 7). In both basins, the amplitude of Oxfordian structural relief exceeds that of all younger horizons.

Limited Oxfordian–Valanginian (JO–KV) deposition was confined to the Vulcan Graben and a depocentre in the central Browse Basin (Fig. 7b), whilst the Valanginian–Aptian (KV–KA) isopach only records a depocentre in the Browse Basin (Fig. 7c). This limited deposition in both the Browse and Bonaparte basins at this time reflects a combination of protracted post-Oxfordian underfill of the Browse Basin (Longley *et al.* 2002) and late Jurassic uplift and Aptian erosion of the Bonaparte Basin (Duddy *et al.* 2004). Both are consistent with structural relief between the two basins during the early Cretaceous and greater accommodation space within the Browse Basin at that time.

Infill of Oxfordian structural relief within the Browse Basin was completed during the late Cretaceous (Longley *et al.* 2002). Peak eustatic

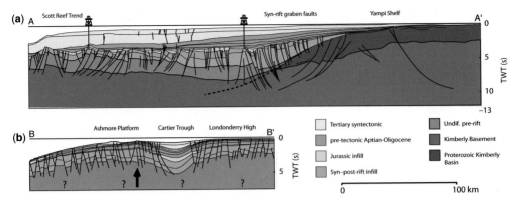

Fig. 3. Published cross-sections across the (**a**) Browse Basin (AGSO, 1994) and (**b**) Bonaparte Basin (Harrowfield *et al.* 2003). Black arrow marks approximate axis of saddle topography. See Figure 2 for section locations.

sea levels during the Turonian (Blevin *et al.* 1998) culminated in onlap of the Scott Reef Trend (Fig. 3a) and infill of relief across the Browse–Bonaparte Transition (Fig. 7d), permitting convergence of Maastrichtian fan systems across the two basins (Blevin *et al.* 1998). The core of the Aptian–base Tertiary (KA–T) depocentre lay adjacent to the mouth of the Vulcan Graben and well inboard of the Scott Reef Trend (Fig. 7e). The Bonaparte Basin, having been eroded to a low-relief shelf during the Aptian (KA), was subsequently covered by a relatively uniform Aptian–Miocene blanket that has no obvious sensitivity to older topography (Fig. 5d) (Harrowfield *et al.* 2003). Apparent thinning of this blanket across the

Ashmore Platform (Fig. 7e) reflects subsequent Neogene erosion (Hillis 1992). The Oligo-Miocene unconformity (Fig. 5e) preserves a similar topography to that of the Aptian unconformity. This topography must therefore post-date deposition of the Aptian–Oligo-Miocene succession.

In the Bonaparte Basin the Neogene–Recent isochore (Fig. 5f) illustrates thick deposits in the Cartier and Nancar troughs and Malita Graben, mimicking those seen in the top Permian surface (Fig. 5a). Thickness variations in this Neogene to Recent isochore reflect infill of the underlying base Tertiary (TO) unconformity (Fig. 5e) and corresponds to Neogene fault trends across the North West Shelf (Fig. 2).

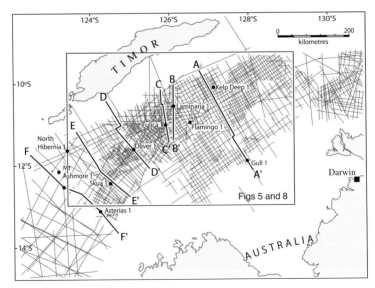

Fig. 4. Seismic base map of the Timor Sea region illustrating open-file seismic lines and selected commercial wells used in the course of this study. The locations of strike-normal (cross-sections (A–F) and the location of Figures 5 and 8 are also shown.

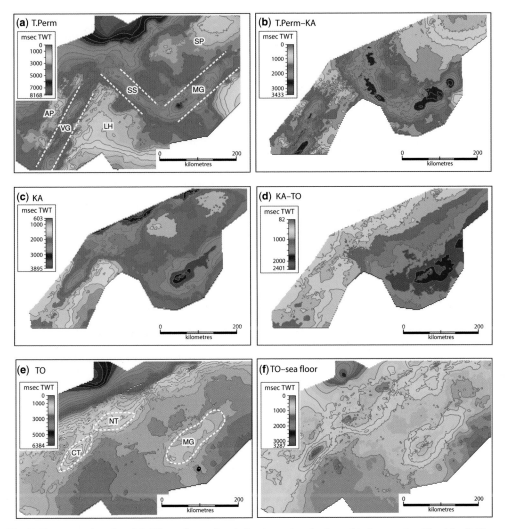

Fig. 5. Tectonostratigraphy of the Timor Sea region, indicating major physiographic features (see Fig. 4 for field of view): (**a**) Top-Permian (T.Perm) time surface map with two-way travel time (TWT) contoured at 400 ms intervals; (**b**) Top-Permian–Aptian (KA) isochore, contoured at 200 ms intervals; (**c**) time-surface map of the KA unconformity, contoured at 200 ms intervals; (**d**) Aptian–Oligo-Miocene (TO) isochore contoured at 200 ms intervals; (**e**) time-surface map of the TO unconformity contoured at 200 ms intervals; (**f**) TO–sea floor isochore contoured at 200 ms intervals. VG, Vulcan Graben; SS, Sahul Syncline; MG, Malita Graben; AP, Ashmore Platform; LH, Londonderry High; SP, Sahul Platform; CT, Cartier Trough; NT, Nancar Trough.

The Neogene sedimentation history of the Bonaparte Basin therefore mimics that of the underlying Permian surface, and all major Neogene–Recent depocentres (Vulcan Graben, Malita Graben, Sahul Syncline) directly overlie older Palaeozoic–Mesozoic troughs (compare Fig. 5a, b & f). This virtually identical topographical growth in the post-Permian and the Neogene occurs despite the change in tectonic regime from extensional to contractional in the intervening 120 Ma of continuous passive margin sedimentation. The

distribution of Neogene sediments appears to have been structurally controlled and associated with a fault-propagated topography (Figs 2 & 5f).

In the Browse Basin the longevity of the depocentres is more subtle than in the Bonaparte Basin. Depocentres in the base Tertiary-water-bottom isopach (Fig. 7f), differ significantly from those in the upper Cretaceous interval (Fig. 7d & e) in that the Tertiary depocentre did not form along-strike from the palaeo-Vulcan Graben (compare Fig. 7e & f), even though that feature experienced

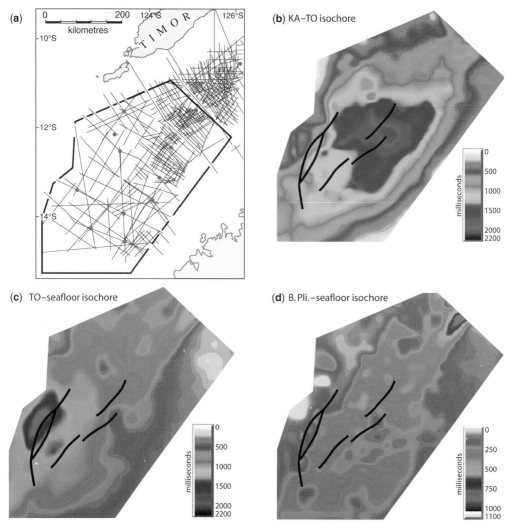

Fig. 6. Detail of the late Cretaceous and Tertiary (Albian-seafloor) history of the Browse Basin, mapped from (**a**) local 2D seismic grid: (**b**) pre-tectonic Aptian (KA)–Oligocene (TO) isochore; (**c**) early syn-tectonic Oligocene (TO)–base Pliocene isochore; and (**d**) base-Pliocene–water bottom isochore. Major basement faults as per Figure 2.

subsidence during the Neogene (Chen *et al.* 2002; Harrowfield *et al.* 2003). Instead, deposition migrated westward and southward (Fig. 6a & b), with the greatest thicknesses accumulating above the deepest regions of Oxfordian structural relief (compare Fig. 7a & f). The Pliocene–Recent component of this depositional wedge is bound by a margin-parallel trough with linear discontinuities that coincide with syn-rift basement faults (Fig. 6d).

Tertiary sedimentation in the Browse Basin therefore reflects a combination of depocentre progradation and the influence of structural relief associated with the Scott Reef Trend, Oxfordian

depocentre and Browse/Bonaparte Transition. These features were not relics of Jurassic architecture, which had been infilled during the mid-late Cretaceous (Figs 6 & 7). Neogene rejuventation of these structural elements was spatially and temporally associated with Neogene faulting and syntectonic sedimentation across the Browse and Bonaparte basins.

Neogene deformation

In the Bonaparte Basin the top Permian surface (Fig. 5a) displays fault-bound grabens associated

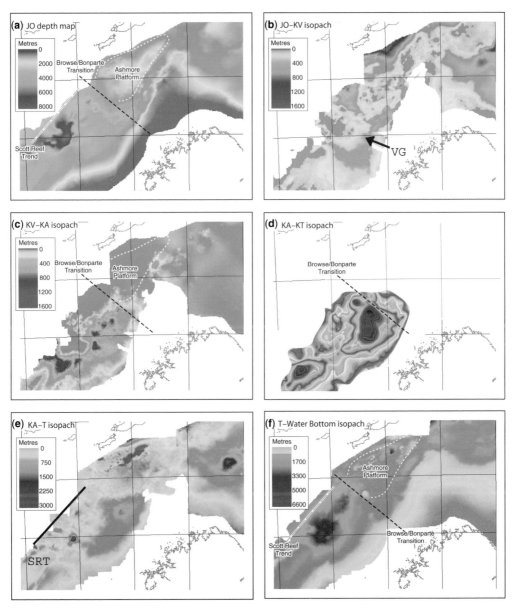

Fig. 7. Major tectonostratigraphic intervals across the Browse and Bonaparte basins after Longley *et al.* (2002), courtesy of Woodside Energy Ltd. (**a**) the Oxfordian (JO) unconformity, the oldest and deepest horizon that may be traced continuously across the two basins; (**b**) the Oxfordian–Valanginian (KV) isopach; VG, Vulcan Graben; (**c**) the Valanginian–Aptian (KA) isopach; (**d**) the Aptian–Turonian (KT) component (Blevin *et al.* 1998; no scale given) of (**e**) the Aptian (KA)–base Tertiary (T) isopach; black line shows position of the Scott Reef Trend (SRT); and (**f**) base Tertiary–water bottom isopach. See Figure 2 for location.

with deep-seated listric detachments (e.g. Australian Geological Survey Organisation (AGSO) North West Shelf Study Group 1994; O'Brien *et al.* 1999). The Oxfordian surface in contrast (Fig. 7a) reflects Jurassic subsidence and renewed

subsidence of pre-existing toughs, with infill of these lows prior to the Aptian (e.g. Longley *et al.* 2002).

Internally, the Aptian–Oligocene sequence (Fig. 3b) displays continuous sedimentary packages that prograde offshore, and generally reflects an advancing sedimentary wedge. This sequence has been distorted about a younger saddle-like topography (Fig. 3b).

Neogene–Recent sedimentation reflects infill of the fault-bound saddle-like topography (since the onset of plate collision), with portions of the sequence thinning across developing highs or thickening above deepening troughs (Fig. 8). As the margin is currently shortening, resulting in an overall decrease of accommodation space, the thinning and thickening of sediments reflect only apparent uplift and apparent subsidence. The coincidence of thinned, fault-bound segments in successive packages (Fig. 8) indicates that thinning was related to both differential uplift and topographic drape. In all cases, synsedimentary thinning and apparent uplift appear to have begun in the late

Oligocene or early Miocene and to have continued well into the Plio-Pleistocene.

Structural highs bounded by brittle normal faults in the Bonaparte Basin have previously been attributed to a horst-like architecture (Woods 1988; de Ruig et al. 2000; Chen et al. 2002). However, these highs (Fig. 8) are not associated with discrete structural thickening. Between major faults the Tertiary horizons commonly exhibit convex-up geometries (Fig. 8), that are harmonic throughout the stratigraphy and are thought to reflect minor distributed shortening within fault-bound segments. Neogene depocentre margins are marked by prominent normal faults (Fig. 8), many of which are coincident with down-to-basement faults at Mesozoic levels. Apparent subsidence and fault growth appear to have peaked during the late Miocene or Pliocene.

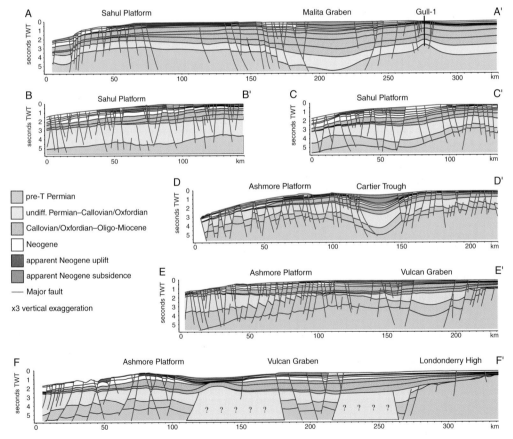

Fig. 8. Interpretation of apparent Neogene topography, based on variations of sedimentary thickness (×3 vertical exaggeration). Deepening depressions in the unconformity at the top of the Oligo-Miocene (orange) were bound outboard by diffuse horst-like structural highs. The Cartier Trough, (C–C′) is also bound inboard by zones of lesser uplift; an apparently similar phenomena on the inboard margin of the Malita Graben (A–A′) reflects a salt diapir beneath the Gull-1 well. Locations of cross-sections given on Figure 4.

The proliferation of seaward-dipping and landward-dipping normal faults, commonly coincident with the older syn-rift architecture at depth (Woods 1988; Nelson 1993; O'Brien *et al.* 1993) makes characterizing Neogene deformation kinematics difficult. However, in the Bonaparte Basin, clear relationships between normal faulting, distortion of pre-collisional cover and the distribution of syn-tectonic (collisional) sediment assist the identification of long wavelength deformation kinematics and four structural domains (Fig. 9):

(I) a zone of dominantly seaward-verging normal faults that may be traced around the inboard margins of the Vulcan Graben;

(II) a zone of dominantly landward-verging normal faults, bounding the outboard margin of the Vulcan Graben;

(III) a zone of dominantly seaward-verging fault kinematics that envelope the outboard flank of the Ashmore Platform; and

(IV) weak, dominantly outboard-dipping normal faults in the vicinity of the Scott Reef Trend, along strike from the Lynher/Lombardina trend of the outer Browse Basin (Fig. 10).

In the central Bonaparte Basin these Neogene faults commonly preserve modern seafloor offsets (Fig. 9A–A'). Domains I and II (Figs 9 & 10) illustrate down-warping of Cretaceous horizons beneath the Neogene fill of the Vulcan Graben; in domains II and III faults shed pre-collisional cover from the rising and eroding Ashmore Platform (Figs 9 & 10).

Reduced structural relief in the Browse Basin makes extrapolation of these domains from the Bonaparte Basin into the Browse Basin difficult, and is exacerbated by the low intensity of brittle deformation and the thinness of the Neogene fill in the Browse Basin. However, coarse extrapolation of the structural domains may be achieved via correlation of Neogene subsidence/uplift, Pliocene sedimentary growth and, locally, by rare kinematic consistency of normal faults (Fig. 11).

The structural grain of Neogene faults across the Bonaparte and Browse basins changes from NE–SW-trending across the Ashmore Platform and Vulcan Graben, the Browse–Bonaparte Transition and the northern reaches of the Browse Basin to east–west trending in the centre of the Browse Basin (Fig. 10). There is no discrete structural

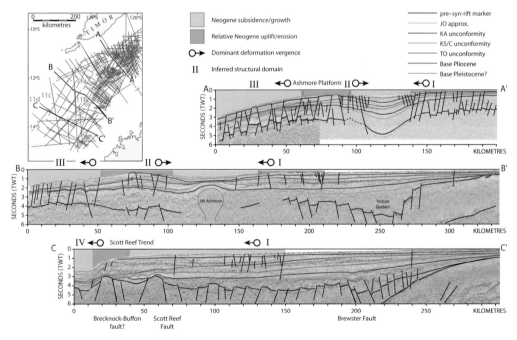

Fig. 9. Neogene deformation vergence, extrapolated southward from the Bonaparte Basin (A–A') on the basis of syn-tectonic Mio–Pliocene sedimentation. Dissection of the Ashmore Platform is continuous with buckling of Cretaceous–Oligocene horizons and sedimentary thinning west of Mt Ashmore. These zones of uplift bound Plio/Pleistocene depocentres within the Vulcan Graben and above Mt Ashmore (B–B'). The central Browse Basin is dominated by sparse, NW-verging faults and deformation associated with the Scott Reef Trend (C–C'). Approximate vertical exaggeration × 12.

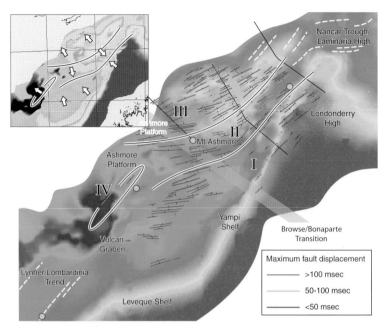

Fig. 10. Interpreted Neogene fault trends across the Browse and Bonaparte basins, coloured according to maximum post-Oxfordian TWT offset. Inferred structural zonation and generalized fault vergence directions (inset) are extrapolated southward from the Bonaparte Basin (Fig. 11).

expression of the NW-trending Browse–Bonaparte Transition. We make several observations of Neogene deformation in the Browse Basin:

- Neogene faults are predominantly confined to the centre of the basin (Fig. 10);
- individual fault segments have negligible expression in Tertiary surface/isochore maps (Figs 6 & 7f) and rarely have maximum displacements greater than 100 ms;
- faults do not penetrate the Yampi Shelf or vicinity of Mt Ashmore; and
- pervasive faulting north and west of Mt Ashmore is continuous with deformation of the Ashmore Platform (Fig. 10).

Neogene modification of the Browse Basin is also manifested as continuous deformation of pre-collisional strata. The present-day bathymetric profile across the Browse–Bonaparte Transition coincides with continuous down-warping of Cretaceous–Miocene horizons (and ponding of Pleistocene–Recent sediments above the Mt Ashmore intrusion) (Fig. 9B–B′).

Continuous Neogene deformation is also observed along the outer margin of the Browse Basin, with Mio-Pliocene prograde expansion and concave-up warping on the outboard side of the Scott Reef Trend (Fig. 11c), and increased relief between the Scott Reef Trend/Browse Basin and

Scott Plateau (O'Brien *et al.* 1993). Likewise, tapering of the Pliocene wedge behind this topographic front (Fig. 9b), corresponding to linear expressions in the Tertiary isopach and Pliocene isochore (Figs 6c & 7f) suggests uplift or amplification of the Scott Reef Trend. The uplifted outer flank of the Scott Reef Trend and its along-strike equivalents formed a locus for Pliocene canyon development (Fig. 11c & d).

Throughout the region, and particularly in the Bonaparte Basin, Neogene faults commonly coincide with larger displacements at Mesozoic levels (Fig. 9) (e.g. Woods 1988; de Ruig *et al.* 2000; Chen *et al.* 2002). This inheritance of extensional architecture, seemingly at odds with the contractional setting of Neogene deformation, has been variously explained in terms of tensional (Woods 1988), strike-slip (Keep *et al.* 2000) and flexural deformation (Harrowfield *et al.* 2003). Although cover and basement faults are typically continuous in 2D seismic cross-section, their displacement profiles are not continuous down-plane (Woods 1988; de Ruig *et al.* 2000). Typical faults have maximum displacements at late Miocene/Pliocene levels, coincident with peak syn-sedimentary Neogene growth (Fig. 9). This growth declines abruptly below the Base Tertiary unconformity: however, and displacements penetrate pre-collsion levels and decay down-plane towards typical

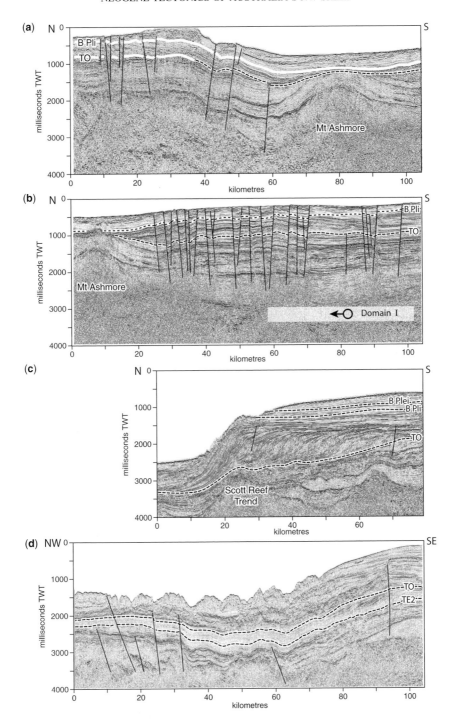

Fig. 11. Continuous Neogene deformation in the Browse Basin (see Fig. 9 for section locations): (**a**) down-warping of Tertiary strata across the Browse–Bonaparte Transition and buckling of pre-tectonic packages above Mt Ashmore; (**b**) rotational distortion of package boundaries between adjacent Neogene normal faults, kinematically consistent at right; (**c**) down-warping of pre-tectonic horizons, and confinement of the Pleistocene wedge across the Scott Reef Trend. Uplift of this trend (c), and its along-strike equivalents (**d**), induced canyon incision on the outboard flank. Approximate vertical exaggeration ×12.

minima around the Campanian or Aptian unconformity (de Ruig *et al.* 2000). Displacement increases abruptly again near the Oxfordian unconformity, culminating in large offsets and growth at syn-rift (Mesozoic) levels (Fig. 9) (Chen *et al.* 2002). Such profiles are not consistent with temporally continuous displacement at all levels of the pile (Walsh & Watterson 1987). Rather, these profiles are thought to reflect juxtaposition of Permian, Jurassic and Neogene offsets. Although fission-track annealing episodes might indicate basinal brine transport and basement fault reactivation (Duddy *et al.* 2004), the connectivity of Lower Cretaceous hydrocarbon seals suggests that such reactivation was not necessarily continuous with brittle deformation of the upper sedimentary pile (de Ruig *et al.* 2000). This uncoupling of basement and cover faulting is thought to have permitted flexure of cover rocks about reactivated basement architecture (Harrowfield *et al.* 2003).

Discussion

We believe Neogene modification of the Bonaparte Basin reflects an amplification of syn-rift basement topography. This amplification appears to have decreased inboard over wavelengths of 200–300 km, penetrating to inboard depocentre margins only in the more highly deformed Cartier and Nancar troughs (Fig. 12). We attribute apparent Neogene subsidence in the Timor Sea to forebulge flexure, and suggest that propagation of this flexure was limited to the leading several hundred kilometres of the Australian margin. This limitation probably reflects the rapid lateral decay of elastic potential and increasing lithospheric thickness toward the continent proper.

Deformation of the Bonaparte Basin is thought to have absorbed minor margin-parallel shortening, oblique to the trajectory of the Indo-Australian Plate (Fig. 1). Although this shortening must have been accompanied by a component of left-lateral deformation (e.g. Shuster *et al.* 1998), our observations suggest that this strike-slip component was partitioned outboard of the major Neogene depocentres, and may have been localized against the outboard margins of the Sahul and Ashmore platforms (Fig. 2) (Nelson 1993; Keep *et al.* 2002).

The Browse–Bonaparte Transition has no discrete structural expression. Neogene fault trends, although oblique to the transition, are continuous across it (Fig. 10). We identify a correlation between the trend and vergence of Neogene normal faults and the architectural topography of the Oxfordian (JO) unconformity. The rotation of Neogene structural grain across the Browse–Bonaparte Transition mimics the curvature of JO

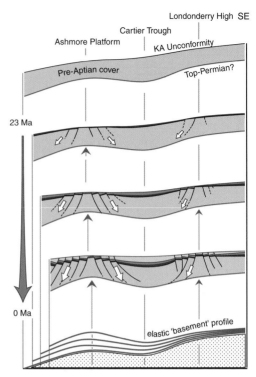

Fig. 12. Conceptual evolution of Neogene architecture. In contrast to these schematic illustrations, Neogene shortening is thought to have been minuscule: approximating a 1.5 km amplitude parabolic flexure across the *c.* 100 km wavelength Ashmore Platform yields an effective shortening of 0.05%.

topographic contours and the arcuate geometry of the Yampi/Leveque Shelf (Fig. 10). This rotation describes an architecture in which normal faults throw broadly perpendicular to JO architectural topography (Fig. 10, inset).

The control on Neogene faulting by basement architecture changes across the Browse–Bonaparte Transition. Neogene deformation of the Bonaparte Basin was tightly controlled by fault-bound basement structural relief (Harrowfield *et al.* 2003), with flexure and normal faults co-axial with syn-rift architecture (Figs 9A–A', 13). This suggests hard-linkage of parallel cover and basement faults (e.g. Nelson 1993; Shuster *et al.* 1998). In the Browse Basin, shallow Neogene normal faults and structural domains trend oblique to syn-rift structure, suggesting Neogene faults were probably soft-linked to basement architecture. For example, in the central Browse Basin shallow Neogene faults localize above structural culminations bound by the JO unconformity. We envisage three probable reasons for this relaxation of basement control: first, reduced amplitude and

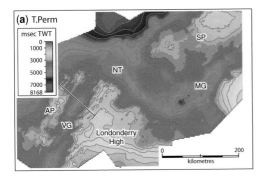

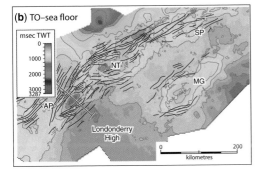

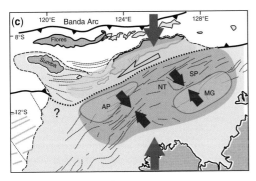

Fig. 13. Neogene deformation of the Bonaparte upper-plate compartment after Harrowfield *et al.* (2003); abbreviations as per Figure 2. The structural relief of the (a) buried Permian rift is mimicked by (b) fault-bound thickness variations (TWT) in the Neogene–Recent isochore. Harrowfield *et al.* (2003) interpreted Neogene faulting to reflect flexure of cover about amplified basement topography; (c) Driven by a north–south remote compressive stress (red arrows), pure-shear flexure of the Bonaparte Basin (blue region and arrows) is inferred to reflect partitioned sinistral strike-slip (i.e. simple shear) deformation outboard of the Ashmore Platform (yellow region).

increased wavelength of Jurassic and syn-rift architecture (Fig. 7a); second, increased basement depth and thickness of Cretaceous–Recent cover (Etheridge & O'Brien 1994; Blevin *et al.* 1998);

and third, reduced Neogene strain accumulation at distance from the collisional margin. The first explanation is consistent with the transition to soft-linked lower-plate rift margin architecture at basement levels (Struckmeyer *et al.* 1998), i.e. syn-rift architecture itself was less controlled by discrete faults, more influenced by ductile relay ramps and thus more continuous over greater length scales than the hard-linked Bonaparte compartment. The second cause is characteristic of increased subsidence of lower plate compartments during post-rift thermal recovery or 'sag' (as per Lister *et al.* 1991) and resultant inter-compartment relief across the Browse–Bonaparte Transition (Fig. 7a). The third reason is consistent with the apparent decline of Neogene structural relief and deformation intensity southward across the Browse–Bonaparte Transition.

Locally, similar rotations of Neogene structural grain are associated with intra-compartment relief and corresponding variations in cover thickness. At the northern end of the Vulcan Graben, low-amplitude Mesozoic architecture and thicker post-Jurassic cover coincide with structural rotations and east–west Neogene fault trends in the Nancar Trough and across the Laminaria High (Fig. 10) (Shuster *et al.* 1998; de Ruig *et al.* 2000). Conversely, in the southern Browse Basin, where post-rift cover thins over the Leveque Shelf, Neogene fault trends and isopach lineaments trend parallel to basement faults of the lower-plate margin (Fig. 10) (Keep *et al.* 2000). Thus the Neogene structural grain is observed to rotate towards greater obliquity with the convergence vector of the Indo-Australian plate (Fig. 1) and inferred driving stress of Neogene deformation with inferred relaxation of basement control.

Neogene modification of the Browse Basin was associated with subtle amplification of Jurassic and older structural relief, accommodated by both faulting and continuous deformation of pre-tectonic Aptian-Oligocene cover (Fig. 9). The Miocene–Recent depocentre was constrained by the Scott Reef Trend, the Browse–Bonaparte Transition and the palaeobathymetry of the Oxfordian depocentre. Thus modification of both the Browse and Bonaparte basins was associated with (1) the subtle amplification of basement structural relief and (2) a continuum of normal faulting. We therefore interpret Neogene deformation of the Browse Basin to be continuous with contractional flexure of the adjacent Bonaparte Basin (Fig. 12) (Harrowfield *et al.* 2003).

In both basins, Oxfordian structural relief was itself a low-amplitude replica of Jurassic architecture (Figs 3 & 9) (Chen *et al.* 2002). Thus both Neogene and Oxfordian structural relief mimicked the architecture of syn-rift basement. These two phases of modification, associated with virtually identical patterns of sedimentary infill (Fig. 7a & f), heightened relief between the Browse and Bonaparte compartments, and both phases resulted in amplification and erosion of outboard highs, subsidence of inboard troughs (O'Brien *et al.* 1993) and a decline in architectural relief southward across the Browse–Bonaparte Transition. Neither compartment shows evidence of any significant shortening or lengthing normal to strike (Chen *et al.* 2002). Whereas Neogene deformation reflects plate-margin collision, Jurassic modification was spatially and temporally associated with seafloor spreading at the continent–ocean boundary (Muller *et al.* 1998). Similar correlations between seafloor spreading and weak contractional modification of passive margins have been described from SE Australia (Holdgate *et al.* 2003), the North American passive margin (Withjack *et al.* 1998), the North Atlantic Margin (Doré *et al.* 1999) and, locally, the diachronously equivalent Cretaceous interval within the Carnarvon Basin (Baillie & Jacobson 1995). However, in the Browse Basin there was one substantial difference between Jurassic and Neogene architecture: whereas Jurassic faults paralleled syn-rift structure (Fig. 2) (Struckmeyer *et al.* 1998), Neogene faults were obliquely oriented (Fig. 10).

Basement and cover fault trends are continuous across and oblique to the architectural relief of the Browse–Bonaparte Transition (Figs 2 & 10). The Browse–Bonaparte Transition is thus more akin to soft-linked rupture-barrier style accommodation zones (i.e. a continuous basement ridge; e.g. Faulds & Geissman 1992) than to transfer style (i.e. fault bound) accommodation zones (e.g. Coffield & Schamel 1989; Hayward & Ebinger 1996). A rupture-barrier style origin, thought to reflect compartmentalization of syn-rift extension (Faulds & Geissman 1992), is consistent with both continuous Neogene amplification of the Browse–Bonaparte Transition and the inferred change in fault linkage mechanism (i.e. uncoupling of the two fault populations) between the Browse and Bonaparte basins. The linear geophysical expression of the Browse–Bonaparte Transition, uncharacteristic of accommodation zones in modern rift settings (e.g. Upcott *et al.* 1996) and apparently unrelated to syn-rift faulting (Fig. 2), possibly reflects inheritance of the older Devonian–Carboniferous structural grain of the Petrel Basin (Fig. 2).

The Browse–Bonaparte Transition compartmentalized infill of both Jurassic and Neogene structural relief. Jurassic flexure, presumed to have been driven by orthogonal seafloor spreading, was coaxial with and hard-linked to syn-rift (Mesozoic) architecture. Neogene flexure, driven by oblique collision, varied complexly between hard-linked/coaxial deformation and soft-linked/oblique deformation because of variations in basement structural relief and cover thickness. Regardless, both episodes caused amplification of long-wavelength relief between the Browse and Bonaparte Basins. Thus, weak flexural deformation, driven by both rifting and early-stage orogenesis, is interpreted to have actively contributed to long-lived compartmentalization of the North West Shelf (Fig. 12).

Conclusions

We conclude that Neogene modification of the Timor Sea region reflects contractional deformation of a collisional plate margin; in effect, early-stage orogenesis. Our model has several interesting ramifications.

1. Any elastic amplification at basement levels (in accordance with Etheridge *et al.* 1991) might have been recoverable following accretion of the Banda Arc. This may explain why Ashmore Reef, a structural high and erosional locus during the Plio-Pleistocene, is now stranded below the apex of shelf topography.
2. Neogene deformation and depocentre growth did not result from penetrative strike-slip modification of the North West Shelf. Neogene depocentres represent troughs of apparent subsidence contained by zones of diffuse uplift.
3. Neogene–Recent tectonism amplified basement topography over wavelengths of several hundred kilometres. This vertical exaggeration was associated with negligible horizontal length change (i.e. very small distributed strain).
4. Shallow Neogene faulting accommodated thin-skinned gravitational collapse of detached sedimentary cover. At depth, Neogene deformation was manifested as continuous flexural shortening. This shortening was oblique to the trajectory of the Australian continent and the inferred tectonic stress.
5. The transcurrent component of Neogene deformation was partitioned outboard of any continuous flexural amplification. We speculate that left-lateral shear was partitioned adjacent to the present-day Timor Trough.

References

AUSTRALIAN GEOLOGICAL SURVEY ORGANISATION (AGSO) NORTH WEST SHELF STUDY GROUP. 1994. Deep reflections on the North West Shelf: changing perspectives of basin formation. *In*: PURCELL, P. G. & PURCELL, R. R. (eds) *The Sedimentary Basins of Western Australia*. Proceedings of the Petroleum Exploration Society of Australia, Perth, 63–74.

BAILLIE, P. W. & JACOBSON, E. 1995. Structural evolution of the Carnarvon Terrace, Western Australia. *Australian Petroleum Production and Exploration Journal*, **35**, 321–331.

BLEVIN, J. E., STRUCKMEYER, H. I. M., CATHRO, D. L., ET AL. 1998. Tectonostratigraphic framework and petroleum systems of the Browse Basin, North West Shelf. *In*: PURCELL, P. G. & PURCELL, R. R. (eds) *The Sedimentary Basins of Western Australia, 2.* Proceedings of the Petroleum Exploration Society of Australia, Perth, 369–420.

CHEN, G., HILL, K. C., HOFFMAN, N. & O'BRIEN, G. W. 2002. Geodynamic evolution of the Vulcan sub-basin, Timor Sea, northwest Australia: a pre-compression New Guinea Analogue? *Australian Journal of Earth Sciences*, **49**, 719–736.

COFFIELD, D. Q. & SCHAMEL, S. 1989. Surface expression of accommodation zone within the Gulf of Suez rift, Egypt. *Geology*, **17**, 76–79.

DE RUIG, M. J., TRUPP, M., BISHOP, D. J., KUEK, D. & CASTILLO, D. A. 2000. Fault Architecture in the Nancar Trough/Laminaria Area of the Timor Sea, Northern Australia. *Australian Petroleum Production and Exploration Journal*, **40**, 174–193.

DORÉ, A. G., LUNDIN, E. R., JENSEN, L. N., BIRKELAND, O., ELIASSEN, P. E. & FICHLER, C. 1999. Principal tectonic events in the evolution of the Northwest European Atlantic margin. *In*: FLEET, A. J. & BOLDY, S. A. R. (eds) *Petroleum Geology of Northwest Europe: Proceedings of the 5th Petroleum Geology Conference.* Geological Society, London, 41–61.

DUDDY, I. R., GREEN, P. F., GIBSON, H. J. & HEGARTY, K. A. 2004. Regional Palaeothermal episodes in Northern Australia. Timor Sea Petroleum Geoscience. *Proceedings of the Timor Sea Symposium.* Petroleum Exploration Society of Australia, 567–591.

ELLIOTT, C. I. 1994. Lineament Tectonics; an approach to basin analysis and exploration. *In*: PURCELL, P. G. & PURCELL, R. R. (eds) *The Sedimentary Basins of Western Australia.* Proceedings of the Petroleum Exploration Society of Australia, Perth, 77–90.

ETHERIDGE, M. A. & O'BRIEN, G. W. 1994. Structural and tectonic evolution of the Western Australian margin basin system. *Petroleum Exploration Society of Australia Journal*, **22**, 45–64.

ETHERIDGE, M., MCQUEEN, H. & LAMBECK, K. 1991. The role of intraplate stress in Tertiary (and Mesozoic) deformation of the Australian Continent and its margins: a key factor in petroleum trap formation. *Exploration Geophysics*, **22**, 123–128.

FAULDS, J. E. & GEISSMAN, J. W. 1992. Implications of palaeomagnetic data on Miocene extension near a major accommodation zone in the Basin and Range Province, northwestern Arizona and southern Nevada. *Tectonics*, **11**, 204–227.

HARROWFIELD, M., CUNNEEN, J., KEEP, M. & CROWE, W. 2003. Early-stage orogenesis in the Timor Sea Region, NW Australia. *Journal of the Geological Society, London*, **160**, 991–1002.

HAYWARD, N. J. & EBINGER, C. J. 1996. Variations in the along-axis segmentation of the Afar rift system. *Tectonics*, **15**, 244–257.

HILLIS, R. 1992. Evidence for Pliocene erosion at Ashmore Reef (Timor Sea) from the sonic velocities of Neogene limestone formations. *Exploration Geophysics*, **23**, 489–495.

HOLDGATE, G. R., RODRIQUEZ, C., JOHNSTONE, E. M., WALLACE, M. W. & GALLAGHER, S. J. 2003. The Gippsland Basin Top Latrobe unconformity and its expression in other southeast Australian Basins. *Australian Petroleum Production and Exploration Association Journal*, **43**, 149–173.

KEEP, M., BISHOP, A. & LONGLEY, I. 2000. Neogene wrench reactivation of the Barcoo sub-basin, northwest Australia: implications for Neogene tectonics of the Australian margin. *Petroleum Geoscience*, **6**, 211–220.

KEEP, M., CLOUGH, M. & LANGHI, L. 2002. Neogene tectonic and structural evolution of the Timor Sea, NW Australia. *In*: KEEP, M. & MOSS, S. (eds) *The Sedimentary Basins of Western Australia 3.* Proceedings of the Petroleum Exploration Society of Australia, Perth, 341–355.

LISTER, G. S., ETHERIDGE, M. A. & SYMONDS, P. A. 1991. Detachment models for the formation of passive margins. *Tectonics*, **10**, 1038–1064.

LONGLEY, I. M., BUESSENSCHUETT, C., CLYDSDALE, L., ET AL. 2002. The North West Shelf of Australia: a Woodside perspective. *In*: KEEP, M. & MOSS, S. (eds) *The Sedimentary Basins of Western Australia 3.* Proceedings of the Petroleum Exploration Society of Australia, Perth, 27–88.

MULLER, R. D., MIHUT, D. & BALDWIN, S. 1998. A new kinematic model for the formation and evolution of the west and -northwest Australian Margin. *In*: PURCELL, P. G. & PURCELL, R. R. (eds) *The Sedimentary Basins of Western Australia 2.* Proceedings of the Petroleum Exploration Society of Australia, Perth, 55–72.

NELSON, A. 1993. Wrench and inversion structures in the Timor Sea region. *Petroleum Exploration Society of Australia Journal*, **29**, 3–30.

O'BRIEN, G. W., ETHERIDGE, M. A., WILLCOX, J. B., MORSE, M., SYMONDS, P., NORMAN, C. & NEEDHAM, D. J. 1993. The structural architecture of the Timor Sea, North Western Australia: implications for basin development and hydrocarbon exploration. *Petroleum Exploration Society of Australia Journal*, **33**, 258–275.

O'BRIEN, G. W., MORSE, M., WILSON, D., QUAIFE, P., COLWELL, J., HIGGINS, R. & FOSTER, C. B. 1999. Margin-scale, basement-involved compartmentalisation of Australia's North West Shelf: a primary control on basin-scale rift, depositional and reactivation histories. *Australian Petroleum Production and Exploration Association Journal*, **39**, 40–61.

PATTILLO, J. & NICHOLLS, P. J. 1990. A tectonostratigraphic framework for the Vulcan Graben, Timor Sea Region. *Australian Petroleum Exploration Association Journal*, **30**, 27–51.

SHUSTER, M. W., EATON, S., WAKEFIELD, L. L. & KLOOSTERMAN, H. J. 1998. Neogene tectonics, greater Timor Sea, offshore Australia: implications for trap risk. *Australian Petroleum Production and Exploration Association Journal*, **38**, 351–378.

STRUCKMEYER, H. I. M., BLEVIN, J. E., SAYERS, J., TOTTERDELL, J. M., BAXTER, K. & CATHRO, D. 1998. Structural evolution of the Browse Basin, North West Shelf: new concepts from-deep-seismic data. *In*: PURCELL, P. G. & PURCELL, R. R. (eds) *The Sedimentary Basins of Western Australia 2*. Proceedings of the Petroleum Exploration Society of Australia, Perth, 345–367.

UPCOTT, N. M., MIKASA, R. K. & EBINGER, C. J. 1996. Along-axis segmentation and isostacy in the Western Rift, east Africa. *Journal of Geophysical Research*, **101**, 3247–3268.

WALSH, J. J. & WATTERSON, J. 1987. Distributions of cumulative displacement and seismic slip on a single normal fault. *Journal of Structural Geology*, **9**, 1039–1046.

WITHJACK, M. O., SCHLISCHE, R. W. & OLSEN, P. E. 1998. Diachronous rifting, drifting, and inversion on the passive margin of Central Eastern North America: an analogue for other passive margins. *American Association of Petroleum Geologists Bulletin*, **82**, 817–835.

WOODS, E. P. 1988. Extensional Structures of the Jabiru Terrace, Vulcan sub-basin. *In*: PURCELL, P. G. & PURCELL, R. R. (eds) *The North West Shelf, Australia*. Proceedings of the Petroleum Exploration Society of Australia, Perth, 311–330.

YEATES, A. N., BRADSHAW, M. T., DICKINS, J. M., ET AL. 1987. The Westralian Superbasin, as Australian link with Tethys. *In*: MCKENZIE, K. G. (ed.) *Shallow Tethys 2*. 2nd International symposium on Shallow Tethys A.A. Balkema, Rotterdam, 199–213.

Fault reactivation in the Port Campbell Embayment with respect to carbon dioxide sequestration, Otway Basin, Australia

CLAIRE ROGERS[1,2], PETER J. VAN RUTH[1] & RICHARD R. HILLIS[1]

[1]*CRC for Greenhouse Gas Technologies, Australian School of Petroleum, The University of Adelaide, South Australia 5005, Australia*

[2]*Present address: Chevron Australia Pty Ltd, 250 St Georges Terrace, Perth, Western Australia (e-mail: claire@chevron.com)*

Abstract: The Naylor structure in the Port Campbell Embayment, Otway Basin, South Australia is proposed as a demonstration site for the subsurface geological storage of carbon dioxide (CO_2). The Naylor structure is a fault-bounded high with normal faults to the north and west to SW. Seismic interpretation shows evidence of recent fault reactivation in the Otway Basin. It is postulated that residual hydrocarbon columns (accumulated and leaked prior to present day) in the Otway Basin leaked due to fault reactivation. Thus, a critical issue in the geological storage of CO_2 in the Port Campbell Embayment is the potential for the reactivation of faults bounding the Naylor structure.

The propensity of faults to be reactivated is assessed by determining the *in-situ* stress field, the mechanical properties of the fault rock and the orientations of the existing faults. The *in-situ* stress field lies on the boundary of a strike-slip and reverse faulting regime in the Port Campbell Embayment. The vertical, minimum horizontal and maximum horizontal stress gradients are 21 MPa km^{-1}, 19 MPa km^{-1} and 38 MPa km^{-1} respectively and the pore pressure gradient is hydrostatic. The maximum horizontal stress in the Port Campbell Embayment is oriented at 150°N.

One planar and two curviplanar faults were identified within the Naylor structure. Two fault segments act to trap accumulations at the crest of the structure. These fault segments have relatively low propensities to reactivate near the crest of the structure. The intended migration pathway of the CO_2 plume does not intersect the identified faults until it reaches the crest of the Naylor structure. However, reservoir heterogeneities such as sub-seismic faults may cause the migrating CO_2 plume to move towards identified fault segments which are not intended to trap the injected CO_2 and have a relatively high propensity to reactivate.

Data from the Vostok ice core indicates that CO_2 concentrations in the atmosphere have until recently remained below 310 ppm for the last 420 000 years (Petit *et al.* 1999). The ice core data also indicate a strong correlation between CO_2 concentration in the atmosphere and its isotopic temperature. The atmospheric concentration of CO_2 has risen to 374.9 ppm (Blasing & Jones 2005) since the industrial revolution in the early nineteenth century, a 20% increase. It is as yet unknown how such a change in atmospheric concentration of CO_2 may affect the temperature of the atmosphere.

Growing concern over the rising concentrations of CO_2 in the atmosphere has led to increased research into greenhouse gas abatement technologies. Geological sequestration of CO_2 allows large volumes of CO_2 to be stored in the subsurface utilizing mature technology from the petroleum industry (e.g. Bachu 2000; Cook *et al.* 2000).

The GEODISC program (concerned with investigating the feasibility of CO_2 storage in Australia) as part of the APCRC (Australian Petroleum Cooperative Research Centre) examined sedimentary basins in Australia to identify possible sites for geological storage of CO_2 (Bradshaw *et al.* 2002). This analysis considered storage capacity, injectivity potential, site economics, containment and existing natural resources such as potable water and hydrocarbons. The GEODISC program identified three sedimentary basins that may be suitable for demonstrating that CO_2 storage is a viable greenhouse gas abatement technology in Australia; the Perth Basin in Western Australia, the Bowen-Surat Basin in SE Queensland and the Otway Basin on the Australian southern margin (Fig. 1).

Successful storage of CO_2 requires a comprehensive understanding of possible CO_2 migration pathways prior to injection. Shipton *et al.* (2004) studied faults bounding CO_2 accumulations in the Colorado Plateau which should act as barriers to fluid flow due to the presence of clay-rich gouges within the fault. This study determined that migration of CO_2 to the surface can be facilitated by faults acting as conduits to fluid flow despite zones of clay-rich gouge.

This study examines the migration potential of faults near the depleted Naylor gas field in the Port Campbell Embayment, Otway Basin. The

From: JOHNSON, H., DORÉ, A. G., GATLIFF, R. W., HOLDSWORTH, R., LUNDIN, E. R. & RITCHIE, J. D. (eds) *The Nature and Origin of Compression in Passive Margins.* Geological Society, London, Special Publications, **306**, 201–214. DOI: 10.1144/SP306.10 0305-8719/08/$15.00 © The Geological Society of London 2008.

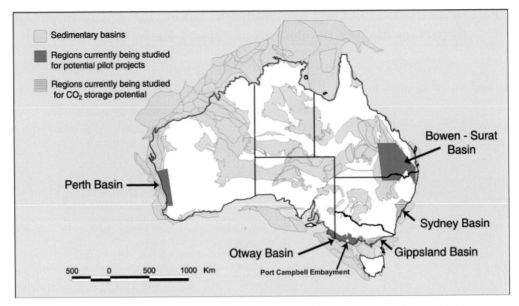

Fig. 1. Basins identified by the GEODISC program as having potential for CO_2 demonstration sites (dark blue). Sedimentary basins are shown in pink and basins currently being researched by the CO2CRC are shown in striped blue. Location of the Port Campbell Embayment is indicated within the Otway Basin.

Naylor structure is the intended location of a demonstration CO_2 storage project run by the CO2CRC (Cooperative Research Centre for Greenhouse Gas Technologies). The Naylor structure is a fault-bound trap formed during the development of the passive margin of southeastern Australia. Previous studies show that the present-day stress field in the Otway Basin has evolved from the normal faulting regime associated with passive margin development during the Jurassic to Cretaceous to a strike-slip or reverse regime (Jones *et al.* 2000; Lyon *et al.* 2005; Nelson *et al.* 2006).

The migration potential of faults is assessed by determining the geomechanical propensity of the fault to reactivate. This propensity is determined using the present-day stress field, a 3D model of the faults and the mechanical properties of the fault rock. The Naylor structure is bound by faults on the northern and western flanks and has anticlinal closure to the south and east.

The Port Campbell Embayment

Geological history

The Port Campbell Embayment is located in the eastern Otway Basin (Figs 1 & 2), with boundaries defined by the pinching out of the early Cretaceous sediments in the east and the disappearance of the late Cretaceous Waarre Formation in the west (Foster & Hodgson 1995).

The Otway Basin is a NW–SE trending basin located on the southern Australian passive margin (Fig. 1). North–south extension associated with the rifting between continental Australia and Antarctica began during the late Jurassic and continued into the early Cretaceous (Yu 1988). This period of initial rifting produced a series of east–west-trending half graben structures in the Port Campbell Embayment into which the Crayfish Group (Fig. 3) was deposited (Hill *et al.* 1994). Initial rifting was followed by a period of subsidence during the Aptian and Albian associated with northward continental drift and the incursion of the Southern Ocean. Localized compression and uplift during the Cenomanian resulted in an erosional unconformity at the top of the late Jurassic Crayfish Group (Fig. 3).

Subsequent extension due to rifting in the Tasman Sea (between the Australian mainland and Tasmania) resulted in renewed movement of the extensional faults formed during the late Cretaceous (Perincek & Cockshell 1995). The Tasman rifting also produced a number of smaller SE-trending normal faults in the Port Campbell Embayment. Most of these SE-trending faults are confined to the Sherbrook Group (Fig. 3) which was deposited during this rift phase (Megallaa 1986). Hydrocarbon and CO_2 accumulations in the Port Campbell Embayment are found in the Paaratte and Waarre Formations in traps bound by faults formed or reactivated during the late

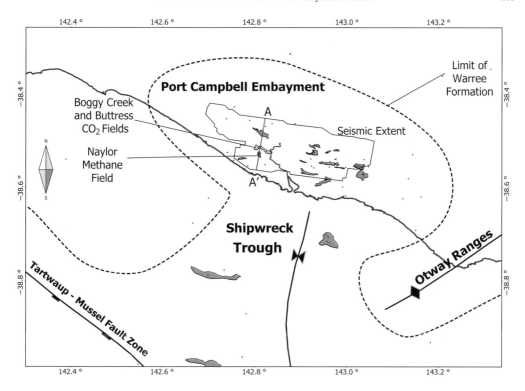

Fig. 2. The Port Campbell Embayment in the eastern Otway Basin including major structural features and stratigraphic extent of the embayment. Location of Naylor (green), Boggy Creek and Buttress (yellow) accumulations also indicated.

Cretaceous (Fig. 4). A period of subsidence with negligible faulting during the Palaeogene saw the deposition of the siliciclastic Wangerrip and Nirranda Groups and the calcareous Heytsbury Group (Megallaa 1986; Fig. 3).

Compressional deformation during the Neogene has been associated with volcanic activity in the Otway Basin (Perincek & Cockshell 1995). This period of compression produced a series of NE-trending anticlines including the Fergusons Hill anticline, the Minerva anticline and the Otway Ranges (Palmowski *et al.* 2004; Schneider *et al.* 2004) and resulted in the reversal of some existing normal faults (Hill *et al.* 1994).

The Naylor structure

The late Cretaceous Waarre Formation in the Naylor structure originally held a methane accumulation which has now been extracted and depleted. It was selected as the location for a CO_2 injection demonstration project due to its many favourable characteristics. Such characteristics include: a high porosity, high permeability reservoir rock; a laterally extensive and thick sealing overburden;

and, a close proximity to the Buttress field, a source of CO_2. Additionally, adjacent to the Naylor trap are the Buttress and Boggy Creek accumulations (Fig. 2), which contain gas composed of approximately 85% CO_2, 15% methane and 98% CO_2, 2% methane respectively. The occurrence of natural high CO_2 accumulations in the Port Campbell Embayment demonstrate that traps in the area are capable of containing CO_2 over geological timescales (5×10^3–2×10^6 years; Watson *et al.* 2004). The Naylor, Buttress and Boggy Creek accumulations are bounded by faults that formed during the early to late Cretaceous (Fig. 4).

Fault reactivation

There is much evidence to suggest that faults which are active or have a high geomechanical propensity to reactivate provide permeable conduits for the migration of fluids (e.g. Sibson 1994; Barton *et al.* 1995; Rogers & Evans 2002). Faults with a high propensity to reactivate in the migration pathway of a CO_2 plume could thus allow migration of injected CO_2 away from the intended containment area. Hence it is vital to understand the

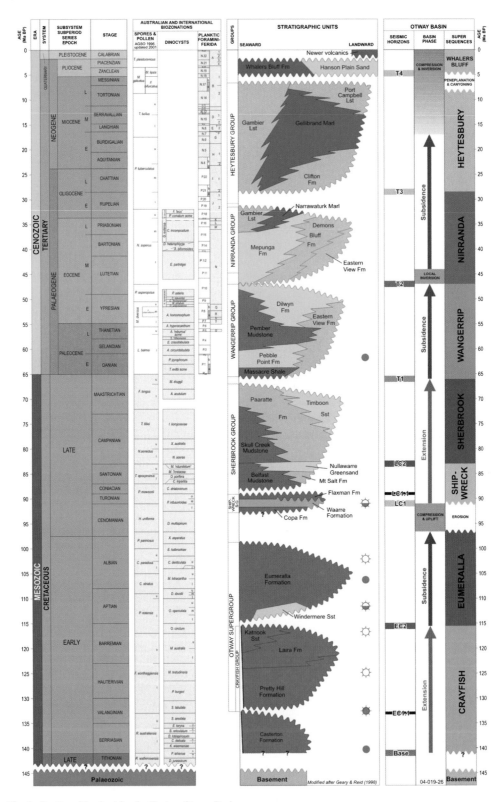

Fig. 3. Stratigraphic chart for the Eastern Otway Basin.

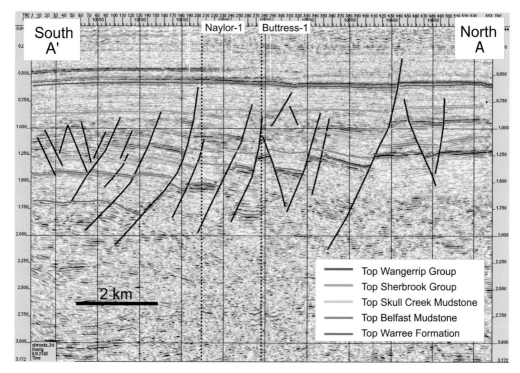

Fig. 4. Seismic section through the Naylor-1 well (see Fig. 2 for location).

geomechanical propensity of faults to reactivate for faults in the migration pathway of CO$_2$ when assessing a site for CO$_2$ storage. The propensity of a fault to reactivate can be judged by determining the pore pressure increase (ΔP) required to reduce the effective normal stress (applied normal stress minus the pore pressure) acting across a pre-existing fault plane such that the fault can slip. The propensity of a fault to reactivate is assessed by determining the present day *in-situ* stress field from drilling data, constructing a 3D structural model of the pre-existing faults and establishing the mechanical properties of the fault rocks in the area.

Pore pressure increase required to reactivate the fault

The principal stresses acting on a fault can be resolved into a shear stress component acting parallel to the fault plane and an effective normal stress component acting perpendicular to the fault plane. The shear stress and normal stress acting on the fault can then be plotted in a Mohr diagram (Fig. 5). The failure envelope describing the stress conditions under which the fault rock fails can also be plotted on the Mohr diagram. The pore pressure increase (ΔP) required for fault reactivation for a given fault orientation can

be determined by evaluating the difference between the effective normal stress acting on the fault and the effective normal stress at which the fault fails. (Fig. 5). Faults with a low ΔP value have a relatively high propensity to reactivate while faults with a high ΔP value have a relatively low propensity.

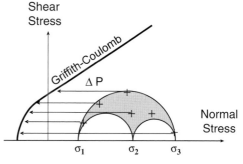

Fig. 5. Representation of ΔP on a Mohr diagram. Principal stresses define the Mohr circles. The failure envelope is defined by the coefficient of friction and the cohesion of the fault rock. Black crosses represent theoretical faults. ΔP is the horizontal distance between the effective normal stress acting on a fault and the failure envelope, represented by arrows.

Geomechanical model

In-situ *stress field.* Assuming the subsurface principal stresses are vertical and horizontal, the *in-situ* stress field can be fully constrained by determining the magnitudes of the three principal stresses, the orientation of one of the horizontal stresses and the subsurface pore pressure. The stress magnitudes are determined using density logs, pressure logs, and leak off tests. The vertical stress, minimum horizontal stress and maximum horizontal stress gradients for the Port Campbell Embayment are 21 MPa km^{-1}, 19 MPa km^{-1} and 38 MPa km^{-1}, respectively (Fig. 6).

Vertical stress magnitude is a result of the weight of the overburden at a particular depth. It is determined by integrating density logs to determine the stress induced by the overburden (McGarr & Gay 1978). The vertical stress was determined by integrating density logs from five wells close to the Naylor structure (Rowans-1, Boggy Creek-1, Curdievale-1, Wallaby Creek-1 and Barton Corner-1). The vertical stress profiles produced from these wells are highly consistent (Fig. 6).

The minimum horizontal stress can be determined using leak-off tests when tensile fractures are formed at the well-bore wall and are propagated into the formation. Leak-off tests (LOTs) are generally performed below the casing shoe to determine the maximum borehole pressure the formation can withstand before fractures are induced (Kunze & Steiger 1991). Drilling fluids are pumped into the open hole (typically 3–10 m) beneath the casing shoe until the formation fails and fractures are formed (Bell 1990). Fractures propagating away from the well-bore open against the least principal stress, thus in normal and strike-slip faulting regimes the fractures open against the minimum horizontal stress (Bell 1996). Fractures close when the fluid pressure within the borehole becomes less than the minimum principal stress, thus in normal and strike-slip faulting regimes the fracture closure pressure is equal to the minimum horizontal stress (Engelder 1993). Leak-off tests do not generally monitor pressure decline and thus cannot provide the fracture closure pressure. However leak-off pressure (defined as the pressure at which the pressure–volume plot deviates from linearity) has been identified as an empirical estimate of the minimum horizontal stress in the absence of closure pressures (Gaarenstroom *et al.* 1993; Zoback *et al.* 2003).

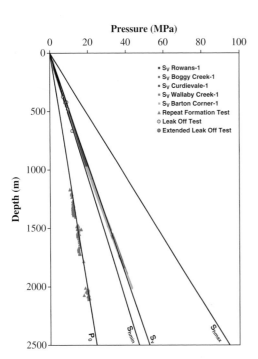

Fig. 6. Data used to determine the magnitudes of the three principal stresses (vertical, minimum horizontal and maximum horizontal) and the pore pressure.

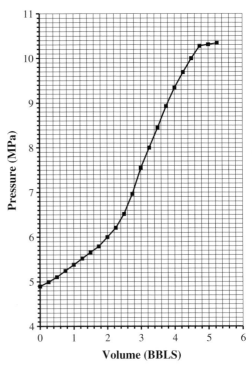

Fig. 7. LOT record from the Naylor-1 well showing volume pumped against pressure. The leak off pressure is 9.48 MPa where the pressure–volume plot deviated from linearity.

The minimum horizontal stress was determined using leak-off pressures from four wells (Lavers-1, Naylor-1, Penryn-1 and Tregony-1, e.g. Fig. 7) and a closure pressure from the McIntee-1 extended leak-off test in the Port Campbell Embayment.

Given the available data, frictional limits theory was the only method by which the maximum horizontal stress could be constrained:

$$\frac{\sigma_1}{\sigma_3} = \left[\sqrt{(\mu^2 + 1)} + \mu \right]^2$$

where σ_1 is the maximum principal stress, σ_3 is the minimum principal stress and μ is the coefficient of friction of the fault rock as used in the failure envelope.

Frictional limits theory assumes that somewhere in the stress field there is an optimally oriented fault on which slip can occur to limit the ratio of maximum to minimum principal stress (Jaeger & Cook 1969). Thus the magnitude of the maximum horizontal stress can be constrained when the magnitude of the minimum principal stress is known (Moos & Zoback 1990). However, frictional limits theory can only be used to constrain an upper bound to the maximum horizontal stress, and only in strike-slip and reverse faulting regimes where the maximum principal stress is horizontal.

Recent inversion of faults in the Port Campbell Embayment seen in seismic sections (e.g. Palmowski et al. 2004) suggests that the stress field is at frictional limits, which implies that the maximum horizontal stress determined using frictional limits is likely to be close to the actual value. Additionally focal mechanisms from eastern Victoria suggest a reverse to strike-slip faulting regime (e.g. Clark & Leonard 2003; Allen et al. 2005) suggesting that the maximum principal stress is horizontal.

The orientations of the horizontal stresses were determined from observations of well-bore break-out and DITFs on image logs. In vertical wells, borehole break-outs are aligned perpendicular to the maximum horizontal stress (Bell 1990; Moos et al. 2003). The orientation of the maximum horizontal stress was determined using an acoustic imaging log from the Dunbar-1 well in the central part of the Port Campbell Embayment. The acoustic image log was run from 1355 to 1740 m TVDSS. Sixteen borehole break-outs were identified from 1504 to 1736 m TVDSS with a total length of 79.2 m. The orientation of the maximum horizontal stress was interpreted as 150°N with a standard deviation of 6.7°. This orientation is consistent with other stress orientation indicators from the western Otway Basin and offshore of the Port

Campbell Embayment (e.g. Hillis et al. 1995; Nelson et al. 2006).

Pore pressure is determined using drill stem and formation interval tests. These tests sample and determine the pressure of the formation fluids. The production history of the Port Campbell Embayment spans over 20 years (Foster & Hodgson 1995) and includes the drilling of over 55 wells. Production testing has generally encountered hydrostatic pore pressure gradients (9.8 MPa km^{-1}). Repeat formation tests from thirteen wells were examined from the Port Campbell Embayment which verified hydrostatic gradients (Fig. 6).

Failure envelope. The failure envelope describes the stress conditions under which the fault rock will fail. The Griffith–Coulomb failure envelope is defined by combining the Griffith failure criterion:

$$\tau^2 = 4T\sigma'_n + 4T^2$$

(Griffith 1921) in tension and the Coulomb failure criterion:

$$\tau = C + \mu\sigma'_n$$

(Coulomb 1773) in compression where τ is the shear stress acting on the fault, T is the tensile strength, C is the cohesive strength and μ is the coefficient of friction of the fault rock. This merging of these two criteria satisfies the empirical observation that $C = 2T$ (Sibson 2000). The tensile strength and coefficient of friction are ideally determined by lab testing of fault rock samples (e.g. Dewhurst & Jones 2002; Mildren et al. 2005). However such samples are not always available and standard values or rock samples from nearby faults must be utilized. There were no fault rock samples from the Port Campbell Embayment. The cohesive strength of the fault rock was determined to be 5.44 MPa from mechanical lab tests on a fault rock sample from the Penola Trough in the eastern Otway Basin (Dewhurst & Jones 2002) which suggests that the tensile strength is 2.72 MPa. The standard value for the coefficient of friction (0.6) was used as determined by Byerlee (1978).

Fault geometry/orientation. Fault orientation must be determined to establish the shear stress and normal stress acting on the fault. The geometry and orientations of pre-existing faults are determined by interpreting 3D seismic data. Faults in the vicinity of the Buttress, Boggy Creek and Naylor structures were interpreted using the

Nirranda–Heytsbury 3D seismic survey (Fig. 4). The Nirranda–Heytsbury survey was shot in March 2002 and covers and area of 83.56 km^2 (Fig. 2). The data is post-stack time migrated and is of high quality at and above reservoir level. Fault plane reflections can be seen clearly on large offset faults allowing faults to be picked with confidence.

The Waarre formation in the Naylor structure is bound by normal faults to the north and west and the reservoir horizon dips towards the SE (Fig. 8). The fault to the west of the Naylor structure (Fault A) dips to the west. It strikes north–south at the crest of the structure and curves to strike to the SE down the flank of the structure. The fault to the

north of the Naylor structure (Fault B) dips to the south and strikes to the SSE at the crest of the structure and curves to strike to the east on the flank of the structure. Additionally, there is a fault in the flank of the structure that does not act to trap accumulations in the Naylor Structure (Fault C). Fault C strikes SSE and dips towards the SW (Figs 8 & 9).

The above *in-situ* stress field, failure envelope and fault geometry data were used to determine the propensity of reactivation for faults in the vicinity of the Naylor structure (Figs 10 & 11). Fault polygons are coloured by the propensity of faults to reactivate based on the ΔP value with red being a high and blue being a low propensity for fault reactivation.

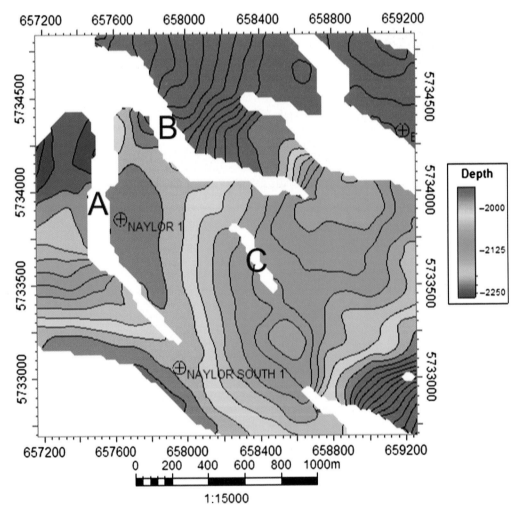

Fig. 8. Map view of the Waarre reservoir horizon. White indicates sections that are faulted. The Naylor structure is bound by faults to the north, west and SW and dips towards the SE.

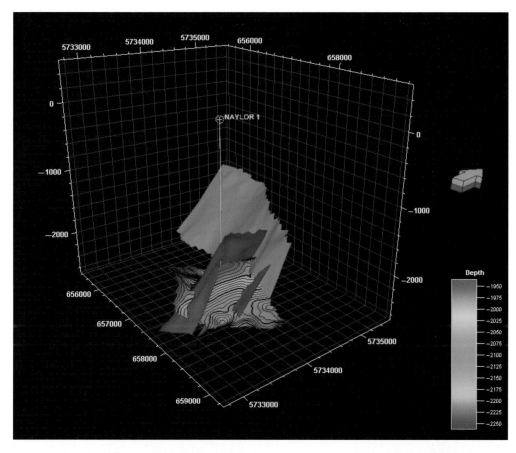

Fig. 9. 3D depth model of the Naylor structure. Faults are shown in purple (A), blue (B) and pink (C) and the Waarre reservoir horizon is coloured and contoured. Naylor-1 well location is shown by the yellow trajectory. North is indicated by the green arrow.

Limitations. Several assumptions were made to constrain the geomechanical model. The *in-situ* stress field in this study was assumed to be either normal or strike-slip such that fractures propagating from the borehole open against the minimum horizontal stress. In a reverse faulting regime the minimum principal stress estimated by LOTs is the vertical stress. Leak-off pressures examined for this study were slightly less than the vertical stress suggesting that the current faulting regime is strike-slip and that the leak-off pressures are an estimate of the minimum horizontal stress.

Additionally, all LOTs were performed at relatively shallow depths (less than 700 m). Thus the gradient for the minimum horizontal stress is not well defined and the minimum horizontal stress at depth may be inexact.

Mechanical rock properties are ideally derived from sample loading and frictional sliding experiments on fault rock samples from the fault in question. No such samples were available from the Port Campbell Embayment. The nearest relevant fault strength data are the aforementioned fault rock samples from the Penola Trough located in the western Otway Basin. The fault rock samples analysed by Dewhurst & Jones (2002) are cataclasites from the early Cretaceous Pretty Hill Formation which is deeper than the Waarre reservoir horizon in the Naylor structure (Fig. 3).

The coefficient of friction used for constraining the maximum horizontal stress and for the geomechanical risking was taken from Byerlee (1978) who gathered frictional data from civil engineering, mining engineering and geophysical literature. Byerlee (1978) determined that the coefficient of friction for two rock surfaces is approximately 0.6. However, the coefficient of friction for faults

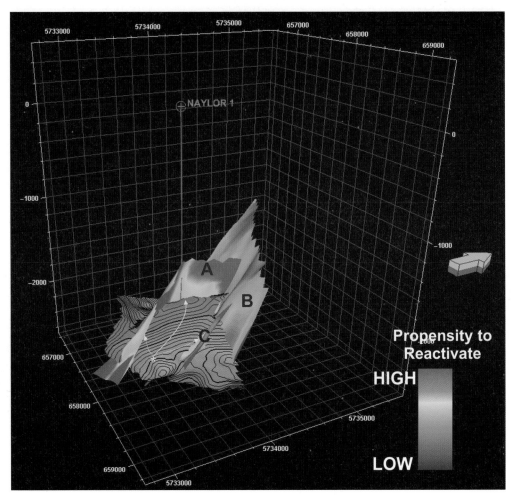

Fig. 10. Propensity of faults to reactivate for faults near the Naylor structure. Top reservoir is blue and faults are coloured according to their ΔP value. Red areas have low ΔP values and are at relatively high risk of reactivation and blue areas have high ΔP value and are at relatively low risk of reactivation. View is towards the WNW (north indicated by the green arrow). Intended migration pathway is shown by the solid yellow line and alternative migration pathways are shown by the yellow dashed lines.

containing gouge can be much lower. As a result, the coefficient of friction for natural faults is highly dependant on the composition of any gouge within the fault plane. The value for the coefficient of friction could not be more accurately defined for faults near the Naylor field due to lack of fault rock samples.

The limitations described above result in large uncertainties in the ΔP value derived from the geomechanical risking method. Therefore the geomechanical risking methodology presented herein should be used as a qualitative risking tool to delineate the most suitable site for injecting CO_2 rather than a quantitative to calculate the

maximum pore pressure increase a fault can withstand before reactivation occurs.

Naylor structure fault reactivation

Faults A, B and C described above are potentially in the migration pathway of injected CO_2 in the Naylor structure (Figs 10 & 11). The fault segments which bound the Naylor structure and are at the crest of the Naylor structure (the northern segment of A and the western segment of B) will ultimately trap the injected CO_2. These fault segments have relatively high ΔP values and thus have a relatively low propensity to reactivate (Fig. 10). Fault B to

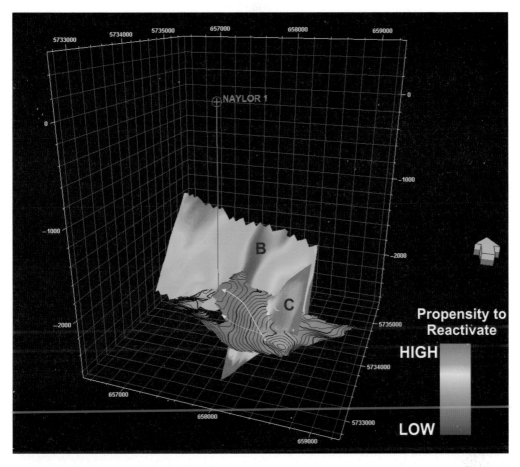

Fig. 11. Probability of fault reactivation for faults near the Naylor structure. As for Figure 10 but viewed towards the north. Fault A is not shown to enable faults B and C to be seen.

the north of the Naylor structure also has a relatively low propensity to reactivate on the flank of the Naylor structure where the fault strikes towards the east. As Fault A curves to strike more towards the SE on the flank of the Naylor structure the propensity to reactivate increases. Fault C which is not a bounding fault in the Naylor structure has a relatively high propensity to reactivate (Fig. 11).

Importance of risking all faults in the migration pathway

The Naylor structure consists of two-way dip closure and two-way fault closure (Figs 8 & 9). It is a depleted gas field and as such we know that the sections of faults bounding the structure are currently barriers to fluid flow as they are capable of

holding a methane accumulation. However, faults not acting as boundaries to the accumulation provide no evidence as to whether they are sealing or acting as a conduit.

A possible injection location for the Naylor structure is down dip of the crest of the structure such that the Naylor-1 well may be used as a monitoring well (Fig. 8). This injection location is thought to be below the original gas–water contact. It is intended and that the CO_2 will migrate up dip towards the crest of the structure (Figs 10 & 11). The injected CO_2 plume is not expected to intersect any of the known faults until the CO_2 reaches its final containment location. However, unforeseen circumstances (e.g. reservoir heterogeneities or sub-seismic faults) may result in the CO_2 migrating along the lower part of Fault A or along Fault C. It is not known whether these fault segments are acting as conduits to fluid flow and may facilitate the migration of CO_2 away from the intended containment area. These fault segments are also the areas which have a higher propensity to reactivate. All three faults cut through the regional seal to the Paaratte Formation above.

Although Fault C does not act as a bounding fault to the Naylor trap, the possibility of migrating CO_2 intersecting this fault highlights the need to consider all faults in the migration pathway of the CO_2, rather than exclusively faults which ultimately will trap the CO_2. Care thus needs to be taken that the CO_2 plume migrates directly up dip as intended and the CO_2 does not migrate towards either Fault C or the lower part of Fault A as these fault segments may not be sealing.

Injection location

The injection location presented herein is situated such that the predicted high porosity, high permeability, relatively homogeneous reservoir conditions will result in the CO_2 plume not intersecting any resolvable faults until it reaches the crest of the Naylor structure. The fault segments at the crest of the structure have relatively low propensities to reactivate thus the CO_2 plume will not intersect any fault segments with high propensities as it migrates up dip.

Pore pressure build-up close to the injection location can result in decreases in effective normal stress and thus possibly fault slip. The intended injection location for the demonstration project is situated to maximize the distance from all identified faults. Additionally, preliminary modelling indicates that pore pressure build-up as a result of CO_2 injection will be minimal due to the high porosity and permeability of the Waarre Formation determined from core samples. The lack of pore pressure build-up and the distance of the injection location from the identified faults should ensure that fault reactivation is not triggered by pressure build-up due to injection.

Future work

Planned future work includes soil gas sampling to verify results of the geomechanical probability of fault reactivation presented herein. The main fault bounding the Boggy Creek accumulation runs parallel and adjacent to Fault B in the Naylor structure. The Boggy Creek fault has a relatively high risk of reactivation and extends close to the surface in places. Soil–gas sampling and subsequent gas analysis can determine the volume percentage and isotopic signature of CO_2 in the soil profile. Previous soil-gas studies over hydraulically conductive faults above CO_2 sources in both the western Otway Basin and along the San Andreas fault have detected elevated levels of CO_2 in the soil gasses (e.g. Lewicki *et al.* 2003; Lyon *et al.* 2005). Hence elevated levels of CO_2 over the Boggy Creek fault can verify whether the fault is acting as a conduit for fluid flow and thus the applicability of geomechanical risking for prediction of fault leakage.

Conclusions

The Naylor structure in the Port Campbell Embayment is intended as a demonstration site for the geological storage of CO_2. The Naylor structure is bound by a SSE to east striking fault at the north of the trap and a north to NW striking fault at the west of the trap. Additionally there is a SSE striking fault on the flank of the Naylor structure.

Shipton *et al.* (2004) demonstrated that faults bounding natural CO_2 accumulations in the Colorado Plateau are acting as conduits for the flow of CO_2 to the surface. This leakage can be attributed to recent activity on these faults. Hence a concern for CO_2 injection in the Naylor structure is the potential for the trap-bounding faults to act as conduits for the injected CO_2. Recent reactivation of faults has been linked with the leakage of CO_2 along trap-bounding faults in the western Otway Basin (Lyon *et al.* 2005). There is no evidence of recent activity on the faults bounding the Naylor structure, however future reactivation may lead to migration of CO_2 along the faults.

The propensity of faults to reactivate was assessed using a geomechanical model. The model utilized the *in-situ* stress field, the mechanical properties of the fault rocks and the orientations of the fault to assess the relative propensity of faults to reactivate.

The present-day state of stress in the Port Campbell Embayment is on the border of strike-slip and reverse with the maximum horizontal stress oriented 150°N. This state of stress assigns the greatest propensity of reactivation to faults striking north and ESE that dip approximately 90°. Thus, Fault C has the highest propensity to reactivate. The westerly part of Fault B and the southerly part of Fault A also have high relative propensities to reactivate.

References

ALLEN, T. I., GIBSON, G. & CULL, J. P. 2005. Stress-field constraints from recent intraplate seismicity in Southeastern Australia. *Australian Journal of Earth Sciences*, **52**, 217–229.

BACHU, S. 2000. Sequestration of CO_2 in geological media: criteria and approach for site selection in response to climate change. *Energy Conservation and Management*, **41**, 953–970.

BARTON, C. A., ZOBACK, M. D. & MOOS, D. 1995. Fluid flow along potentially active faults in crystalline rock. *Geology*, **23**, 683–686.

BELL, J. S. 1990. Investigation of stress regimes in sedimentary basins using information from oil industry wireline logs and drilling records. *In*: HURST, A. LOVELL, M. A. & MORTON, A. C. (eds) *Geological Application of Wireline Logs*. Geological Society, London, Special Publications, Blackwell Scientific Publications, Oxford, 305–325.

BELL, J. S. 1996. *In-situ* stresses in sedimentary rocks (Part 1): measurement techniques. *Geoscience Canada*, **23**, 85–100.

BLASING, T. J. & JONES, S. 2005. *Current Greenhouse Gas Concentrations*. CDIAC.

BRADSHAW, J., BRADSHAW, B. E., ALLINSON, G., RIGG, A. J., NGUYEN, V. & SPENCER, L. 2002. The Potential for geological sequestration of CO$_2$ in Australia: preliminary findings and implications for new gas field development. *APPEA Journal*, **42**, 25–46.

BYERLEE, J. 1978. Friction of rocks. *Pure and Applied Geophysics*, **116**, 615–626.

CLARK, D. & LEONARD, M. 2003. Principal stress orientations from multiple focal-plane solutions: new insight into the Australian intraplate stress field. *In*: HILLIS, R. R. & MULLER, R. D. (eds) *Evolution and Dynamics of the Australian Plate*. Geological Society of Australia, Special Publication 22 and Geological Society of America, Special Paper, **372**, 91–105.

COOK, P. J., RIGG, A. J. & BRADSHAW, J. 2000. Putting it back where it came from: is geological disposal of carbon dioxide an option for Australia? *APPEA Journal*, **40**, 1–13.

COULOMB, C. A. 1773. Sur une application des régles de Maxims et Minimis a quelques problémes de statique relatifs á l'Architecture. *Academie Royale des Sciences Memoires de mathematiques et de physique parti: divers savans*, **7**, 343–382.

DEWHURST, D. N. & JONES, R. M. 2002. Geomechanical, microstructural and petrophysical evolution on experimentally reactivated cataclasites: applications to fault seal prediction. *AAPG Bulletin*, **86**, 1385–1405.

ENGELDER, T. 1993. *Stress Regimes in the Lithosphere*. Princeton University Press, Princeton, N.J.

FOSTER, J. D. & HODGSON, A. J. 1995. Port Campbell reviewed: methane and champagne. *The APEA Journal*, **35**, 418–435.

GAARENSTROOM, L., TROMP, R. A. J., DE JONG, M. C. & BRANDENBURG, A. M. 1993. Overpressures in the Central North Sea: implications for trap integrity and drilling safety. *In*: PARKER, J. R. (ed.) *Petroleum Geology of Northwest Europe: Proceedings of the 4th Conference*. Geological Society, London, 1305–131.

GRIFFITH, A. A. 1921. The phenomena of rupture and flow in solids. *Transactions of the Royal Society, London*, **A 221**, 163–198.

HILL, K. A., COOPER, G. T., RICHARDSON, M. J. & LAVIN, C. J. 1994. Structural framework of the Eastern Otway Basin: inversion and interaction between two major structural provinces. *Exploration Geophysics*, **25**, 79–87.

HILLIS, R. R., MONTE, S. A., TAN, C. P. & WILLOUGHBY, D. R. 1995. The contemporary stress field of the Otway Basin, South Australia:

implications for hydrocarbon exploration and production. *The APEA Journal*, **35**, 494–506.

JAEGER, J. C. & COOK, N. G. W. 1969. *Fundamentals of Rock Mechanics*. Methuen and Co. Ltd., London.

JONES, R. M., BOULT, P. J., HILLIS, R. R., MILDREN, S. D. & KALDI, J. 2000. Integrated hydrocarbon seal evaluation in the Penola Trough, Otway Basin. *APPEA Journal*, **40**, 194–211.

KUNZE, K. R. & STEIGER, R. P. 1991. Extended leak off tests to determine in situ stress during drilling. *In*: ROEGIERS, J.-C. (ed.) *Rock Mechanics as a Multidisciplinary Science*. Balkema, Rotterdam.

LEWICKI, J. L., EVANS, W. C., HILLEY, G. E., SOREY, M. L., ROGIE, J. D. & BRANTLEY, S. L. 2003. Shallow soil CO$_2$ flow along the San Andreas and Calaveras Faults, California. *Journal of Geophysical Research*, **108**; doi:10.1029/2002JB002141.

LYON, P. J., BOULT, P. J., WATSON, M. & HILLIS, R. R. 2005. A systematic fault seal evaluation of the Ladbroke Grove and Pyrus Traps of the Penola Trough, Otway Basin. *APPEA Journal*, **45**, 459–476.

MCGARR, A. & GAY, N. C. 1978. State of stress in the Earths crust. *Annual Review of Earth and Planetary Sciences*, **6**, 405–476.

MEGALLAA, M. 1986. Tectonic development of Victoria's Otway Basin – A seismic interpretation. *In*: GLENIE, R. C. (ed.) *Second South East Australia Oil Exploration Symposium*. Melbourne, PESA, 201–218.

MILDREN, S. D., HILLIS, R. R., DEWHURST, D. N., LYON, P. J., MEYER, J. J. & BOULT, P. J. 2005. FAST (Fault Analysis Seal Technology): a new technique for geomechanical assessment of the risk of reactivation-related breach of fault seals. *In*: BOULT, P. J. & KALDI, J. (eds) *Hedberg 2: Evaluating Fault and Cap Rock Seals*, **Volume 1**, AAPG.

MOOS, D. & ZOBACK, M. D. 1990. Utilization of observations of well bore failure to constrain the orientation and magnitude of crustal stresses: application to continental, Deep Sea Drilling Project, and Ocean Drilling Program Boreholes. *Journal of Geophysical Research*, **95**, 9305–9325.

MOOS, D., PESKA, P., FINKBEINER, T. & ZOBACK, M. D. 2003. Comprehensive wellbore stability analysis utilizing quantitative risk assessment. *Journal of Petroleum Science and Engineering*, **38**, 97–109.

NELSON, E., HILLIS, R. R., SANDIFORD, M., REYNOLDS, S. D., LYON, P. J., MEYER, J. J., MILDREN, S. D. & ROGERS, C. 2006. Present-day state-of-stress of Southeast Australia. *APPEA Journal*, **46**.

PALMOWSKI, D., HILL, K. C. & HOFFMAN, N. 2004. Structural-stratigraphic styles and evolution of the offshore Otway Basin—A structural seismic analysis. *In*: BOULT, P. J., JOHNS, D. R. & LANG, S. C. (eds) *PESA Eastern Australasian Basins Symposium*, **II**, Adelaide 2004. Petroleum Exploration Society of Australia Special Publication, 75–96.

PERINCEK, D. & COCKSHELL, C. D. 1995. The Otway Basin: Early Cretaceous rifting to Neogene inversion. *The APEA Journal*, **35**, 451–466.

PETIT, J. R., JOUZEL, J., RAYNAUD, D. *ET AL*. 1999. Climate and atmospheric history of the past 420,000 years from the Vostok ice core, Antarctica. *Nature*, **399**, 429–436.

ROGERS, S. F. & EVANS, C. J. 2002. Stress-dependent flow in fractured rocks at Sellafield, United Kingdom. *In*: LOVELL, M. & PARKINSON, N. (eds)

Geological Application of Well Logs. AAPG Methods in Exploration, **13**, 241–250.

SCHNEIDER, C. L., HILL, K. C. & HOFFMAN, N. 2004. Compressional growth of the Minerva Anticline, Otway Basin, Southeast Australia—evidence of oblique rifting. *APPEA Journal*, **44**, 463–480.

SHIPTON, Z. K., EVANS, J. P., KIRSCHNER, D., KOLESAR, P. T., WILLIAMS, A. P. & HEATH, J. 2004. Analysis of CO_2 leakage through 'low permeability' faults from natural reservoirs in the Colorado Plateau, east-central Utah. *In*: BAINES, S. J. & WORDEN, R. H. (eds) *Geological Storage of Carbon Dioxide*. Geological Society, London, Special Publications, **233**, 43–58.

SIBSON, R. H. 1994. Crustal stress, faulting and fluid flow. *In*: PARNELL, J. (ed.) *Geofluids: Origin, Migration and Evolution of Fluids in Sedimentary Basins*. Geological Society, London, Special Publications, **78**, 69–84.

SIBSON, R. H. 2000. A brittle failure mode plot defining conditions for high-flux flow. *Economic Geology*, **95**, 41–48.

WATSON, M., BOREHAM, C. J. & TINGATE, P. R. 2004. Carbon dioxide and carbonate cements in the Otway Basin: implications for geological storage of carbon dioxide. *APPEA Journal*, **45**, 703–720.

YU, S. M. 1988. Structure and development of the Otway Basin. *The APEA Journal*, **28**, 243–254.

ZOBACK, M. D., BARTON, C. A., BRUDY, M. *ET AL*. 2003. Determination of stress orientation and magnitude in deep wells. *International Journal of Rock Mechanics and Mining Sciences*, **40**, 1049–1076.

Index

Note: Page numbers denoted in *italics* refer to figures, those in **bold** refer to tables.